The Buddhist Directory

Whatever conduces to purity, that is my teaching.
Whatever conduces to freedom, that is my teaching.
Whatever conduces to decrease of wordly gains and
  acquisitions, that is my teaching.
Whatever conduces to simplicity, that is my teaching.
Whatever conduces to contentment, that is my teaching.
Whatever conduces to individuality, that is my teaching.
Whatever conduces to energy, that is my teaching.
Whatever conduces to delight in good, that is my teaching.

– The Buddha

The Buddhist Directory

PETER LORIE AND
JULIE FOAKES

BOXTREE

First published 1996 by Newleaf, an imprint of Macmillan
Publishers Ltd, 25 Eccleston Place, London, SW1W 9NF and Basingstoke.

Associated companies throughout the world

ISBN: 0 7522 0595 1

1 3 5 7 9 10 8 6 4 2

A CIP catalogue entry for this book is available from the British Library

Typeset by SX Composing DTP, Rayleigh, Essex
Printed and bound in Great Britain at The Bath Press, Bath
Designed by Roger Lightfoot

Contents

> What we are today comes from our thoughts of yesterday, and our present thoughts build our life of tomorrow: our life is the creation of our mind.
>
> – *The Dhammapada*

CAVEAT

Mention of any teacher, group or centre in this book does not imply endorsement of them by the authors. This is in line with the traditions of Buddhism which has never been a centralised, authoritarian religion with a governing body dispensing or withholding approval. It is therefore up to each individual to test the ground for him/herself, guided by common sense and those indications that the Buddha himself gives in the Scriptures (e.g. the *Kalama Sutta*):

'Believe nothing, O monks, merely because you have been told it . . . or because it is traditional, or because you yourselves have imagined it. Do not believe what your teacher tells you merely out of respect for the teacher. But whatsoever, after due examination and analysis, you find to be conducive to the good, the benefit, the welfare of all beings – that doctrine believe and cling to, and take it as your guide.'

The reader is particularly referred to John Snelling's chapter on The Western Buddhist Spiritual Quest (*The Elements of Buddhism*, published by Element Books) for sound and sensible advice.

ACKNOWLEDGEMENTS

Sincere thanks to the Buddhist community of the UK and Europe for their help in supplying information and for their friendliness, especially as most centres are staffed by voluntary help. In particular, we would like to thank Ard Verboom of the European Buddhist Union, Jim Belither of the New Kadampa Tradition and Dharmachari Vishvaparni of the Friends of the Western Buddhist Order.

INCLUSION IN FUTURE EDITIONS

Buddhist organisations who would like to be in the next edition of this book, should write to Peter Lorie c/o Newleaf, Pan Macmillan, 25 Eccleston Place, London SW1W 9NF giving address, telephone and fax numbers.

USE OF LANGUAGE

Some of the Buddhist terms used within this book are derived from the dead Indian languages of Pali and Sanskrit or from Tibetan. As none of these languages use a Roman alphabet, they are usually transcribed phonetically into European script. When transcribed into English, Pali and Sanskrit versions of the same terms may have slightly different spelling, but are still recognisable, e.g. Dharma (Sanskrit) and Dhamma (Pali). As Pali is the language of Theravada Buddhism and Sanskrit the language of Mahayana Buddhism, we have taken the spelling used by the centre concerned. Tibetan words and names, however, may be spelt differently when transcribed into different European languages, e.g. Kalu Rinpoche (English) and Kalou Rinpouché (French). For ease of use, we have therefore used English versions of Tibetan spellings throughout. In all cases, we have not used diacritical marks or accents for words from these languages.

Introduction

> The adept in Zen is one who manages to be human with the same artless grace and absence of inner conflict with which a tree is a tree. . . . He is all of a piece with himself and with the natural world, and in his presence you feel that without strain or artifice he is completely 'all here' – sure of himself without the slightest trace of aggression.
>
> – Alan Watts *This is IT and Other Essays on Zen and Spiritual Experience*

For anyone wanting to explore Buddhism, this is an exciting time and Europe an exciting place to do it. Not only is Buddhism expanding here and going through changes in its adjustment to our fundamentally different culture, it is also going through a revival in lands where it was once a big influence and having to face the growth of consumerism in the Far East.

Buddhism has throughout its long and varied history of contraction and expansion always been able to change and adapt. When taken to new countries, it has been able to mutate and integrate cultural elements. When Buddhists themselves felt that established practices had become stale, inaccessible or moved away from the original spirit of Buddha's teachings, new schools were born. Great thinkers and mystics have made their own changes, developing new lines of thought or reverting to an idea of something pure from the past. It has also survived being nearly eradicated from some countries, including India, its country of origin.

Buddhism's adaptability stems partly from its tradition of

having no central authority to judge what is and what is not acceptable within an established canon. This is a religion of practice and not of dogma, where the Buddha himself taught that each person needed to find out for himself what the truth was.

As a result, over 2,500 years after the life of the Buddha, there now exists a incredible variety of traditions. These range from the colourful, ritualistic Tibetan lineage with its secret Tantric teachings through to the austere, strictly minimalist approach of Zen and all the degrees in between; at one end of the scale Theravadins emphasise individual responsibility while Nichiren schools emphasise the efficacy of faith alone. And all these schools are now found in the West.

The meeting of a quintessentially Eastern religion with the busy and materialistic West has resulted in a range of responses. Some traditions seek to keep the purity of their original teachings and some have adapted enormously to the needs of Western lifestyles and attitudes. Both teachings and practices are being translated into European languages, some centres now conducting practices in European rather than Eastern languages.

Masters from the East are encountering western psychology and therapeutic techniques and some are integrating this into their work. This is particularly noticeable at the moment due to the diaspora of Tibetan teachers throughout the world following the Chinese invasion of Tibet in the 1950s. Tibetans now seek both to preserve their culture and religion and to adapt to the world outside the previously isolated Tibet. An increasing number of Westerners trained by Eastern masters either here or in the East go on to make a Western input.

Conversely, Buddhism is also influencing Western thinking, particularly in psychology. Some Western therapists now use Buddhist practices in their own systems of self development.

One of the distinctive features of Buddhism in the West is a great movement towards dialogue both between Buddhist traditions and with other religions. Many centres offer teachings from a combination of schools and lineages. Many are open to everyone regardless of religious persuasion, seeing their practices as of use to everyone. The only school which stands aloof from this is the Nichiren Shoshu which has historically avoided relations with other Buddhist groups.

Anyone approaching Buddhism in Europe has an incredible range of options open to them, both in terms of which school to choose and how Westernised it has become. There is something for everyone and if there is a problem, it is the danger of being overwhelmed by the number of options.

When visiting centres also be aware that the physical environment at individual centres may vary considerably. This is not only dictated by the tradition involved, but also the kind of physical space available. Buddhists in Europe practice everywhere from specially constructed and elaborate temples, through hired halls, to people's front rooms. You may find dedicated centres, communities, groups that meet in private homes on a regular basis, individuals that organise retreats and places used by several schools of Buddhism. Some also serve as cultural centres for expatriates of Far Eastern countries.

Although some centres have a missionary aim, Buddhism's aim is to make the Buddha's teachings available to all, but never to impose it on others. You are encouraged to investigate various schools and centres before choosing which one is best for you. Be aware that if you don't like one school or centre, others may be very different in style and approach.

> In Buddhism there is no place for using effort. Just be ordinary and nothing special. Eat your food, move your bowels, pass water, and when you're tired go and lie down. The ignorant will laugh at me, but the wise will understand.
>
> *– Lin-chi*

In 1980 there were only four Buddhist centres in Britain; today there are around 200. Throughout Europe, numbers have increased at a similar rate and European Buddhists now number between one and three million. People in the West are opening up to spiritual alternatives, often becoming disillusioned with their own spiritual traditions which they feel are too authoritarian in an increasingly individualistic society and unable to keep pace with changing values. Buddhism is attractive in that it emphasises the role of the individual in finding his or her own path while offering sound spiritual methods tested over many centuries and able teachers.

There also continues to be substantial academic interest in Buddhist psychology, philosophy and art.

HOW THIS BOOK WAS COMPILED

About 1,500 requests for information were sent out and entries for each centre have been compiled from replies to a questionnaire, brochures and other literature received in reply. Only centres which replied have been included. We have tried to be true to the spirit of each centre's information as given to us although it has had to be adapted to a standard format. Entries for each centre are based upon the information sent by the centres themselves and do not reflect the personal opinion of the authors. All entries are necessarily brief – contact centres direct for more information.

> What do you have to do?
>
> Pack your bags,
> Go to the station without them,
> Catch the train,
> And leave your self behind.
>
> Quite so: the only practice – and once.
>
> – Wei Wu Wei, *Open Secret*

HOW TO USE THIS BOOK

To find a Buddhist centre in a particular locality: Within each country, the method of ordering is written at the start of that country.

To find a Buddhist centre of a particular tradition: See listing of centres organised by school on page 339.

To find a particular teacher: All teachers are listed in the index.

If you still haven't found what you want: This Directory is by no means an exhaustive list of everything available in the UK and Europe. Apart from centres which did not reply to the questionnaire, there are also groups of Buddhist who meet regularly to study and practice but have no permanent premises – none of these are listed. Buddhism is also an expanding religion and centres are opening or moving to larger premises all the time. To track down these unlisted centres and groups, see the chapter on Finding Other Centres, Groups and Organisations.

USEFUL INFORMATION ON ENTRIES FOR CENTRES

Length of entry depends upon the amount of information sent by the centres themselves and is no indication of relative size or importance to a particular school.

The name of the school of Buddhism practised is in brackets after the name of the centre – see section on *Schools* for more information.

When applicable, there is information on retreats and these vary in content according to the tradition followed and the topic of the retreat. At some centres, there is a fairly relaxed attitude about attending sessions, at others, the behaviour asked of you is very strict and may require you to comply fully with monastic life and behaviour.

Apart from directly spiritual practices, other activities may be offered. These may be methods of self-development (physical or psychological), cultural activities, meditative practice or creative expression. For Tibetan Buddhism, this may be Thangka painting; for Zen, archery, calligraphy or tea ceremonies. Many traditions have started using Western psychotherapeutic techniques. Exercises such as tai chi chuan and hatha yoga combine physical exercise with meditative practice.

Founder/Guru The term Guru generally refers to Tibetan Buddhism, entries for other traditions referring to founders. H.H. = His Holiness. See *Glossary* for meanings of titles.

Residents Where applicable, numbers of both lay and

monastic residents are noted.

Festivals   As Buddhists use a lunar calendar, the dates for festivals vary from year to year, so the names only have been included – refer to the section on *Festivals* for more information.

Food   Although most centres offer vegetarian food, the Buddha refused to make vegetarianism compulsory. For him it was more important that the Sangha who lived by begging for their food should eat with gratitude whatever was put in their bowls.

Fees   Most Buddhist centres are non-profit making or charity organisations entirely dependent on donations. There is a general policy of making the teachings accessible to everyone who is interested, so most will accommodate differing financial states of people wanting to attend. Generosity is a Buddhist virtue and giving (*dana*) is a central part of Buddhist practice. The way this is expressed may vary. Some make no charge for teachings, but only to cover costs, some expect participants to donate what is appropriate to their income and some have concessionary prices for those on a low or no income.

Languages   Languages spoken by people at the centre do not necessarily mean that teachings happen in that language – check with centre where this is not clear.

Expected behaviour   This varies tremendously from place to place, ranging from the most casual to very strict adherence to set rules. There are also sometimes cultural dictates, such as the Thai custom of not showing the soles of the feet to either another person or to a Buddha image. Often either the Five or the Eight Precepts are specified – see Appendix: Precepts for details.

How to get there   Travel instructions are usually confined to public transport. Contact centre for fuller instructions if necessary.

Schools of Buddhism represented in this directory

> My teaching is not a philosophy. It is the result of direct experience. The things I say come from my own experience. You can confirm them all by your own experience. . . . Only direct experience enables us to see the true face of reality.
>
> – Thich Nhat Hanh, *Old Path White Clouds*

Association Zen Internationale A Soto Zen school. Soto Zen was brought to Europe by Taisen Deshimaru Roshi in 1967; until then, it had been known in Europe only through books. Kodo Sawaki Roshi, from whom Tasien Deshimaru received Transmission, endeavoured throughout his life to return Zen to its purest source – the teaching of Dogen Zenji and the practice of zazen. By 1982 when he died, Deshimaru Roshi had left a long line of books and publications, a large centre in Paris, a centre in the French countryside capable of accommodating 400 people, over 100 meditation centres and several thousand followers.

Ch'an Chinese Zen (see also Zen) that developed in the sixth and seventh centuries and stressed the possibility of sudden and direct enlightenment.

Changpa Kagyu See Tibetan and Kagyu.

Dachang Kagyu See Tibetan and Kagyu.

Drikung Kagyu See Tibetan and Kagyu.

Drukpa Kagyu See Tibetan and Kagyu.

Dzogchen A Tibetan school which has its roots in the the pre-Buddhist Bon religion of Tibet. It cannot be classified as a religious or philosophical tradition or as a school or sect; it is knowledge that Masters have transmitted without being limited by religious or scholastic tradition. It is not based on intellectual understanding but on awareness of the individual's true condition. Over the centuries it has been practised by adepts from all schools and traditions, although historically it has spread mostly in the Bon and Nyingma traditions. Can be taught, understood and practised in any cultural context.

Foundation for the Preservation of the Mahayana Tradition (FPMT) A Tibetan Gelug school founded in 1975 by Lama Thubten Yeshe. The majority of the FPMT centres are set up around the central activities of study and meditation, providing the means for their students to hear the teachings and meditate upon them. The FPMT seeks to integrate Buddha's teachings with the relief of physical as well as mental suffering and so runs healing centres around the world. In Bodh Gaya in India (the place of Buddha's enlightenment) a statue of Maitreya is being planned for placing in a specially created meditation grove. Two years after Lama Yeshe passed away, a Spanish child, Osel Hita Torres, was recognised as his reincarnation. He was ordained as a novice monk by the Dalai Lama at the age of three and is now studying and training as a monk and future master to prepare him to continue the work he started in his previous life. Lama Zopa Rinpoche is currently the FPMT spiritual director. The FPMT strives to follow the example and inspiration of His Holiness the Dalai Lama in his compassionate service to humanity.

Friends of the Western Buddhist Order (FWBO) Founded by Venerable Sangharakshita, a London-born Buddhist monk, in 1967. Draws from all main Buddhist traditions to take what is useful for the spiritual needs of Westerners. Most centres also offer classes in various indirect means of development, such as Hatha Yoga, Tai Chi Chuan, karate and massage. Either men or women may lead classes and meetings. There is only one ordination in the FWBO, the Dharmachari (for men) or Dharmacharini (for women). There are also Mitras who have formulated a special connection with the FWBO, neither monastic nor lay in that these distinctions are more to do with lifestyle than commitment to the Three Jewels. Some members live in monastic celibacy, some in communities and some in families. The FWBO places special emphasis on friendship as the Buddha stated that friendship is the whole of the spiritual life. The two main meditation techniques taught initially are Mindfulness of Breathing, which enhances awareness and peace of mind and Metta Bhavana which develops loving kindness. The main magazine of the FWBO is *Golden Drum*, from Windhorse Publications, Top Left, 3 Sanda Street, Glasgow G20 8PU.

Gelug A Tibetan school. Founded by the chief disciples of Tsongkhapa (1357–1419), a Tibetan monk who wanted to restore Tibetan Buddhism to the purity of its Indian sources and stressed the importance of ethics and the monastic virtues for monks. He encouraged study and rigorous intellectual evaluation so that practitioners might have a clear understanding of the nature and aim of the Buddhist path. Its highest award for philosophical study is the title Geshe. The Gelugpas held spiritual and temporal preeminence in Tibet from the sixteenth century through to 1959. Dalai Lama was the title originally given by the Mongols to the third head of this school and has been carried by its head since. Current practices include debate in Tibetan and English, reflective meditation on the Graduated Path (Lamrim) and Tantric visualisation techniques. Many Gelug centres are directed by Tibetan monk-lamas and although they aim to preserve the purity of the tradition, many now incorporate elements of Western culture, such as psychological approaches. Lay people within this tradition may practise to as high a level as they are able within the constraints of everyday life. Also sometimes referred to as the New Kadampa school.

International Meditation Centre (IMC) An organisation of Theravada centres worldwide. Founded in 1979 by the Sayagyi U Ba Khin Memorial Trust to provide for the instruction and practice of Theravada Buddhist Meditations. Its main centre is in Yangon, Myanmar (formerly Rangoon, Burma) and was founded by Sayagyi U Ba Khin.

International Zen Institute of America (IZIA) A Rinzai Zen organisation which aims to disseminate Zen Buddhist teaching and practice in Western society. Founded in 1983 by Venerable Gesshin Myoko Prabhasadharma Roshi who is its President. Now has formal branches in Florida, Germany, The Netherlands and Spain and many meditation groups in the USA and Europe.

Jodo Shin Lit: The School of the Pure Land. Present school founded by Honen (1133–1212 BCE). Unlike Jodo Shinshu, it has a monastic life. See also Pure Land.

Jodo Shinshu Lit: The True School of the Pure Land. Founded by the Japanese Buddhist Shinran Shonin (1173–1262 BCE) who taught that the actual recitation of the Nembutsu was not so important as the quality of faith underlying it, and that is a gift of pure grace. He saw that Buddhist life could be lived by ordinary people outside monasteries so taught a lay tradition and himself married and had children. See also Pure Land.

Kagyu A Tibetan school. Founded in the eleventh century by Gampopa. It is about practical mysticism rather than scholarship. It emphasises meditation and has produced many successful solitary meditators. Naropa (1016–1100 BCE), after a life of scholarship had a vision of an old crone who revealed the hard truth that the knowledge he had acquired was merely dry intellectual stuff, not the transrational knowledge of the heart. This shock drove him to the verge of suicide, but he was saved by discovery of his guru, Tilopa (988–1069 BCE) and underwent a gruelling twelve-year training in Tantra. After suppression of first transmission of Buddhism to Tibet, the Tibetans collected gold and went to India to obtain scriptures. One of them, Marpa (b. 1012) studied with Naropa among other great masters. Among the teachings he received were the Six Yogas of Naropa and Mahamudra. On returning to Tibet, Marpa settled down to ordinary life as a farmer and family man. His most famous disciple and heir to the lineage was Milarepa (1052–1135) who avoided both institutions and ordination as a monk – he is the prototype of the free wheeling yogi and poet following his own spontaneous spiritual path in lonely places. His most influential disciple was Gampopa (1079–1153), author of the classic text *The Jewel Ornament of*

Liberation and from his many disciples stem the three Kagyu sub-schools – Druk, Drikung and Karma. His main spiritual heir was the first Gyalwa Karmapa. Since that time, the Karmapas have reincarnated again and again to guide their tradition. The present Karmapa is the seventeenth and was discovered in Tibet in 1992.

Kanzeon Sangha Basically Soto Zen in the lineage of Hakuyu Taizan Maezumi Roshi but also includes teaching of the Rinzai school.

Karma Kagyu See Tibetan and Kagyu.

Mahayana Whereas Theravada Buddhism is about individuals attaining Enlightenment for themselves, Mahayana stresses the ideal of the Bodhisattva who aspires to Buddhahood solely that he might help others. All schools that are not Theravada are Mahayana.

New Kadampa Tradition (NKT) A Tibetan Gelug school. Founded by Geshe Kelsang Gyatso, a Tibetan Master resident in the UK since 1977, it seeks to promote the Buddha's teachings and practice in a form that is suited to the modern world and way of life. There are NKT centres worldwide.

Nichiren A Japanese tradition founded by Nichiren Shonin (1222–1282 CE) who espoused the doctrine that the Lotus Sutra represents the embodiment of the genuine teachings of the Buddha. This belief is affirmed by chanting Namu Myoho Renge Kyo, meaning Adoration to the Sutra of the Lotus of the Perfect Truth and Nichiren schools believe Buddhahood can be attained through recitation of this formula. It teaches that our destiny lies in our own hands and we must take responsibility for our own lives and make the necessary positive moves to settle our problems and release our full potential. Members are therefore actively counselled, helped and supported by the movement, and are encouraged to take up a three-fold practice involving faith, study and chanting. Faith is in the power of the Gohonzon, a scroll on which Nichiren Shonin wrote Namu Myoho Renge Kyo in mandalic form. The orginal is at head temple (Minobusan Kuonji in Japan, established by Nichiren Shonin in 1274), but members obtain their own copy and chant before it twice daily. Emphasis is on the earthly Buddha realm and Buddhist sociopolitical action. They strive to engender peace within themselves and throughout the world by actively disseminating their teachings. See also Nichiren Shu and Nichiren Shoshu.

Nichiren Shu (Lit: The School of the Lotus of the Sun.) Unlike the Nichiren Shu, they have a priesthood.

Nichiren Shoshu (Lit: True School of Nichiren.) Venerates Nichiren as a Buddha and is a lay organisation with no priesthood. Currently unique within Buddhism in avoiding relations with other Buddhist groups and for having a highly active policy for promoting itself. See also Soka Gakkai and Reiyukai. Other sub schools include Rissho Koseikai (an offshoot of Reiyukai) and Nipponzan Myohoji.

Non-sectarian Tolerance is part of the Buddhist tradition. In coming to the West, there have been great moves for dialogue both between other schools of Buddhism and other religions. Many Buddhist centres are also members of organisations that promote these ends.

Nyingma A Tibetan school which dates back to the first transmission of Buddhism to Tibet. They are more anarchic and less inclined to monastic life, leaning more towards magic than the other newer Tibetan traditions. They also particularly venerate Padmasambhava (also known as Guru Rinpoche), a Tantric adept who transmitted Buddhism to Tibet in the seventh century and who is also highly esteemed by other Tibetan traditions. He did not deliver all his teachings at that time, however, but hid some both geographically and in the mind for dicovery later when people would be better prepared to understand them.

Pure Land Unlike other forms of Buddhism which emphasise one's own efforts to attain Enlightenment, Pure Land schools emphasise the role of faith and ask Amitabha (Japanese: Amida), the Buddha of Infinite Light, to intercede spiritually on their behalf. Also known as Other-power Buddhism, because it teaches reliance on, or surrender to, the Power of the Buddha, rather than relying on our own efforts. The basic sutra of Pure Land tells how Amida, whilst still a Bodhisattva Lokeshvararaja vowed that he would found a 'Pure Land in the West' and not become a Buddha until all living things were redeemed. 'Whoever relies on my vow and calls my name will without exception be taken into my pure land.' The principal practice is the recitation of the name of Amida Buddha in the Japanese form, Namu Amida Butsu, known as the Nembutsu. It was the first really democratic form of Buddhism, concentrating on a simple theology of faith and Nembutsu practice and adherents remain firmly anchored in everyday life. It stresses humility rather than attainment, study and mediation being distrusted as leading to intellectual and spiritual arrogance. Great emphasis on good works, generating much charitable work. In Japan it is the most widespread school of Buddhism with twelve million followers. Jodo Shu and Jodo Shinshu (see separate entries) are Japanese but there are also Chinese and Vietnamese forms.

Reiyukai (pronounced Ray-You-Kye) is based in Nichiren. A unique movement whose philosophy is human-centred and focused on the untapped human potential of all men and women. Its aim is to help create a better human society for all – a world of sanity and compassion, awareness and integrity that we would wish to bestow on future generations. To help promote the process of self-development, members regularly recite the Blue Sutra. It started in Japan in 1919 and has since spread throughout the world. See also Nichiren.

Rigpa A Tibetan Nyingma school. International network of centres and groups named Rigpa where the teachings of Buddha are followed under the guidance of Sogyal Rinpoche.

Rime A Tibetan school started in Tibet in the last century by Jamyang Khyentse Wangpo and Jamgon Kongtrul Rinpoche which seeks to overcome sectarianism within Tibetan Buddhism and has especially influenced the Karma Kagyu and Nyingma schools.

Rinzai Zen A Japanese Zen school. Meditation is usually practised sitting in straight lines facing a partner. After meditative practice to bring about calmness and concentration, there is usually koan practice. Koans are riddles used by early masters in real life situations to enlighten their students. They are extremely active devices for throwing the student against the ultimate question of his or her own nature.

Sakya A Tibetan school that enjoyed great spiritual and temporal power in Tibet in the twelfth and thirteenth centuries. Its most important doctrinal and meditation cycle is 'The Path and Its Fruit', a systemisation of both Sutra and Tantric teachings credited to the ninth century Indian adept, Virupa, and based on the Hevajra Tantra. By following this path it is apparently possible to gain Enlightenment in a single lifetime. Present supreme head is H.H. Sakya Trizin.

Serene Reflection Meditation Tradition A Soto Zen school founded by Rev. Master Jiyu-Kennet, Abbess and Spiritual Director of Shasta Abbey. Can be followed as either a lay person or a monk. Their monastics are known as The Order of Buddhist Contemplatives and men and women have equal status and recognition, training together in the priesthood. All ranks and both sexes are addressed as Reverend and are referred to as monks and priests.

Shambhala International A Nyingma and Kagyu Tibetan school. Teachings on study and practice originally from Chogyam Trungpa Rinpoche and carried on by Sakyong Mipham Rinpoche. Involves the Shambhala Training programme of meditation and study and the Nalanda traditions of contemplative arts, education, health and livelihood. Classes and trainings include the Sacred Path of the Warrior.

Shin is an abbreviation of Jodo Shinshu – see Jodo Shinshu and Pure Land Buddhism.

Shingon Shingon is a Japanese esoteric and ritualistic school of Buddhism, and the word means 'School of the True Word'. Founded by Kukai (776–835 BCE) who developed it from Chinese Tantrism and took it to Japan in the first century BCE. It is a mystical teaching which seeks to awaken direct experience of

Enlightenment through study and practice of the Three Mysteries of Body, Speech and Mind. Methods include studies in Ritual Gesture (Mudra), Mandala and Chanting.

Soka Gakkai A Nichiren Shoshu school. (Lit: Scientific Society for the Creation of Values.) Modern Buddhist movement founded by Makiguchi Tsunesabwo in Japan in 1930, its current President being Daisaku Ideka. See Nichiren and Nichiren Shoshu.

Soto Zen A Japanese Zen school. Founded by Dogen Zenji (1200–1253), its meditation practice (Zazen or Shikantaza) is usually done facing a blank wall and is not about concentration, introspection or any kind of thinking – there should be no expectations or endeavour of any kind. The practice and realisation are the same thing – just to sit is to be a Buddha and it makes no distinction between new and advanced students.

Tarab Ladrang Institutes A Tibetan school founded by Tarab Tulku Rinpoche to teach and research Tibetan philosophy, psychology and psychotherapy and to undertake comparative studies of Western and Tibetan theory in these areas. Teachings interpret Buddhism for daily Western life and explain how to use the psychological and psychotherapeutic tools developed by Tarab Tulku. Tarab Rinpoche advises as to what is suitable for each individual. There are institutes in Denmark, France, Belgium, Germany and Austria.

Thai Forest Tradition A Theravada school which flourishes in the North-east of Thailand with a strong tradition of highly effective meditation and vinaya practice. It came to England after a visit in 1977 by the Venerable Ajahn Chah, a highly respected teacher from Thailand. Responding to requests from English Buddhists, he asked his senior Western disciple, Venerable Ajahn Sumedho to remain in England and continue teaching, assisted by other Western monks. The community has rapidly expanded, establishing four monasteries in England, with branch monasteries in Europe, Australia and New Zealand.

Theravada Thai, Sri Lankan and Myanmar are represented in Europe and vary slightly due to cultural differences. The earliest form of Buddhism still surviving today. All forms of Buddhism use the Pali Canon, but Theravada uses it exclusively. Has a strong monastic tradition and monks shave their heads and wear traditional ochre or orange robes. They are committed to a life of poverty, mendicancy and chastity and are bound at all times by numerous precepts and rules. The daily routine is austere and hierarchy is important. Monastics and lay people have a special relationship, the monastery being the spiritual focus of a community. In the West, there is usually a lay association which takes care of the monks' material welfare as the usual custom of monks making daily alms rounds with a begging bowls is not feasible. There is a school of thought that maintains that real practice is possible only for the ordained Sangha, but intensive lay practices have been established in the West, most notably by Mahasi Sayadaw and U Ba Khin.

Tibetan Buddhism The most colourful and ritualistic school of Buddhism present in the West. Seclusion of Tibet enabled Tibetans to preserve the Mahayana and Tantric Buddhism of India for over a millennium and create a uniquely rich spiritual culture. 'Unfortunately in 1950, the Chinese Communists felt the need to "liberate" these people from the thrall of Western imperialism. Despite the fact that there were virtually no Westerners – and certainly imperialists – in Tibet at the time, the Chinese went ahead ... and became imperialists themselves, taking over the government of what had hitherto effectively been an autonomous nation, colonising it, plundering its mineral and natural wealth, and making the Tibetans themselves virtual aliens in their own land. The Tibetans voted with their feet against this "liberation", and when the Chinese finally – and bloodily – completed their takeover in 1959, tens of thousands fled to exile in India. The virtual destruction of Buddhism in Tibet was completed during the Cultural Revolution (1966–76). Yet these violent and destructive events did have one positive outcome: they made the spiritual riches of Tibetan Buddhism accessible to Westerners for the first time.' John Snelling, *The Elements of Buddhism*. Several schools are currently represented in the West – see Kagyu, Nyingma, Gelug, Rime and Sakya.

Vipassana centres often do not consider themselves to be

Buddhist as they are often non-denominational. Vipassana may be practised by people of any culture or religion, although it was devised by the Buddha and is unique to Buddhism. It involves opening the mind and whatever arises in the field of attention is observed. It is a form of psychotherapy in which old fears, traumas and repressions, if merely treated to bear attention, simply pass away. See *Finding Other Centres, Groups And Organisations* for addresses of main centres in Europe.

Zen Probably originated in India but came into its own in China in the sixth and seventh centuries and is now found mainly in Japan and Korea. Places great emphasis on sitting meditation. Tends not to rely on words and logical concepts for communicating the Dharma, but stresses the primary importance of the enlightenment experience more than any other school. Teaches the practice of Zazen (or sitting meditation) as the shortest, albeit the steepest, way to awakening. See also Soto Zen and Rinzai Zen.

Buddhist teachers

If a man speaks or acts with a pure mind, joy follows him as his own shadow.

– The Dhammapada

This section is intended to cover the main teachers mentioned in this Directory and is not intended to be an exhaustive list. Abbreviations: H.H. = His Holiness. See *Glossary* for meanings of titles, e.g. Tulku or Ajahn.

Akong Rinpoche (Tibetan – Karma Kagyu) Spiritual director of Samyedzong in Dublin, Ireland. Trained as Abbot and doctor of traditional Tibetan medicine. Escaped from Tibet to India in 1959. Came to England in 1963 on study scholarship and worked as hospital porter to support himself. In 1967 founded Samye Ling with late Trungpa Rinpoche, first Tibetan Buddhist centre in Western Europe and has been Abbot and Director since. Is married with three children. Spiritual director of more than a dozen centres in Europe and South Africa which are associated with Samye Ling. Abbot of several Tibetan monasteries and nunneries in Tibet for which rebuilding schemes have been permitted by People's Republic of China. Recently, very active in raising and distributing funds for many educational and health care projects in rural Tibet. Also involved in establishing Tibetan Medical College in Scotland.

Ayang Rinpoche, Venerable (Tibetan – Drikung Kagyu) Born 1941 in Tibet. Lived in monastery age nine to eighteen. 1959 left

Tibet. Founded monastery in Southern India. Specialist in Phowa practices and carries blessings of the three Phowa lineages – Nyingma, Drikung and Namcho Phowa. At request of Dalai Lama, taught Phowa in Japan and frequently visits Europe and USA where he conducts Phowas courses and teaches at his various centres.

Ayya Khema (Theravada) Born 1923 in Berlin and is mother and grandmother. Founded Thai forest monastery in Australia in 1978 and ordained as nun in Sri Lanka in 1979. Founded a meditation centre for women near Colombo in Sri Lanka. In 1984 opened the Parappuduwa Nuns Island in Sri Lanka for women of all nationalities who want to live for an extended time in a monastery. Tours Europe, Australia, etc. Founder/resident teacher of Buddha-Haus in Germany. Author of books on Buddhist teachings which have been translated into nine languages.

Bokar Rinpoche, Venerable (Tibetan – Kagyu) (Karma Shedrup Yongdu Pal Zangpo) Born 1939 near Baar Monastery, where previously incarnated. Recognised as Tulku at age four by 16th Karmapa. Initially studied at Bokar monastery and age twelve to fourteen studied at Karmapa's main seat. 1959 went to Sikkim. From 1967, three-year retreat practising the Six Yogas of Niguma and then another three-year retreat under the direction and guidance of Kalu Rinpoche at Darjeeling. Later became retreat master at Sonada, India and was appointed master of three-year facility at Rumtek. Founded retreat centre at Mirik, Darjeeling, India.

Chah, Ajahn (Theravada – Thai) Meditation master of the Thai Forest tradition. Born in rural North-east Thailand. Ordained at early age. Studied basic Dhamma, discipline and scriptures as a young monk and later practised meditation under several masters of the forest tradition. Lived as an ascetic for several years, then spent short time with Ajan Mun and eventually settled in a thick forest grove near his birthplace. Large monastery grew up around him (Wat Pah Pong) and from this, numerous branch temples have sprung up in NE Thailand and elsewhere. Wat Pah Nanachat set up in 1975 as special training monastery for Westerners. Visited UK and USA in late seventies. Author of several books.

Chime Rinpoche, Lama (Tibetan – Karma Kagyu) Active in UK. Born in Tibet, recognised as Tulku. Received instruction in Mahamudra from Nyentrul Rinpoche and in Dzogchen from Dilgo Khyentse Rinpoche. Sent to West by Gyalwa Karmapa. In 1972 resigned as monk and married. Set up Kham Tibetan House in the UK in 1973 and Cho Khor Ling in 1987. Works for the British Library with their Tibetan manuscripts.

Dagpo Rinpoche (Tibetan – Gelug) Also known as Bamcho Rinpoche. Born in Tibet in 1932. Recognised as the reincarnation of the previous Dagpo Lama by the 13th Dalai Lama and studied calligraphy, reading and rituals at Bamcho monastery. Moved to Dagpo Shedrupling monastery at thirteen and studied the five great subjects of logic and tantra, and a special study of Lam Rim. Thirteen years later completed studies at Drepung Gomang monastery under some thirty-four teachers, including several retreats, astrology, grammar, poetry and history. Left in 1959 due to Chinese occupation. Arrived in France in 1960, teaching at the INLCO university and writing several books on Tibet and Buddhism in collaboration. Founded Centre Bouddhiste Tibetain Guepele Tchangtchoup Ling in 1978 and teaches there and at other Buddhist teaching centres in France, Italy, Switzerland, Holland, Belgium, Germany, Singapore and Indonesia. Often visits India to see his spiritual masters and teachers. Fluent in French.

Dagyab Kyabgon Rinpoche (Tibetan – Gelug) 9th Dagyab throneholder. Born Tibet 1939. Recognised as reincarnation of throneholder at early age and began education in 1946. Fled to India in 1959. Received Lharampa Geshe degree 1964. Studied five great subjects: Logic, Prajnaparamita, Madhyamaka, Abhidharma and Vinaya. Moved to Germany and became member of University of Bonn Central Asian Seminar. Spiritual guide to the Chodzong Buddhist Centre and teaches around Germany and other countries. Author of a number of books, articles and translations. Fluent in German and English.

Dalai Lama, H.H. the 14th (Gyalwa Tenzin Gyatso) (Tibetan) Spiritual and temporal head of the Tibetan people. Born 1935 in Tibet and recognised as Dalai Lama reincarnation at age two.

Taken to Lhasa in 1939 and formally enthroned 1940. Began education at six years old at Sera, Drepung and Gendun monasteries. Awarded Lharampa Geshe degree with honours at age twenty-four. Assumed full temporal powers early at age sixteen due to Chinese threat. Held discussions in Peking in 1954 on behalf of his people, but unsuccessfully. Left Tibet 1959 and given sanctuary in India. Since then has campaigned for peaceful return of Tibet to independence. In 1963 promulgated draft democratic constitution for Tibet and has since conducted his government-in-exile in Dharamsala, India, along those lines. Worked very successfully to resettle 100,000 Tibetan refugees and preserve Tibetan culture. Travels worldwide teaching and lecturing and has met political and spiritual leaders, scientists, doctors, writers and philosophers. Impresses people everywhere with his Buddhist message of peace and kindnesss. Author of several books. Considered one of the great Dalai Lamas along with the 5th and 13th. Won Nobel Peace Prize in 1989.

Damcho Yonten, Venerable Geshe (Tibetan – Gelug) Born 1930, Tibet. Entered Tibetan university at age six and studied Buddhist philosophy, psychology, logic, debate, scriptural subjects and meditation for twenty-three years. Completed studies in Ladakh and India after Chinese invasion of Tibet. Became Abbot of Samtenling Gompa Norba in Ladakh. Was requested by Western students he met in India to teach in West and Lam Rim Buddhist Centre in Wales was established for him to be Spiritual Director.

Deshimaru Roshi, Taisen (Zen – Soto) (1914–1982) Japanese who started religious training with Kodo Sawaki late in life and received Dharma Transmission. Settled in France in 1967 and based himself in Paris. Founded Association Zen Internationale in 1970 which now has centres in France, Belgium, Germany, USA, North Africa and South America. Died in Tokyo after teaching in France for fifteen years. Author of a number of books.

Dhammawiranatha Nayaka Thera, Most Venerable (Theravada – Myanmar) Born in Den Haag, The Netherlands. In 1977 he went to Indonesia and studied under Jinamitto Nayaka Thera. Founder and head monk of the Buddhayana centres in Europe. Divides his time between these viharas and centres.

Dharmapala, Anagarika (David Hewavitarne 1864–1933) (Theravada) Worked for the acceptance of Buddhism worldwide. Born in Sri Lanka and joined Theosophical Society at an early age. Attended American Parliament of World Religions in 1893. Campaigned for return of Bodh Gaya (one of the most sacred and historical Buddhist sites in India) to Buddhists. Sri Lanka was a part of the British Empire at this time and he fought against their attempts to uproot Buddhism. Realised his ambition to found the London Buddhist Vihara, the first Buddhist centre in Europe, in 1926 and thus took Buddhism to the capital of the British Empire. Also founded the Maha Bodhi Society of Sri Lanka

Dilgo Khyentse Rinpoche, H.H. (1910–1991) (Tibetan – Nyingma) Born in Tibet. Head of the Nyingma School and one of main lineage holders of the Dzogchen Longchen Nyingthig tradition. Recognised as an incarnation while still unborn and entered monastery at eleven. Enthroned as the wisdom-mind emanation of Jamyang Khyentse Wangpo (1820–92) by his teacher, Zhechen Gyaltsab Rinpoche who imparted to him all the essential instructions and empowerments of the Nyingma tradition. Has studied intensively with many great masters and scholars from all four lineage traditions. Practised for years in remote caves and solitary hermitages. Whilst in Tibet spent more than twenty years in retreat. Went into exile after Chinese occupation, establishing Zhechen Tenyi Dhargye Ling monastery in Nepal and became spiritual advisor to the Bhutan royal family. Built new stupa at Bodh Gaya and planned construction of seven other stupas in pilgrimage places associated with life of Buddha. Travelled extensively thoughout India, South-east Asia and the West. One of the most outstanding Nyingma masters and renowned for his Dzogchen practices. Author and famous for outstanding scholarship and wisdom. Important in preserving Tibetan spiritual heritage. One of founders of Longchen Foundation in the UK.

Dorje Lopon Lama Ngawang, Venerable (Tibetan – Kagyu) Born in Tibet 1927 and became a monk at the age of eight. Has spent long periods in retreat and on pilgrimages in Tibet. Fled to India in 1959 and completed three-year retreat at Sonada under the guidance of the Kalu Rinpoche. Invited to go to Stockholm, Sweden in 1976 through the assistance of the Gyalwa Karmapa and is now Director of Karma Shedrup Dargye Ling and Karma Dechen Osel Ling where he leads three-year retreats.

Drikung Kyabgon Chetsang, H.H. (Tibetan – Drikung Kagyu) The 37th Drikung Kyabgon was born in 1947 in Tibet to a famous family. Recognised as incarnation of previous Drikung Kyabgon in 1950 and at five received ordination from the Dalai Lama. Forced to leave his monastery in 1959 and went to live with a former tutor. Student of Chinese schools from 1960–1969 and then worked in communes in Tibet. Escaped to India in 1975 and resumed spiritual training. Studies included practices of Phowa, Mahamudra and the Six Yogas of Naropa. Since 1976 has travelled to many monasteries worldwide and toured extensively in the USA, Canada and the Far East.

Dudjom Rinpoche, H.H. (1904–1987) (Tibetan – Nyingma) Born into a noble family in Tibet. Recognised as an incarnation of a famous discoverer of many hidden teachings (Termas). Studied with many of the most outstanding lamas of his time. Only receiver of transmissions of all the existing teachings of the Nyingma tradition. Great *terton* (discoverer of hidden teachings) whose Termas are now widely taught and practised. Leading exponent of Dzogchen. A master of masters. Prolific author and meticulous scholar. Founded centres in India, Nepal and the West, including Urgyen Samye Choling in France.

Dzogchen Rinpoche, H.E. (Tibetan – Nyingma) Born 1964 in Sikkim. Recognised as 12th incarnation of Dzogchen Pema Rigdzin (1625-97). Enthroned 1972 and has received teachings from Dudjom Rinpoche (last head of the Nyingma school, a married lama who died in France in 1987) and Dilgo Khyentse Rinpoche among others. Education closely supervised by the Dalai Lama. Currently rebuilding Dzogchen Monastery (formerly foremost Nyingma centre in Tibet) in Mysore, India. Has visited Europe and USA at invitation of Sogyal Rinpoche. Thought to have great potential as a future Nyingma teacher. One of the spiritual directors of Rigpa.

Gendun Rinpoche, Lama (Tibetan – Kagyu) Born 1918 in Tibet. Began studies at seven. At seventeen fully ordained. Three-year three-month retreat on the Six Yogas of Naropa at twenty-one. Main teacher Lama Tulku Tenzin. Went on pilgrimage through Tibet and Nepal, meditating in caves blessed by great siddhas of the past. In 1959, went to India where 17th Karmapa gave him directorship of a monastery in Bhutan. After three years went into semi-retreat for twelve years, visiting Karmapa for instruction once every year. In 1975 Karmapa advised him to go to France and he took up residence at Dhagpo Kagyu Ling. Has visited many Buddhist centres in Europe and since 1986 has also directed the three-year retreat centre of Thong Drol Ling in Germany.

Gonsar Tulku Rinpoche, Venerable (Tibetan – Gelug) Born into aristocratic Tibetan family in 1949. At three recognised by the Dalai Lama as the reincarnation of a famous lama. At the age of six, joined Seraje Monastery and studied under the late Geshe Rabten. In 1959, went with him to India. In 1974 accompanied him to Switzerland to reside at Rabten Choeling where he is now Abbot and director of its teaching centre. Has collaborated in the translation of many books on Mahayana Buddhism.

Govinda, Lama Anagarika (E.L. Hoffmann 1898–1985) (Tibetan) Of Bolivian and German extraction. Studied architecture, archaeology and philosophy in Europe. Was also an artist and lived for a while in an artistic colony on Capri. Went to Sri Lanka in 1928 to study stupas and got interested in Buddhism. First interest was in Theravada and he ordained as an anagarika. In 1931 met Tibetan Buddhism at a Buddhist conference in Darjeeling and met his guru, Tomo Geshe Rinpoche, in whose memory he set up Arya Maitreya Mandala after his death. During 1930s and 1940s studied Buddhism in Ladakh, Sikkim and Tibet. Wrote *The Way of the White Clouds* and *Foundations of Tibetan Buddhism*, the first comprehensive account of Tibetan Buddhism by a Westerner practitioner.

Hogen Daido (Yamahata) Roshi (Zen – Soto). Japanese non-resident teacher of Jiko An in Spain, an Open Way Zen Buddhist Community. Abbot of Chogenji (Japan). Trained in both Rinzai and Soto schools. Leads soto-style sesshins in Europe each year that incorporate hatha yoga with traditional elements.

Hookham, Michael (Lama Rigdzin Shikpo) (Tibetan – Nyingma)

Born 1935 in London. Mathematician interested in possible relations between Buddhism, Western science and psychotherapy. Studied Theravada for nine years before meeting his Tibetan teacher, Trungpa Rinpoche in 1965 who asked him to begin teaching in 1975. Established Longchen Foundation under Trunpa Rinpoche's direction and established Nitartha School.

Humphreys, Christmas (1901–83) One of the first propagators of Buddhism in the West. Born in London and educated at Cambridge. Long and distinguished career in criminal law. Visited Japan after World War II to sit on International War Crimes Tribunal. Married. Founded the Buddhist Lodge which later became the Buddhist Society in 1924. Great public speaker, broadcaster and writer on Buddhism. Author of books on Buddhism, theosophy and an autobiography as well as books of poetry.

Ikeda, Daisaku (Nichiren Shoshu) President of Soka Gakkai International. Born 1928 in Tokyo. Came across Soka Gakkai when about nineteen 'and knew instantly that this was a way of life he must follow'. Became President on death of previous incumbent in 1960. Set out to raise membership to three million, which he did by 1962. Formed Soka Gakkai International in 1975 and began holding dialogues with eminent world leaders and leading intellectuals, arranging cultural exchanges, etc. UN Peace Award in 1972. Author of a number of books.

Jampa Thaye, Lama (Tibetan – Sakya) Co-founder with Karma Thinley Rinpoche of the Dechen community – an association of meditation centres and groups in the UK. Born in England in 1952. Began study and practice of Vajrayana Buddhism in 1972. Later appointed as Karma Thinley Rinpoche's spiritual representative. Has PhD in Tibetan religious history and author of a number of books and articles. Married with three children. One of the few Westerners qualified and authorised to give Vajrayana empowerments.

Jiyu-Kennett, Reverend Master (Peggy Teresa Nancy Kennett) (Zen – Soto) Born in England and trained at Trinity College of Music, London. Ordained in 1962 in Malaysia. Studied Soto Zen in Japan. Installed as Abbess of a temple in Japan and taught her own Western students. Recognised as Roshi (Master). Travelled to the West to promote Soto Zen in the West and founded abbeys in the USA, Canada and in 1972 the Throssel Hole Priory in the UK. Author of several books.

Kalu Rinpoche (1904–1989) (Kagyu – Dachang) Born 1905 in Tibet to parents who were Rime students. Recognised as Tulku but not ordained, wandering freely instead and educated by father. At thirteen began formal studies. Received ordination from 11th Tai Situpa. Studied sutra and tantra teachings, receiving empowerments from many great lamas. At sixteen underwent three-year retreat under direction of Norbu Tondrup from whom he received complete transmission of teachings of Karma Kagyu and Shangba Kagyu traditions. At age twenty-five went into twelve-year solitary retreat. Became Director of three-year retreats at Palpung at request of Tai Situpa. Recognised by 16th Gyalwa Karmapa as incarnation of Jampgon Kontrul Lodro Thaye. Toured Tibet in 1940s and asked to leave in 1955 by Karmapa. Established two centres in Bhutan and ordained 300 monks. Pilgrimages to India. In 1965 established headquarters in Darjeeling, India and another three-year retreat. Invited to the West in 1971. With the blessing of the Dalai Lama and the Karmapa founded Karma Ling in 1980. The tradition passed to his disciple Lama Denys Teundrop. Founded several centres for practice of Chenrezig Sadhana in France and USA. Principal centre in North America in Vancouver. Began three-year retreats for Westerners in France at his two centres. Author of a number of books. Venerated by all lines of Tibetan Buddhism.

Karma Thinley Rinpoche (Tibetan – Sakya) Co-founder with Lama Jampa Thaye of the Dechen community – an association of meditation centres and groups in the UK. Born in Tibet in 1931 and subsequently recognised as an incarnate lama. Studied with some of the most distinguished masters of Tibetan Buddhism. Vajrayana meditation master and highly renowned poet and artist. Settled in Toronto, Canada, in 1971 and has founded numerous centres throughout the world. Principal seat at Legshay Ling Monastery in Nepal.

Karmapa, H.H. the 16th Gyalwa (Rangjung Rigpe Dorje 1923–

1981) (Tibetan – Kagyu) Born in Tibet. Recognised as new incarnation early on. At age seven received ordination from Tai situpa and Vajra Crown and Karmapa robes one year later. Enthroned by Situ Rinpoche at Palpung. Studied for four years with Beru Khyentse Rinpoche and Bo Kangkar Mahapandita. Received empowerments and transmissions from Situ Rinpoche in 1937. Intensive practice and pilgrimage 1940–1944. Full monk ordination 1945. Became master of Mahamudra in 1948. Visited Beijing with Dalai Lama in 1954. Given empowerment of the thousand-armed Avalokiteshvara from Dalai Lama. Started to send lamas out of Tibet in 1957 and left himself in 1959 for Bhutan, then Sikkim where he set up headquarters at Rumtek. World tour in 1974. Established number of centres, notably Dhagpo Ling in France in 1977 and Karma Triyana Dharmachakra in USA in 1981. Died in Chicago.

Karmapa, H.H. the 17th Gyalwa (Urgyen Trinley Dorje) Born 1985 in Tibet. Enthroned 1992.

Karta, Lama (Tibetan) After education in India both at English school and Kalu Rinpoche's monastery, he decided to become a monk at the age of seventeen. When twenty-three, sent to France to teach and has been in Belgium since 1987. Has produced a cassette of sacred Tibetan songs. Lives in Yeunten Ling in Belgium.

Kelsang Gyatso Rinpoche, Venerable Geshe (Tibetan – Gelug – New Kadampa Tradition) Born 1932 in Tibet. Ordained and entered Jampa Ling monstery in 1940. Moved to Sera monastery. Left Tibet in 1959 and undertook intensive meditation retreats in Nepal and India until 1977. Awarded Geshe degree in 1972. Resident in Britain since 1977. Now a naturalised British citizen. Founded the New Kadampa Tradition and is Spiritual Director of the worldwide community of NKT centres. Author of a number of books.

Khemadhammo Mahathera, Venerable (Theravada – Thai) Born in England in 1944. Interest in Buddhism took him to Hampstead Vihara and FWBO. Took up training seriously under a Thai Bhikkhu resident in Hampstead. Co-founder of Wat Buddhapadipa Lay Buddhist Association in London until 1971 when he went to Thailand. Began vipassana training at Wat Mahadhatu, Bangkok. Took samanera ordination. Went to stay with Ven Ajach Chah in 1972 and was resident at his wats for next few years where he took Bhikkhu ordination. Visited England with Ajahn Chah and Ven. Sumedho Bhikkhu and began visiting prisons. Esablished vihara on Isle of Wight in 1979 and Buddha-Dhamma Vihara at Kenilworth in 1984. Launched Agulimala in 1985 and became its spiritual director. Moved to The Forest Hermitage in Warwick in 1985 and beame resident Ajahn. Lectures at Warwick Univeristy and still travels extensively to visit prisons. Founder and teacher of Wat Pah Santidhamma in Warwickshire.

Kyabje Gosok Rinpoche, H.E. (Tibetan – Gelug) Born 1948 in Tibet. Recognised as a reincarnation of a lama by the Dalai Lama at the age of four and studied at Sera, one of the three great monastic universities of Tibet. Left Tibet in 1959 after the Chinese occupation. Named Abbot of Monastery University of Gyurme, and started the reconstruction work in India in 1988. In 1989, a group of ten artists from Sera Med under his direction created 'Sacred Dance and Music' which toured Europe to raise funds for the Sera Med community.

Lobsang Tengye, Venerable Geshe (Tibetan – Gelug) Qualified as Geshe after twenty-five years of study in the five main subjects at the Seraje monastery both in Tibet and in exile in India. On the instruction of the Dalai Lama, in 1969 he was sent to Thailand for eight years to study on a scholarship awarded by the Thai goverment. Went to France in 1978, first two years at the Linhson Vietnamese Monastery in Paris and then becoming the resident teacher at Institute Vajra Yogini in 1980.

Maezumi Roshi, Taizon (Zen – Rinzai) Born 1931 in Japan. Ordained Zen monk at eleven. Degrees in Oriental literature and philosophy from Komazawa University. Dharma transmission from two major lines of Rinzai Zen. Holds credentials as Training Master. Went to Los Angeles in 1956 as priest of Zenshuji Temple. Founded Zen Center of Los Angeles in 1967 and Kuroda Institute for Transcultural Studies in 1976. Founding influence behind Zen Arts Center in New York. Author of a number of books.

Mahasi Sayadaw, H.H. (U Sobhana Mahathera 1904–1982) (Theravada – Myanmar) Began studying in monastery at age six. Became Samanera at twelve and Bhikkhu at twenty. Studied with U Narada and after intensive meditation course worked as teacher of Buddhist scriptures. Passed government-sponsored Pali and scholastic exams with distinction. Asked to give meditation instruction in Rangoon in 1949 by Prime Minister and another member of Buddha Sasananuggaha Association where he held intensive training courses. An estimated 45,000 received instruction at the centre and 600,000 across the nation. Many ancillary centres set up in Myanmar and also spread abroad to Thailand, Bangladesh, India, Sri Lanka, Europe, South Africa, Australia and USA. Author of several books.

Merzel Sensei, Dennis Genpo (Zen – Soto/Rinzai Synthesis) Born 1944 in New York. Degree in economics and educational administration. Taught for eight years before moving to Zen Center of Los Angeles in 1972 where began studying with Maezumi Roshi. Ordained Zen monk in 1973 and assisted Maezumi Roshi in guiding student practice in 1978. Completed koan study and appointed Dharma Holder in 1979. Received Dharma Transmission in 1980. Travelled to Japan for installation as Zen priest in 1981. Lived with wife at ZCLA until 1984 and was executive vice-president. Since June 1984 has been guiding the Kanzeon Sangha in England, Poland, Holland, France and Germany – its headquarters are in Salt Lake City, Utah. Genpo Sensei has taught in Europe since 1982.

Mother Sayamagyi (Theravadan – Myanmar – International Meditation Centre) Mahasadhammajotikadhaja Sayamagyi Daw Mya Thwin first started teaching Theravada Vipassana meditation at the IMC in Yangon, Myanmar (formerly Rangoon, Burma) under Sayagyi U Ba Khin, whom she assisted from 1953 until his demise in 1971. Was able to follow Sayagyi U Ba Khin's teachings completely. From 1971 until 1978, Mother Sayamagyi (as she is known to her students), together with her husband, Sayagyi U Chit Tin, continued to run the IMC Yangon and to teach meditation there. In 1978 Mother Sayamagyi and Sayagyi U Chit Tin left Myanmar and soon became based at IMC UK, from where they regularly visit student groups around the world including four other IMCs.

Namkhai Norbu Rinpoche, Chogyal (Tibetan – Dzogchen) Born in 1938 in Tibet. Recognised as reincarnation of the great Dzogchen master Adzam Drukpa (1842–1934). Lived in the West since 1960, when invited to collaborate at the Is.M.E.O. cultural institute in Rome. Subsequently Professor of Tibetan Langauge and Literature and Mongolian Language and Literature from 1964 to 1992 at the Istituto Universitario Orientale in Naples. Deep knowlege of Tibetan culture, especially history, literature, medicine and astrology. Well known for activities in aid of the Tibetan people and their culture. Founder and resident teacher at Merigar in Italy. Has established Dzogchen study centres throughout the world, the main ones being in Italy, the United States and Argentina. Teaches also in Australia, Japan, Russia, etc.

Narada Mahathera, Venerable (Sumanapala Perera 1898–1983) (Theravada – Sri Lanka) Born in Sri Lanka and English-educated. Entered Sangha at eighteen and received traditional monastic education but also studied philosophy, logic and ethics at University. First travelled abroad to India in 1929 and later travelled widely in South-east Asia and developed close ties with Indonesia and Vietnam. Promoted Theravada Buddhism in Western Europe. Elected President of the Buddhist Vihara Society in London. Author of many books.

Ngawang, Venerable Lama Thurman (Tibetan – Gelug) Born 1931 of nomad family in Tibet. Studied at Dhargyey monastery from age fourteen. At twenty-five moved to Seraje monastery and was taught by Geshe Rabten. Moved to India in 1959. Studied and gained Geshe Lharampa degree 1975–79. Spiritual head of Tibetisches Zentrum in Germany. Various publications in German.

Nichiren Shonin (1222–1282) (Nichiren) Japanese founder of Nichiren schools. Sent to monastery to study at age eleven and ordained at fifteen. From early age wondered why there were so many schools of Buddhism while the Buddha expounded only one. After considerable study of all the schools, he concluded that the Lotus Sutra represented the perfect culmination of the teaching of the Buddha. In 1253, started preaching at a time when Japan was in turmoil due both to political factions and natural disasters and the people in a state of panic amidst famine and plague. Wrote *Rissho Ankoku Ron* (Treatise on Spreading Peace Throughout the Country by Establishing Righteousness), in which he attributed the disasters to 'the foolishnesss of the government and the degeneracy of the people who were superstitious and misguided religous beliefs'. He suggested they convert to his faith. Despite persecution, his missionary zeal continued and he wrote several more works. Buried at Mount Minobu.

Ohtani, H.E. Lord Patriarch Kosho (Pure Land) Chief Abbot Emeritus of Nishi Honganji, Kyoto. Has visited Europe several times and conducted services and ceremonies here.

Ole Nydahl, Lama (Tibetan – Karma Kagyu) After studying philosophy in Copenhagen, he studied meditation practice from 1968 with H.H. Gyalwa Karmapa. With his wife, he was his first Western student. Authorised to teach Dharma. Has worked as a meditation teacher round the world and has founded many centres in the name of the Karmapa.

Prabhasadharma, Venerable Gesshin Myoko (Zen – Rinzai) Zen Master and Bhikshuni trained in Japanese and Vietnamese Rinzai Zen tradition. Entered Zen training in 1967 in Los Angeles under Japanese Zen Master, the Most Venerable Joshu Kyozan Denkyo-Shitsu Roshi. In 1973 and 1974 trained in Zen monastery in Kyoto, Japan. In 1985 received the 'Dharma Mind Seal Transmission of a Great Master' from the Most Venerable Dr. Thich Man Giac, and became the 45th Generational Heir in the Vinitaruci lineage of Vietnamese Rinzai Zen. Dedicated to deeper understanding between world religions and the strengthening of the position of women in religious traditions. Founding member of American Buddhist Congress. Founder and president of International Zen Institute of America which also has centres in Europe. Author of several books and publications.

Rabten, Geshe (1920–1986) (Tibetan – Gelug) Born into farming family in Tibet. Entered Seraje monastery at eighteen under teacher Geshe Jhampa Khedup. Became adept at rigorous philosophical debate and underwent frequent meditation retreats. Suffered poverty and undernourishment until appointed tutor to

Gonsar Tulku. Fled Tibet in 1959 and set up courses of study. Awarded Lharampa Geshe in 1963 then moved to Dharamsala and became personal assistant to Dalai Lama. Began instructing Westerners at Namgyal monstery. Sunyata retreat 1970. Invited to Europe 1974 and became Abbot of Tibetan Monastic Institute at Rikon in Switzerland in 1975. Founded centre at Mont Pèlerin in 1977 and taught in USA and other European countries, establishing centres in Germany, Italy and Austria. Author of a number of books.

Rewata Dhamma, Venerable Dr. (Theravada – Myanmar) Spiritual Director of Birmingham Buddhist Vihara and other centres in Britain and Europe. Has been teaching in England and in the West since 1975. Ph.D. in the Philosophy and Psychology of Buddhism and has published on the subject. Conducts yearly courses of meditation in England, Scotland, Holland, Belgium, Germany, France, the former Czech Republic and Switzerland.

Sakya Trizin, H.H. (Tibetan – Sakya) Born in Tibet in 1945 of royal family descent. Head of the Sakya tradition since age of seven upon the death of his father. Has received intensive training in the study and practices of the Sakya tradition. Seven-month retreat whilst still a child. In 1959 at age fourteen left Tibet and went to India and received instruction on the Rime collections, the Collection of Tantras and the Lamdre. Holds the three main Sakya lineages of Sakya, Tsar and Ngor. Also holds complete teachings of both the Iron Bridge and Great Perfection lineages of Nyingma. Has founded numerous monasteries throughout India and East Asia. Seat in exile is at Rajpur, India. Since 1974 has made several world tours, teaching in Europe, USA and South-east Asia. Fluent in English.

Sakyong Mipham Rinpoche (Tibetan – Nyingma and Kagyu – Shambhala) Eldest son of Chogyam Trungpa Rinpoche. Born in India in 1962 and moved to Scotland to be with his father at the age of eight. Joined his father in the USA in 1972 after a two year separation where he continued his Western education and started extensive training in the Buddha dharma and Shambhala arts. Empowered as the Sawang (Earth Lord) and heir to the Shambhala lineage in 1979, and continued his training under close guidance from his father, gradually taking on responsibilities and starting to teach. After the death of Chogyam Trungpa in 1987, he returned to Asia to train with H.H. Dilgo Khyentse Rinpoche, who asked him to return to the West and lead the Shambhala community in 1990. Recognised as a tulku by H.H. Pema Norbu Rinpoche, head of the Nyingma lineage, who continues to teach him. Enthroned as Sakyong Mipham Rinpoche in 1995.

Sangharakshita (D.P.E. Lingwood) (Friends of the Western Buddhist Order) Founder of the Friends of the Western Buddhist Order (FWBO). English Buddhist monk born 1925 in London who spent 20 years in India, practising, studying, teaching and writing. Ordained as Theravadin monk in 1949 after living as a wandering ascetic and meeting many spiritual teachers. When Dr. B.R. Ambedkar died a few weeks after founding a movement for mass conversion to Buddhism of ex-'Untouchables' to remove them from the terrible stigma imposed on them by the caste system, Sangharakshita stepped into the breach. Following the Chinese invasion of Tibet, he met many eminent lamas who had fled to India. Received Bodhisattva precepts from the Venerable Dhardo Rinpoche and Vajrayana initiations from others, including Jamyang Khyentse Rinpoche, Dilgo Khyentse Rimpoche and Dudjom Rinpoche. Returned to the UK in 1964 and established the FWBO in 1967. Author of many books.

Sayagyi U Ba Khin (Theravadan – Myanmar – International Meditation Centre) Founder of the International Meditation Centre in Yangon, Myanmar (formerly Rangoon, Burma) and it is after him that the Sayagyi U Ba Khin Tradition of Theravada Buddhist meditation is named. Lived in Myanmar from 1899 to 1971 and taught meditation from 1941 until his death. Established the IMC Yangon in 1952 with the construction of a Dhamma Yaung Chi Ceti (Light of the Dhamma Pagoda). At the same time as being an eminent meditation teacher, was Accountant General of Myanmar from 1948 to 1953 and subsequently held a number of senior posts in government. Learned meditation from a lay teacher, Saya U Thetgyi who, in turn, studied under the well-known and much respected Myanmar monk, Venerable Ledi Sayadaw.

Sayagyi U Chit Tin (Theravadan – Myanmar – International Meditation Centre) Saddhammajotikadhaja Sayagyi U Chit Tin is one of the leading disciples of the late Sayagyi U Ba Khin of Myanmar (formerly Burma) under whom he studied Theravada Vipassana meditation from 1950 until Sayagyi U Ba Khin's demise in 1971. From 1953 onwards Sayagyi U Chit Tin and his wife, Mother Sayamagyi, assisted their teacher in his work at the Centre and carried on his work there after his demise until 1978. An officer in the Accountant General's Office and also Chief Accountant to the Sixth Buddhist Synod, held in Yangon from 1954 to 1956. Left Myanmar with his wife for the West in 1978, where they have since established five more Sayagyi U Ba Khin Centres. Has either written or edited over twenty publications about the Buddha Dhamma for the Sayagyi U Ba Khin Memorial Trust, UK.

Sheng-yen, Venerable Dr. (Ch'an) Abbot of monastery of Taiwan and Head of Institutes of Chung Hwa Buddhist Culture in Taiwan and New York. Founder of Bristol Ch'an Group and Western Zen and Ch'an Retreat Centre at Shipham, UK. Second generation teacher in lineage of the Great Master Hsu Yun who did so much to restore Ch'an in China in the early years of this century. Has trained within the tradition of the great Harada Roshi, from whom several lineages of American Zen are currently descended. Received doctorate in Buddhist Studies in Japan and is a considerable scholar.

Shenphen Dawa Rinpoche, H.E. (Tibetan – Nyingma) Born in Tibet in 1950, son and Dharmaheir of Dudjom Rinpoche. Received transmissions from an early age, gaining a particularly full personal training from his father in the Nyingma tradition. Conventional education at European schools in India. Fluent in English. Travelled widely in Europe and North America, setting up centres in Spain, England, Switzerland and the USA. Committed to the continuance of Dudjom Rinpoche's teachings. Lives in the Dordogne in France.

Sherab Dorje, Lama (Tibetan – Kagyu) Born in Bhutan in 1941. Studied main Kagyu texts for twenty years in Bhutan and performed three-year retreat on the Six Yogas of Niguma under the Kalu Rinpoche in India. Currently director of Kagyu Ling in

France. Particularly skilled in painting, sculpture and architecture.

Sherab Gyaltsen Amipa, Venerable Geshe (Tibetan – Sakya) Works closely with Dalai Lama. Born in Tibet and sent to Europe to found the Tibetan Institute of Rikon in Switzerland after short stay in India. Teaches in various European Sakya centres. Founder of the European Institute of Tibetan Buddhism in Kuttolsheim in France.

Shifu Nagaboshi Tomio (Dr. T Dukes) (Shingon) Primary teacher in Britain of the Kongo Raiden Ha (Branch) of Shingon Buddhism. Initiated by the Venerable Fa-Tao-Meng, himself the direct student of the Acarya Chin-Kang Tsu, head of the Chinese Order. By initiating a Westerner, the Venerable Fa-Tao fulfilled a prophecy made several generations previously. Shifu has also studied many other forms of Buddhist doctrine and practice with Tibetan, Thai, Korean, Chinese and Japanese teachers.

Shinran Shonin (b. 1173) (Pure Land – Jodo Shinshu) Japanese founder of Jodo Shinshu. Born near Kyoto and orphaned early in life. Became a monk on Mount Hiei, the greatest centre of Buddhist learning at the time and studied learning, discipline and meditation. After more than twenty years, he was still very much aware of his imperfections and inability to attain what he so desperately sought. In desperation, he left the monastery and soon after met Honen Shonin, who was the founder of Jodo Shu and whom he acknowledged as his teacher. He married and had children and referred to himself as neither monk or lay man.

Sogyal Rinpoche (Tibetan – Nyingma – Rigpa) Born in Tibet in the early 1950s. Raised mostly at Dzongsar monastery in the care of the renowed lama Jamyang Khyentse Chokyi Lodro who recognised him as the reincarnation of Terton Sogyal, a discoverer of many hidden texts and a Dzogchen master. Learnt poetry, drama, logic and various Buddhist texts from private tutors. Taken to Sikkim in 1954 due to growing Chinese occupation. Following the death of his root lama, he continued his studies with Dudjom Rinpoche and Dilgo Khyentse Rinpoche and also began to study English in 1959. University in Delhi studying Indian philosophy and took up a scholarship to Cambridge University in England to study comparative religion. Served as translator and aide to Dudjom Rinpoche, the inspiration for his work in the West, for a number of years. Has established a number of teaching centres in Europe and North America, the Rigpa Fellowship who practise under his guidance. Spends most of his time travelling and teaching around the world, specialising in presenting the Tibetan views on death and dying and Dzogchen. Author of several books.

Sonam Gyaltsen, Geshe (Tibetan – Gelug) Born in Tibet in 1926. Became monk at age of five and began elementary studies. Transferred to Ganden Jangtse monastery when eighteen where he stayed until 1959. Completed his studies and gained Lharampa Geshe degree in India. Entered lower tantric college and gained Ngagrampa degree. Took acarya degree and doctorate in Buddhist studies at Institute for High Tibetan Studies at Varanasi. Appointed tutor to several students in 1977. Moved to France in 1980 and taught at Guepele Tchantchoup Ling and other teaching centres in France and Italy. Appointed leader of ritual at Gyume monastery in India in 1990.

Sotetsu Yuzen Sensei (Dr Klaus Zernickow) (Zen) Leader of Zendos in Germany, Poland and Austria. Worked as a doctor. Trained by Seki Yuho Roshi in Rinzai Zen. Ordained as Zen monk at the age of forty. Studied also under the Master Che Hua in China where he became a Ch'an master of the Lin-Chi school.

Sumedho, Ajahn (Theravada – Thai) American-born Theravada meditation master who founded various Western monasteries. Far East and Asian studies in America with visits to Far East due to army service, Peace Corps to teach English in Thailand. Ordained on vacation in Laos, later became disciple of Ajahn Chah at Wat Pah Pong. Became Abbot of the international Wat Pah Nanachat in 1974. Established Chithurst Forest Monastery in England in 1979 and various other centres have sprung from this. Abbot of Amaravati in Hemel Hempstead, England and goes on regular world tours. Honorary President of the Buddhist Society. Author of several books.

Tai Situpa Rinpoche, H.E. 12th (Pema Dongak Nyingshe Wangpo) (Tibetan – Kagyu) Born in Tibet in 1954. Identified by the 16th Karmapa as the reincarnation of Situ Tulku. When six, left for Bhutan due to Chinese occupation, then on to Sikkim. Joined Rumtek monastery. Received full range of empowerments from the 16th Karmapa and undertook a rigorous programme of study. Trained in the arts associated with Tibetan Buddhism. Assumed full traditional responsibility in 1975. Early 1980s founded Sherab Ling monastery in North India and established his headquarters there. Since 1980 has toured extensively in Western countries and visited Tibet in 1984. Founded Maitreya Institute in USA in 1984 – now has branches in USA and France. Organises and participates in international conferences. One of the regents heading the Karma Kagyu tradition until the new Karmapa is instated. Author of a few books.

Taikan Jyoji (Zen – Rinzai) Spent twelve years in Japan, seven in the Zen monastery of Shofuku-ji in Kobe under the direction of Yamada Mumon Roshi, a famous Rinzai master. Between retreats he was initiated into the arts of Japanese Zen archery and Zen calligraphy. On his return to France in 1974, founded the Centre du Taillé (since renamed Centre de la Falaise Verte). In 1989 received the title Kaikyoshi, Master founder of Zen for Europe. Author of several books on Zen.

Tarab Tulku Rinpoche (Tibetan) 11th incarnation of Tarab Tulku. Educated in Tibet in Buddhist psychology, philosophy and metaphysics as well as in meditation disciplines including Tantra. Currently head of the Tibetan section of the Royal Library and the Tibetan section of Copenhagen University. Has lectured at universities in Europe and the USA and published articles on Buddhist psychology and philosophy. Has compiled and developed an all-encompassing personal and transpersonal psychology and psychotherapy adapted to modern life while still maintaining its Indian and Tibetan essence. Teaches courses in Europe and the Americas and has established Tarab Ladrang Institutes in Denmark, France, Belgium, Germany and Austria.

Teundrop, Lama Denys (Tibetan – Kagyu) French disciple of Khyabje Kalou Rinpoche. Head of Karma Ling in France. After university study and twenty-year training as lama, took on the transmission of the Vajrayana tradition from his teacher.

Thich Nhat Hanh (Vietnamese Rinzai Zen) Born in Vietnam. Student at Columbia University in the USA, but recalled to Vietnam to help with an attempt at an alternative to the corruption of Saigon and the communism of Hanoi. Established Van Hahn University and the School of Youth for Social Service which went out to help the peasantry in war-torn rural areas. Coined the term 'Engaged Buddhism'. Author of several books. Now lives in exile at Plum Village in France. Poet and peace activist.

Thrangu Rinpoche, Very Venerable (Tibetan – Karma Kagyu) Scholar holding the teaching degree of Geshe Rabjam – highest qualification within all Tibetan Buddhist scholarly traditions. Founder of Thrangu House in Oxford. Resides mostly at his monastery in Nepal, Thrangu Tashi Choling. Visits Britain annually to give teachings at Samye Ling in Scotland and Thrangu House.

Thubten Ngawang, Geshe Tibetan scholar and meditation master, resident teacher at Tibetisches Zentrum in Hamburg, Germany. Entered Sera Monastery in Tibet at age eleven. 1959 fled to India. After thirty-seven years of intensive study and practice, passed final examination and received title of Lharampa Geshe.

Trungpa Rinpoche, Chogyam (1939–1987) (Tibetan – Kagyu) Born in Tibet and recognised as the 11th throneholder of the Trungpa lineage at the age of eighteen months. Left Tibet in 1959 after Chinese invasion and came to England to study at Oxford University. Co-founded Samye Ling in 1968 in Scotland. In 1969 relinquished monastic vows and married. Moved to USA and founded Karme Choling Buddhist Meditation and Study Center in Vermont and Vajradhatu, an international Tibetan Buddhist association. In 1974 established the Nalanda Foundation for non-sectarian education which includes Shambhala Training, a secular meditation programme, and the Naropa Institute, an arts college. Author of many books.

Yeshe, Lama Thubten (1935–1984) (Tibetan – Gelug) Tibetan exiled from Tibet, went to live in India. Met first Western students in 1965 and by 1971 had settled at Kopen, near Kathmandu in Nepal. Due to demand began teaching with his disciple, Lama Thubten Zopa Rinpoche, to increasing numbers of travellers, who in turn started groups and centres in their own countries. In 1975, Lama Yeshe named this fledgling network the Foundation for the Preservation of the Mahayana Tradition. Author of several books. Since his passing away, Lama Zopa Rinpoche is the Spiritual Director of the Foundation. Lama Yeshe's reincarnation, a Spanish child called Osel Hita Torres, is now studying and training to prepare him to continue the work he started in his previous life.

Zopa Rinpoche, Lama Thubten (contemporary) (Tibetan) Disciple of Lama Thubten Yeshe and succeeded him as Spiritual Director of the Foundation for the Preservation of the Mahayana Tradition after his death. Tours extensively, teaching at the Foundation's sixty odd centres worldwide.

Main Buddhist Festivals

> In the Buddhist approach, life and death are seen as one whole,
> where death is the beginning of another chapter of life. Death is
> a mirror in which the entire meaning of life is reflected.
>
> – Sogyal Rinpoche, *The Tibetan Book of Living and Dying*

GENERAL

All Buddhist traditions celebrate Buddha's Birth, Buddha's
Attainment of Enlightenment (Bodhi Day), and Buddha's death
(Parinirvana). Some traditions mark all three on the same day of
the year (Wesak or Buddha Day). Also celebrated is Preaching of
Buddha's First Sermon in Benares, India (called variously Asala,
Dharma Day, Dhammachakra or Turning of the Wheel of Dharma
Day). Other celebrations vary according to the major figures
(Bodhisattvas or founders) in a particular tradition and
national/ethic influences and these are shown in the listings
below.

Dates for celebrations also vary from tradition to tradition and
from year to year due to the use of a lunar calendar.

Celebration of festivals at different centres varies as to how
public or private they are, some being open to the public and
others involving religious ceremonies suitable only for experienced practitioners. Others have a programme of events, some of
which are suitable for beginners, others only for more experienced
practitioners.

TIBETAN

Chokhor Duchen – Buddha's First Sermon – June/July
Dalai Lama's Birthday – 6 July
Lha Bab Duchen – Ascent into the Tushita Heaven – October
Losar – New Year Festival – four days followed by a long religious ceremony – February
Ngacho Chemo – Je Tsongkhapa Day – November
Padmasambhava Day – in honour of the founder of Buddhism in Tibet
Saga Dawa – Buddha Day – May

JAPAN

Hana Matsuri – Buddha's Birth – 8 April
Higan – Spring equinox marking time of change and remembrance of dead – around 21 March
Nehan – Buddha's Enlightenment – 15 February
Obon – Spirits of the dead welcomed back to their home area – four days beginning 13 July
Rohatsu – Buddha's Enlightenment
Setsubon – Driving out evil spirits – early February
Shubun no hi – Autumn equinox marking time of change and remembrance of dead – around 20 September

Japanese Zen

As for Japanese festivals plus:
Bodhidharma Day – October
Daito Zenji – 22 November
Dogen Zenji – 28 August
Keizan Zenji – 15 August
Rinzai Zenji – 10 January

Nichiren

Buddha Nirvana Day

Nichiren Shonin's Birthday – 16 February
Buddha's Birthday – 8 April
Proclamation of the establishment of a new order – 28 April
Nichiren Shonin's Exile to Izu Peninsula – 12 May
Matsubagayatsu Persecution – 27 August
Tatsunokuchi Persecution – 12 September
Sado Exile – 10 October
Oeshiki (Nichiren Shonin's death) – 13 October
Komatsubara Persecution – 11 November

Pure Land

Main Buddhist festivals plus:
Shinran Shonin's Birthday – 21 May
Ho Om Ko – Shinran Shonin's Death – varies according to Head
Temple followed

THERAVADA

Rains Retreats follow the Buddha's custom of monks and nuns
going into retreat for about three months during the rainy season.
Dates vary according to when the rainy season is in various countries.

Kathina Day (October/November) marks the end of Rains
Retreat with the laity presenting monks with cloth for making into
robes on the same day.

Uposatha Days are observed weekly at full, new and quarter
moons; full and new moons being the most important. On these
days religious activites are more intense. The way they are
observed varies considerably among the different traditions.

Myanmar

Asalha – Buddha's first sermon/ start of Rains Retreat – July
Kathina – November
New Year – April
Thitingyut – End of Rains Retreat – October

Wesak – Buddha's Birth, Enlightenment and Death Day – May/June

Thailand

End of Rains Retreat – October
Kathina – November
Loykrathong – Festival of Lights – November
Magha Puja – All Saints Day – February
Songkrang – New Year – April
Vassa – Rains Retreat – July-October
Visakha Puja – Buddha's Enlightenment – May
Wan Atthami – Buddha's Cremation – May/June

Sri Lanka

Poya – Five full moon days of special importance named after the lunar months in which they occur. They are Duruthu, Navam, Wesak, Poson and Esala.
Duruthu – Sanghamitta's arrival in Sri Lanka (female counterpart of Poson) – December
Esala/Asalha – Buddha's first sermon – July
Kathina – September
New Year – April
Poson – Establishment of Buddhism in Sri Lanka – June/July
Wesak – Buddha's Birth, Enlightenment and Death Day – May/June

WESTERN BUDDHISM

Sangha Day – expression of the spiritual community of all Buddhists – November

Centres in the UK and Ireland

> So here we have the whole practice of the Buddha: refrain from evil and do good, live simply, purify the mind. That is, be watchful of our mind and body in all postures; know yourself.
>
> *– Venerable Ajahn Chah*

ENGLAND

Arranged with London at the beginning, followed by each UK county in alphabetical order.

LONDON

Arranged alphabetically according to postcode area

London Buddhist Centre (LBC) (Friends of the Western Buddhist Order)
51 Roman Road
London E2 0HU
Tel: 0181 981 1225
Fax: 0181 980 1960
e-mail: ilbc@alanlbc.demon.co.uk

Principal centre of Friends of the Western Buddhist Order. Converted six-storey fire station with attached shop, restaurant and office complex.
    Friends of the Western Buddhist Order (FWBO) was

established in 1976 in Britain by a London-born Buddhist monk, Sangharakshita. It draws from all the main traditions of Buddhism, not with an attitude of eclecticism, but to take what is useful according to the spiritual needs of Westerners today. Each centre is autonomous, but linked by common practice and friendship between Order members.

Classes and meetings led by both men and women Order members. Wednesdays 7.15pm – a thorough introduction to one or two meditation techniques given, plus talks on meditation and Buddhism. Retreats held both for weekends and longer (especially holiday periods) often at The Water Hall Retreat Centre which is administered through the LBC for its own use. Right Livelihood businesses and a Buddhist Arts Centre nearby and over 100 people are housed in Buddhist communities in the area. Nearby Right Livelihood businesses include The Cherry Orchard vegetarian cafe, Jambala Bookshop, Evolution (a gift shop) and Friends Foods healthfood shop. See separate entries for the **Water Hall Retreat Centre** (p113), **The Buddhist Arts Centre** (p47) and **Bodywise Natural Health Centre** (p47) which are associated with this centre.

Founder/Guru	Sangharakshita
Teachers	Order members
Opening times	Monday – Friday 10am–5pm
Residents	No
Festivals	Wesak, Dharma Day, Sangha Day, Parinirvana Day and Padmasambhava Day and FWBO Day
Facilities	Shrine room, library, study room, bookshop
Accommodation	No
Food	No
Booking	For classes, no booking required. For courses, book in advance with 50% deposit
Fees	See programme
Expected behaviour	No smoking and no shoes in the shrine room
How to get there	Nearest tube station is Bethnal Green

Bodywise Natural Health Centre (Friends of the Western Buddhist Order)
119 Roman Road
London E2 0QN
Tel: 0181 981 6938

Affiliated to and nearby the **London Buddhist Centre** (see separate entry on p45). Right Livelihood business established in 1986. Run by four women working on a basis of cooperation and Buddhist ethics. Aim to provide a high standard of complementary health care. Twenty-five practitioners offer different therapies to prevent and treat ill-health and to support and maintain good health and well-being. Following treatments are available: acupuncture, Alexander Technique, aromatherapy, art therapy, Bach Flower Remedies, counselling, Feldendrais Method, herbal medicine, homeopathy, hypnotherapy, karate, massage, Movement Psychotherapy, naturopathy, NLP, nutritional therapy, osteopathy, Polarity Therapy, reflexology, reiki, shiatsu, tai chi and yoga. Also offer Massage Diploma course.

Friends of the Western Buddhist Order (FWBO) was established in 1976 in Britain by a London-born Buddhist monk, Sangharakshita. It draws from all the main traditions of Buddhism, not with an attitude of eclecticism, but to take what is useful according to the spiritual needs of Westerners today. Each centre is autonomous, but linked by common practice and friendship between Order members.

How to get there   Two minutes' walk from Bethnal Green tube

London Buddhist Arts Centre (Friends of the Western Buddhist Order)
Eastbourne House
Bullards Place
London E2
Tel & Fax: 0181 983 4473
e-mail: postbox@lbac.demon.co.uk

Aim to provide a forum in which to develop an understanding of the place of the arts in Buddhist life. To this end they offer workshops, seminars, lectures, performances, exhibitions and classes in various artistic disciplines – all with the aim of stimulating and developing the imaginal faculty through which, as Sangharakshita has suggested, one perceives spiritual truths. Most events are for those involved with the FWBO, but some are also open to non-Buddhists.

Topics such as drawing, Cezanne, William Morris, Contact Improvisation (dance), film-making, poetry-making, Midsummer Night's Dream and portraiture.

Their main studio is also available for hire as a rehearsal space.

Friends of the Western Buddhist Order (FWBO) was established in 1976 in Britain by a London-born Buddhist monk, Sangharakshita. It draws from all the main traditions of Buddhism, not with an attitude of eclecticism, but to take what is useful according to the spiritual needs of Westerners today. Each centre is autonomous, but linked by common practice and friendship between Order members.

Founder/Guru	Sangharakshita
Teachers	Various
Opening times	As per programme
Residents	No
Festivals	No
Facilities	Contact centre
Accommodation	No
Food	Bring lunch to share on day/weekend events
Booking	Phone the London Buddhist Centre on 0181 981 1225 or the number above, then send one-third of cost as deposit
Fees	See programme
Languages	English
Expected behaviour	Normal decent behaviour
How to get there	Nearest tube is Bethnal Green or No 8 bus to Roman Road

Rigpa Fellowship (Tibetan – Nyingma – Rigpa)
330 Caledonian Road
London N1 1BB
Tel: 0171 700 0185

Rigpa is an international association of Buddhist meditation centres in Europe, the USA and Australia under the direction of
Sogyal Rinpoche. The Rigpa London Centre aims to encourage a
true understanding of the teachings of the Buddha, through offering a full and varied programme of courses, workshops and international retreats on topics such as meditation, compassion,
healing and caring for the dying. Regular evening and weekend
courses on meditation and compassion practices. Contact the
office for an up-to-date programme of events.

The Ripga shop, Zam Trading, offers a wide selection of
Buddhist books, Tibetan artifacts and audio and video tapes of
teachings by Sogyal Rinpoche and other masters. Shop hours:
Tuesday to Friday 2–6pm and Saturday 1–5pm.

Founder/Guru	Sogyal Rinpoche and H.E. Dzogchen Rinpoche
Teachers	Senior students of Sogyal Rinpoche and Buddhist teachers of all traditions visit
Opening times	According to programme of events
Residents	No
Festivals	Losar
Facilities	Two shrine rooms
Accommodation	No
Food	Tea
Booking	See programme
Fees	See programme
Languages	English
Expected behaviour	No smoking in building
How to get there	Nearest tube station is Caledonian Road. Nearest train station is Caledonian Road & Barnsbury on the North London Line

North London Buddhist Centre (Friends of the Western Buddhist
Order)
St Marks Studio
16 Chillingworth Road
London N7 8QJ
Tel: 0171 700 3075
Fax: 0717 700 3077

Founded 1992. Introductory classes to meditation Tuesday evenings and Tuesday and Thursday lunchtimes each week. Introduction to Buddhism and Introduction to Meditation day events or courses running one evening a week for six weeks. Day and weekend retreats suitable for beginners or those wanting to deepen their practice. FWBO network of centres also runs events for different groups as a way of responding to particular needs they may have, for example meditation courses for women, gay men or lesbians.

Friends of the Western Buddhist Order (FWBO) was established in 1976 in Britain by a London-born Buddhist monk, Sangharakshita. It draws from all the main traditions of Buddhism, not with an attitude of eclecticism, but to take what is useful according to the spiritual needs of Westerners today. Each centre is autonomous, but linked by common practice and friendship between Order members.

Founder/Guru	Sangharakshita
Teachers	Members of the Western Buddhist Order
Opening times	Monday – Friday 11am–6pm
Residents	No
Festivals	Four a year
Facilities	Shrine room and small library
Accommodation	No
Food	Tea available
Booking	Not necessary for classes. For courses and events send 50% deposit
Fees	See programme, concessions available
Languages	English, Spanish and German
Expected behaviour	Normal decent behaviour
How to get there	Nearest tube stations are Holloway and Highbury and Islington. Buses also pass nearby

Heruka Buddhist Centre (Tibetan – Gelug – New Kadampa Tradition)
13 Woodstock Road
Golders Green
London NW11 8ES

Tel: 0181 455 7563
Fax: 0181 905 5280
e-mail number: heruka@rmple.co.uk

House in a residential area of Golders Green. Relaxed and friendly atmosphere. Aim to make the Buddhadharma available to as many as possible whether or not interested in becoming Buddhists. At the time of writing, the centre was looking for funding to buy larger premises in Kilburn.

Regular pujas, meditation sessions, retreats, etc. for newcomers and for more experienced practitioners. Lunchtime meditations and one meditation evening followed by a meal each week. Meditation classes open to all both at Golders Green and other branches every night of the week. The classes are designed to be directly applicable to today's world, enabling people to integrate their lives with spiritual practice. There is a full and varied programme of retreats and courses. Subjects include Dealing with Anger, Working with Relationships, How to Meditate, The Wisdom of Compassion.

All NKT centres form a family spiritually following the same direction. Its very core is the Three Study Programmes, of which this centre offers:

• The General Programme – a basic introduction to Buddhist view, meditation and action in a form that is suitable for beginners. It also includes advanced teachings and practices of both Sutra and Tantra.

• The Foundation Programme – an opportunity to deepen our understanding and experience of Buddhism through systematic study of five of Geshe Kelsang's books. It takes about four years to complete.

• The Teacher Training Programme is designed for people who wish to train as authentic Dharma Teachers. This seven-year programme involves studying twelve of Geshe Kelsang's books, observing certain commitments with regard to behaviour and way of life, and completing a number of retreats.

Ring to be put on their mailing list.

Founder/Guru	Venerable Geshe Kelsang Gyatso Rinpoche
Teachers	Resident nun, Venerable Ani-la Kelsang Chowang, and occasional visits by teachers

	from Manjushri Mayhayana Buddhist Centre
Opening times	According to programme of events
Residents	One monk, two nuns and four lay people
Festivals	Buddha's Enlightenment Day, Parinirvana Day, NKT Day (first Saturday in April). There is also a Spring Festival (three days in May) and Summer Festival (two weeks) celebrated at the Manjushri Centre
Facilities	Gompa and sitting and dining area
Accommodation	Contact centre
Food	See above
Booking	Contact centre
Fees	See programme
Languages	English and French
Expected behaviour	Visitors are welcome to join in or to sit quietly and observe
How to get there	Three minutes' walk from Golders Green tube station and bus station

Jamyang Meditation Centre (Tibetan – Gelug – Foundation for the Preservation of the Mahayana Tradition)
The Old Courthouse
Renfrew Road
London SE11
Tel: 0171 820 8787
Fax: 0171 820 8605
e-mail: jamyang@cix.compulink.co.uk

Beautiful Victorian listed building which was originally a courthouse – moved into these premises in January 1996.

Classes Monday to Thursday 7.30pm and Sundays (times vary). Special events on many weekends and during Christmas and Easter holidays. Study classes are held on Wednesday evenings and Sundays on such topics as Dependent Arising, Mind and Mental Factors, Buddha Nature, Joyful Perseverance, Patience and the Seven Limbs. Monday and Tuesday classes are suitable for newcomers. Plans for healers, Yoga, Tai Chi, etc on the premises.

All offers of help or donations towards building renovation are welcome. Contact centre for more information.

Founder/Guru	Lama Thubten Yeshe
Teachers	Resident teacher – Geshe Tashi Tsering; many visiting teachers including Glenn Mullin, Kathleen McDonald
Opening times	Daily from 2pm (closed Fridays)
Residents	One monk and one lay housekeeper
Festivals	Contact centre
Facilities	Library, bookshop, quiet meditation room
Accommodation	Ring for details
Food	In-house cafe; tea and biscuits before and after classes; meals for long-term visitors and helpers
Booking	Contact centre
Fees	Teachings are given free, but suggested donations are £4 for the regular programme and £6 for guest lecturers and teachers
Languages	English; by arrangement Tibetan, German, French, Spanish
Expected behaviour	No shoes in the shrine room and please enjoy yourself
How to get there	Nearest tube station Kennington on the Northern line

The Buddhist Society (Main Buddhist traditions)
58 Eccleston Square
London SW1V 1PH
Tel: 0171 834 5858

Town house in south London square. Founded 1924 as a lodge of The Theosophical Society and became independent body in 1926 because of philosophical differences. Initial interest was in Theravada Buddhism which later expanded to cover Mahayana Buddhism. Now aims for impartial presentation of main Buddhist traditions. Shrine room, meeting room, a general office and a room where members can meet for refreshments. Extensive library of about 2,500 volumes which includes book sales and an enquiries section. Tapes of talks for sale.

Object is 'to publish and make known the principles of Buddhism and to encourage the study and practice of these principles'. Arrange a variety of classes and activities, and provide facilities to both members and non-members. Works together with other Buddhist organisations in the UK, represents the Buddhist community at national level, participates in international conferences and has achieved an internationally recognised status.

Courses on Theravada Buddhism, Zen, Introductions to Buddhism, Tibetan Buddhism, Mahayana Sutras and correspondence course. Informal classes on meditation, Zen and public lectures are held once a month. Annual summer school at the end of August in the Cotswolds. Retreats as part of some classes. Information available on retreats arranged by other Buddhist organisations.

Membership on an individual basis from £14 to £20 per annum; joint membership between £18 and £28 per annum; cost depends on where one lives. Members receive *The Middle Way* and may attend members-only classes and occasional functions and receptions.

Open to members and non-members during opening hours.

Publish various books and *The Middle Way* – a quarterly journal.

Founder/Guru	Founder: Christmas Humphreys
Teachers	Various from different schools
Opening times	2–6pm on weekdays and 2–5pm on Saturdays, except holidays
Residents	No
Festivals	See programme
Facilities	See above
Accommodation	No
Food	Refreshments room
Booking	Contact centre
Fees	See above
Languages	English
Expected behaviour	Contact centre
How to get there	Close to Victoria rail and coach stations

Shambhala Centre London (Tibetan – Kagyu & Nyingma – Shambhala)
27 Belmont Close
London SW4 6AY
Tel: 0171 720 3207

Former church in Clapham. Founded 1985 as London Dharmadhatu from the nucleus of the London Dharma Study Group. Affiliated to Shambhala International whose headquarters are in Canada.

They offer three paths: The Shambhala Training (or Sacred Path of the Warrior) which is a non-denominational systematic training in meditation as a way to secular enlightenment; The Vajradhatu Gate which is a programme of Buddhist teaching and practice; and The Nalanda Gate which embraces all other cultural activities such as the Japanese art of archery, ikebana (Japanese flower arranging) and calligraphy.

Weekend programmes normally run from approximately 9am–7pm and generally include much sitting meditation practice. Month-long retreats arranged through the parent organisation, together with some other residential programmes. For individual and group retreats, the centre has a farm cottage in Welsh Border countryside which is also available for family holidays. You can speak to a meditation instructor any time you visit the centre.

Founder/Guru	Chogyam Trungpa Rinpoche, now headed by Sakyong Mipham Rinpoche
Teachers	Various visiting teachers
Opening times	Monday 7.30–9.30pm; Wednesday 7.30–9.30pm; First Sunday of month 10.00am–7.30pm
Festivals	Contact centre
Facilities	Shrine room and meditation instruction rooms
Accommodation	For weekend programmes, they try to arrange accommodation with London participants
Food	May be provided as part of programme
Booking	Booking not usually required
Fees	See programme

Languages	English
Expected behaviour	Normal decent behaviour
How to get there	Nearest tube station is Clapham Common

The Buddhapadipa Temple (Theravada – Thai)
14 Calonne Road
Wimbledon
London SW19 5HJ
Tel: 0181 946 1357
Fax: 0181 944 5788
Lay Buddhist Association: 0181 337 2173

Thai-style temple opened to the public 30 October 1982. Also a monastery and affiliated to the Royal Thai Embassy in London. Resident monks have been chosen to propagate the teachings of the Buddha abroad by the Sangha Supreme Council of Thailand. Buddhist school for children (in Thai). Large, wooded garden, part of which is set aside for meditation during the summer. Several lay organisations: Young Buddhist Group of the UK and the Lay Buddhist Association. Most visitors are Thai.

Weekend classes in Abhidhamma study for beginners, for intermediate students or for advanced students. Walking and sitting meditation followed by discussion; talk in English, chanting and discussion; same in Thai; Buddhist school for children (in Thai). Correspondence Course in Basic Buddhism from 1 March to 31 August. Spring, summer and winter retreats of around one week; Monthly meditation retreats Saturdays 9am–5.30pm. Daily morning and evening meditation and chanting.

Founder/Guru	Founded by Thai people
Teachers	Resident missionary monks
Opening times	For visits to the temple: Saturdays and Sunday 1–5pm, weekdays by appointment only.
Residents	Five monks
Festivals	Seven times a year
Facilities	Shrine room, study room and library
Accommodation	No
Food	Occasionally at festivals

Booking	Not necessary
Fees	Visitors are expected to make a donation
Languages	Thai and English
Expected behaviour	To be decently dressed; no shoes or hats while inside the temple or monks' houses
How to get there	93 Bus, District Line tube or local trains to Wimbledon

London Fo Kuang Temple (Pure Land and Zen)
84 Margaret Street
London W1N 7HD
Tel: 0171 636 8394
Fax: 0171 580 6220

Two storeys of four-storey Victorian building converted from a church school. Established October 1992. Part of Buddha's Light International Association (BLIA) – worldwide organisation for Chinese Buddhism based in Taiwan. Most visitors are Chinese from all over the Far East.

Different types of services Sundays at 10.30am usually chanting or light offering services. Daily chanting sessions at 7am and 4pm. Newcomers should make an appointment and will be introduced to the various practices of the centre. Amitabha Pure Land retreat which lasts seven days. Possibility for individuals to undertake one- or two-day retreats.

As well as Buddhist practices, during term times also offer classes in acrobatics, dancing and other cultural activities.

For some events, e.g. Wesak and Sangha Dana they need to hire a larger space, e.g. in Chinatown in the West End of London.

Also a BLIA centre in Manchester – telephone 0161 236 0494.

Founder/Guru	Master Shing Yun
Teachers	Three resident teachers; visiting teachers
Opening times	Every day 9am–5pm
Residents	Three nuns and two lay people
Festivals	Most Buddha and Boddhisattva celebrations
Facilities	Shrine room, library and study room and a big hall

Accommodation	Limited space for those on one- or two-day retreats
Food	Provided during services and festivals only
Booking	Phone for appointment
Fees	Payment by donation
Languages	Chinese, English, Cantonese, etc.
Expected behaviour	Most visitors are already aware of the behaviour expected of Buddhists
How to get there	Oxford Circus tube station or any bus to Oxford Street

West London Buddhist Centre (Friends of the Western Buddhist Order)
94 Westbourne Park Villas
London W2 5PL
Tel: 0171 727 9382
e-mail: 100305.642@compuserve.com

Started fifteen years ago in a residential neighbourhood close to Westbourne Grove. Small but friendly centre.

Five Level I meditation courses a year suitable for newcomers and two Level II courses for the more experienced Monday evenings for five weeks. Meditation and seven-fold puja every Friday night except the last Friday of the month. There are also regular Dharma courses and study retreats. Drop-in classes three times a week. Regular weekend retreats .

Friends of the Western Buddhist Order (FWBO) was established in 1976 in Britain by a London-born Buddhist monk, Sangharakshita. It draws from all the main traditions of Buddhism, not with an attitude of eclecticism, but to take what is useful according to the spiritual needs of Westerners today. Each centre is autonomous, but linked by common practice and friendship between Order members.

Founder/Guru	Sangharakshita
Teachers	Resident: Dharmachari Moksaraja and visiting Order members
Opening times	1–5pm daily and class times
Residents	Men's community of six

Festivals	Parinirvana Day, Dharma Day, Wesak Day, Padmasambhava Day, Sangha Day, FWBO day
Facilities	Shrine room, library which will loan to regular members and two study rooms
Food	Tea and biscuits
Booking	Call the office for a programme
Fees	Five-week course £60 (£30 concessions)
Languages	English, German and French
Expected behaviour	Normal decent behaviour
How to get there	Five minutes' walk from Royal Oak tube station

The London Buddhist Vihara (Theravada – Sri Lankan)
Dharmapala Building
The Avenue
Chiswick
London W4 1UD
Tel: 0181 995 9493
Fax: 0181 994 8130

First established in 1926 in Ealing, the oldest Buddhist Temple outside Asia. Moved to present premises in May 1994. Internationally recognised as the leading centre for Theravada Buddhism in Europe.

Has three functions: Centre for Buddhist devotion, mainly serving more orthodox Sri Lankan Buddhists; missionary instruction centre, offers information to Westerners wishing to investigate the Dhamma; and a cultural centre for Sri Lankan expatriates needing a meeting place with a religious atmosphere to keep their heritage alive.

An eight-week Introduction to Buddhism course – Friday evenings

Meditation (*Bhavana*) instruction and practice for all levels – Wednesday evenings and the last Saturday of each month except August and December

Children's classes – Sundays

Pali language class – Tuesday evening

Sinhala language class for mature students – Thursday evening.

Puja, Dhamma class, meditation and Pirith chanting – Sunday evening
Theravada Buddhism (London University Extra-Mural Studies) – Thursday evening
One-day retreats are held on the last Saturday of each month except August and December.

Founder/Guru	Anagarika Dharmapala
Teachers	Resident monks and occasional visiting teachers
Opening times	Daily from 9am–9pm
Residents	Contact centre
Festivals	*Rahula Dhamma* Day (children's day) and Sinhala New Year in April. Vesak, Poson, Esala (Dhamma Day), Founder's Day (open day) in September, Kathina, Sanghamitta Day, Poya (full moon) days
Facilities	Library of about 3,000 books, shrine room, and study room
Accommodation	No
Food	Offered without charge on festival days
Booking	No booking needed
Fees	Contact centre
Languages	English and Sinhala
Expected behaviour	Removal of shoes before entering shrine room and modest dress
How to get there	Two minutes' walk in a northerly direction from Turnham Green tube station

British Buddhist Association (Non-sectarian)
11 Biddulph Road
London W9 1JA
Tel & Fax: 0171 286 5575

Established 1974 by Dr. Horner (President of the Pali Text Society), The Most Venerable Dr. Vajiragnana (Sangha Nayaka of Great Britain) and A. Haviland-Nye (Dhammacariya). Special expertise in Abhidhamma.
    Promotes education, religious and meditation aspects of the

Buddha's teaching at evening and weekend sessions both in London and at country retreats to augment private study and practice. Activities generally ordered to a structured form both for those who have a professional interest in the Buddha's teaching and for interested members of the public who are able to give systematic attention and radical reflection.

Evening sessions and weekend schools for newcomers specially geared to Westerners at which students have the opportunity to meet tutors and assess whether they wish to commit themselves to study and practice with the BBA either in London or at a distance.

Supporters and students use the service book for daily offices. Group meetings held periodically and weekend schools bimonthly. Seminars, religious festivals and retreats mark the Buddhist calendar and supplement courses. Contact the BBA for further information.

Founder/Guru	See above
Teachers	Scholar monks led by A. Haviland-Nye
Opening times	By appointment only
Residents	None
Festivals	Yes
Facilities	Shrine room, library and study room
Accommodation	No
Food	No
Booking	By post
Fees	No formal fee structure, but rely on contributions appropriate to income
Expected behaviour	Five Precepts
Languages	English
How to get there	Nearest tube station Maida Vale

> Wealth is like dew on a blade of grass,
> so give alms without covetousness.
>
> – *The Message of Milarepa*

Greater London

Buddha Dhamma Association (Theravada – Sri Lankan)
12 Featherstone Road
Southall
Middlesex UB2 5AA
Tel: 0181 995 9495

Inaugurated three years ago with the purchase of a large four-storey building which had been gutted by fire. Following total renovation, opened April 1996 with a peace procession. Shrine room on the top floor; library on Buddhism, Dr. Ambedkar and general interest; downstairs hall for lectures, etc.; shrine room for individual study, reflection, meditation, worship, etc.; monks quarters, the Dharmasala (visitors' rooms); a large hall for receptions and lectures and a kitchen.

Anti-caste, integrationist, missionary, inter-faith and multi-racial. Non-denominational, but will follow Theravada to reflect the majority of its Indian Buddhists. Expect a mixed congregation of Indian and English Buddhists and will cater for both. The particular aim is to fight Untouchability discrimination and all forms of discrimination of race, religion, and ethnicity (their Dharmasala will welcome ex-Untouchables who might otherwise have difficulty finding accommodation in the area). Will also spread knowledge of Buddhism, cooperate with clergy of other religions and emphasise missionary activity rather than advanced study.

'Most Indian ex-Untouchables have great faith in Buddhism but little experience and therefore all lectures, scripture study and meditation classes will be kept very simple. There will be no advanced classes so newcomers will find no difficulty and experienced practitioners will find plenty of opportunity for revision.'

Scripture study Wednesdays and meditation (Metta Bhavana and Anapana Sati [meditation on the breath]) lessons Tuesdays. Services in English, Hindi, Punjabi and Pali.

The monks will go out to teach in schools, visit patients in hospital and lecture for newcomers. Most events free because revenue will come from the Dharmasala (hotel).

Founder/Guru   Buddha Dhamma Association
Teachers   Visiting Buddhist monks

Opening times	9am–9pm
Residents	A monk will be appointed
Festivals	Full moon Sri Lankan celebration – Durutu, Navam, Medin (Rahula Day), Bak, Wesak, Poson, Esala, Nikini, Binara, Vap, Katthina, Il (Missionary day), Unduwap
Facilities	See above
Accommodation	Dharmasala or hotel for pilgrims
Food	Mostly traditional vegetarian Indian food which will be given to all who ask regardless of caste, religion, race or colour
Booking	Not necessary
Fees	See above
Languages	English, Hindi, Punjabi – services and lectures will be held in all three languages and also services in Pali
Expected behaviour	No alcoholic drink in the main building. Shoes and headgear to be removed in the shrine; although they may be worn in the rest of the building, most Indians will not out of custom
How to get there	From M4, stop at the Heston Service area, take Fern Lane to Norwood Road, turn right up King Street, turn left at junction at end before Dominion Centre. There is a car park at the rear of the building

> When a man considers this world as a bubble of froth, and as the illusion of an appearance, then the king of death has no power over him.
>
> *– The Dhammapada*

Avon

Bristol Buddhist Centre (Friends of the Western Buddhist Order)
9 Cromwell Road
St Andrews
Bristol BS6 5HD

Tel: 0117 924 9991 (also fax number by arrangment)
e-mail: 100636.3412@compuserve.com.

Urban Buddhist centre currently looking for larger premises in the area. Began in 1981 in Long Ashton, and moved to present premises in 1987. Activities have been developing and expanding fairly constantly through this period. About seventeen Order members in Bristol and about twenty-five working towards ordination.

Classes, courses, and events most evenings and weekends and sometimes on a weekday. Evening courses for beginners and intermediates offered throughout the year, drop-in class every Tuesday evening. Puja and chanting are introduced as people develop their interest and involvement. Weekend retreats, arts events and creative communication courses also run.

Friends of the Western Buddhist Order (FWBO) was established in 1976 in Britain by a London-born Buddhist monk, Sangharakshita. It draws from all the main traditions of Buddhism, not with an attitude of eclecticism, but to take what is useful according to the spiritual needs of Westerners today. Each centre is autonomous, but linked by common practice and friendship between Order members.

Founder/Guru	Sangharakshita
Teachers	Four resident teachers; visiting members of the Order
Opening times	Apart from during classes, 1–4pm Monday and Friday
Residents	No
Festivals	Buddha, Dharma, Sangha, Parinirvana and Padmasambhava Day
Facilities	One large, one subsidiary shrine room, reference book library, loan library for video and audio tapes, bookshop
Accommodation	No
Food	Participants in day events are asked to bring food to share. Tea, etc. at evening classes
Booking	£15 deposit – check to see that places are available
Fees	See programme

Languages	English
Expected behaviour	Normal decent behaviour
How to get there	At the Arches' junction on the A38, one mile north of the city centre

International Zen Association UK (IZAUK) (Zen – Soto – Association Zen Internationale)
Bristol Zen Dojo
91–93 Gloucester Road
Bishopston
Bristol BS7 8AT
Tel: 0117 942 4347
e-mail: c/o Chris Priest wcp@hplb.hpl.hp.com

First Dojo opened in Bristol in 1986 by a monk and nun who were followers of the Japanese Zen Master Taisen Deshimaru. Open to anyone who sincerely wants to practice.

Daily activities involve Zazen practice and a short ceremony with chanting. Session times 6.30am Tuesdays, Wednesdays, and Thursdays, 6pm Tuesdays, Fridays and Saturdays, 8.30am Saturdays and Sundays. Periodic talks and days of zazen practice. Questions and introductory session Saturdays 5pm. Three or four sesshins a year of two and a half days and five days in the Spring. Newcomers and experienced practise together. Sesshins involve three to four sittings of zazen each day, samu and a chance to ask questions to the person directing the retreat. Sesshins held at different locations. In the summer there is a longer sesshin in France (see **Temple Zen la Gendronnière** in France on p190) where people from all over the world gather to practise.

Now some 12 more Dojos around the country, including one in Scotland and three in London.

Founder/Guru	Founders: Jean Baby and Nancy Amphoux; based on Taisen Deshimaru Roshi Tradition
Teachers	Resident: Jean Baby
Opening times	See session times above
Residents	Contact centre
Facilities	Dojo
Accommodation	No

Food	No
Booking	Arrive ten minutes early
Fees	Contact centre
Languages	Contact centre
Expected behaviour	Contact centre
How to get there	Contact centre

Lam Rim Bristol Buddhist Centre (Tibetan – Gelug)
2 Victoria Place
Bedminster
Bristol BS3 3BP
Tel: 0117 963 9089 or 0117 923 1138
Fax: 0117 968 7484

Three-storey building, painted pale yellow in cul-de-sac of terrace houses. In quiet part of town. Building had been a Christian Mission hall and a dance school. Purchased in 1987 and extensively renovated, largely by volunteers. Member of the Bristol Interfaith Group and has regular participants from other faiths. Peaceful, easy-going. Run by volunteers and open to all. Buddhist practice predominantly sutra path.

Meditation Monday evenings and some weekends; Tara Puja Tuesday evenings followed by teachings. Some weekend retreats. Introductory evenings on Thursdays. Teachings by Venerable Geshe Damcho Yonton on Tuesday evenings and some weekends. For more experienced practitioners, Lama Chopa sometimes teaches at weekends or evenings.

Centre includes Centre for Whole Health, for complementary medicine. All practitioners are professionally qualified. Non-sectarian. Therapies offered: relaxation, acupuncture, osteopathy, psychotherapy, counselling, massage, shiatsu, homeopathy (with children's clinic), Tai Chi and Tibetan medicine. Session costs vary.

Founder/Guru	Venerable Geshe Damcho Yonton (resident at **Lam Rim Buddhist Centre** in Wales [see separate entry])
Teachers	Founder and occasionally other visiting teachers

Opening times	Centre for Whole Health 9am–5pm weekdays; Buddhist Centre 7.30–9pm Monday and Thursday, 7–9pm Tuesday, some weekends
Residents	Occasionally – either monks for six-month periods or lay people if no monk resident or to look after Geshe-La if staying at centre
Festivals	Sometimes celebrated
Facilities	Shrine room, library and large hall or therapy rooms for hire
Accommodation	No
Food	Only with weekend courses
Booking	Not for evenings, for weekends prefer at least one week before
Fees	Buddhist Centre: approx £2.50 per class, or £5 per day for weekends
Languages	English, Italian, German, Dutch, Spanish
Expected behaviour	The Five Precepts
How to get there	At the end of East Street, Bedminster. Past London Inn up British Road, first on right

Sakya Thinley Rinchen Ling (Tibetan – Sakya)
121 Somerville Road
St Andrews
Bristol BS6 5BX
Tel: 0117 924 4424

Large house in a quiet area near a beautiful park. Founded 1977. Emphasises traditional Buddhist values in a non-monastic context. Inspired by Rime (non-sectarian) spirit.

Weekly meditation instruction and practice Thursdays 8pm. Thinley Society comprising activities for children held on the first Sunday of every month at 11am. Four part Introduction to Buddhism courses Wednesdays 8pm. Meditation days occasionally. Six-part Middle Way Teachings courses Mondays. Regular courses given by Lama Jampa Thaye and study groups led by senior members. Evening pujas. Retreats every two years at the Dordogne centre.

Member of the Dechen community of Buddhist centres in

Europe. Contact this centre for other addresses.

Founder/Guru	Karma Thinley Rinpoche and Lama Jampa Thaye
Teachers	Lama Jampa Thaye, Karma Thinley Rinpoche and H.H. Sakya Trizin visit
Opening times	Every Thursday evening at 8pm and during scheduled programmes. Other times by arrangement
Residents	Three lay people
Festivals	Pujas on the four great Buddha days
Facilities	Shrine room and library
Accommodation	No
Food	During scheduled courses only – usually vegetarian lunch
Booking	By phone or post
Fees	Contact centre
Languages	English
Expected behaviour	Respect for Buddhism and consideration for the centre
How to get there	Off Gloucester Road, opposite the swimming baths. 121 is on the corner of Sommerville and Wathen Road, near St Andrews Park

Western Zen and Ch'an Retreats (Ch'an/Zen)
c/o Dr John Crook
Winterhead Hill Farm
Shipham
Avon BS25 1RS
Tel & Fax: 01934 842 231

Remote farmhouse in mid-Wales. Western Zen retreats are derived from the enlightenment intensives of Charles Beriver. Ch'an retreats are orthodox Chinese Ch'an as taught by Master Sheng Yen. Founded by John Crook in 1970s to offer intensive retreats in Zen and Tibetan Mahayana. Ch'an Hall was the first purpose-built building for meditative Ch'an retreats in Britain.

Retreats – daily routine varies according to retreat and runs from 4 or 5am till 10pm. Activities include meditation, communication exercises, teachings, walks, Yoga. Meditations include Silent Illumination, Shikantaza, Koans, Mahamudra. Study of Mahayana literature, Introductions to meditation, Tibetan visualisation, literature and teachings in Buddhism. Retreats once every two months approximately, usually not in summer. Mountain walks. Retreats on such topics as: Calming Minds – Raising Doubt; Mahamudra; Exploring the Dharma; Timeless Questions.

Focus for retreats from the Bristol Ch'an Centre and affiliated groups in Swindon, Cardiff, Manchester and Edinburgh. Also contacts in Warsaw, St Petersburg and New York.

Publication of journal, *New Ch'an Forum*.

Founder/Guru	Master Sheng Yen
Teachers	John Crook PhD, DSc; occasional visiting teachers
Opening times	For retreats only
Residents	No
Festivals	Contact centre
Facilities	Shrine room, meditation hall and refectory. (library and study room under construction)
Accommodation	Dormitory facilities for up to twenty people. Showers available
Food	Expert vegetarian cooking
Booking	Write at least one month in advance, £30 deposit
Fees	All inclusive £125–£200, depending on duration, teacher, etc.
Languages	English, French, Modern Greek, some German
Expected behaviour	Silence, punctuality, tidiness, application of practical method
How to get there	Details supplied on acceptance

Learned Audience, you should know that the mind is very great
in capacity, since it pervades the whole Dharmadhatu. When
we use it, we can know something of everything, and when we
use it to its full capacity we shall know all. All in one and one
in all.

– *The Sutra of Wei Lang (or Hui Neng)*,
translated from the Chinese by Wong Mou-Lam

Berkshire

Shantideva Centre (Tibetan – Gelug – New Kadampa Tradition)
39 Devereux Road
Windsor
Berkshire SL4 1JJ
Tel: 01753 864 307

Terrace house in quiet area close to town centre and Windsor
Great Park. Established in 1992 to provide meditation classes for
people in the Windsor/Slough area, which developed into a residential centre.

The New Kadampa Tradition (NKT) is a Mahayana Buddhist
tradition founded by Geshe Kelsang Gyatso, a Tibetan Buddhist
Master resident in the UK since 1977. Its main purpose is to preserve and promote the essence of Buddha's teachings in a form
that is suited to the modern world and way of life.

All NKT centres form a family spiritually following the same
direction and its core is the Three Study Programmes. Of these,
this centre offers:

• The General Programme – provides a basic introduction to
Buddhist view, meditation and action in a form that is suitable for
beginners. It also includes advanced teachings and practices of
both Sutra and Tantra.

• The Foundation Programme – to deepen understanding and
experience of Buddhism through systematic study of five of
Geshe Kelsang's books. It takes about four years to complete.

Regular study classes and special day courses open to all. Daily
and weekly prayers chanted in English. Week-long retreats held
periodically.

Branches in Reading and Richmond. Meditation and talks held at Windsor Boys' School.

Founder/Guru	Venerable Geshe Kelsang Gyatso Rinpoche
Teachers	Resident: Venerable Ani-la Kelsang Chowang
Opening times	Visits arranged informally
Residents	One monk, three lay people
Festivals	Contact centre
Facilities	Shrine room
Accommodation	No
Food	No
Booking	Necessary only for day courses and with deposit
Fees	£5 per class; Foundation Programme £8 per day or £25 per month
Languages	English
Expected behaviour	Contact centre
How to get there	Rail to Windsor and Eton Central or Windsor and Eton Riverside

Soka Gakkai International (Nichiren – Soka Gakkai)
Taplow Court
Taplow
Near Maidenhead
Berkshire SL6 0ER
Tel: 01628 773 163
Fax: 01628 773 055

Country house with a history going back to Saxon times, set in eighty acres of grounds. Headquarters of Soka Gakkai International in the UK. This school of Nichiren Buddhism arrived in the UK from Japan in 1960 and has grown slowly since then, most numerously in France, Italy, UK and Germany. Cultural and administrative centre and not retreat or teaching centre as meetings are usually held in members' homes.

SGI-UK is a lay society of individuals practising Nichiren Buddhism. Dedicated to peace through education and culture. Members in over 120 countries share this vision by challenging their own negative tendencies to reveal the life force, compassion and wisdom inherent in all living beings and helping others to do the same. Collectively involved in many charitable works and cooperate with other organisations towards the relief of suffering.

In each country, activities reflect the local culture. In the UK members carry out their daily practice at home, getting together once a month for small discussion meetings in the local area.

Grand Culture Centre which houses art galleries, the Institute of Oriental Philosophy and is used for courses for members and for cultural activities like Spring Exhibitions and Arts Festivals. Broad variety of study seminars and cultural projects throughout the year. Courses here are organised by and for local SGI-UK groups and are not generally open to the public.

For information about the nearest meeting to you, phone telephone number above or Richmond centre on 0181 948 0381/2 after 4pm and at weekends.

Founder/Guru	Founder: Nichiren Daishonin. President: Daisaku Ikeda
Teachers	Not applicable
Opening times	Open to the public 2–6pm Sunday afternoons, 7 April to 28 July 1998 as an opportunity to see the history, architecture and enjoy the grounds
Residents	Not applicable
Festivals	Contact centre
Facilities	Three halls and Institute of Oriental Philosophy library
Accommodation	No
Food	Canteen for lunch and occasionally supper for organised events
Booking	Not applicable
Fees	Not applicable
Languages	English and Japanese
Expected behaviour	Not applicable
How to get there	By train to Taplow or by car Exit 7 off the M4 or Exit 2 off the M40

> What is enthusiasm? It is finding joy in what is wholesome.
>
> – Shantideva, *A Guide to the Bodhisattva's Way of Life*

Cambridgeshire

Cambridge Buddhist Centre (Friends of the Western Buddhist Order)
25 Newmarket Road
Cambridge CB5 8EG
Tel: 01223 460252

Near the centre of town in a residential area. Occupies two lower floors of a large house. Friendly and open to all. About thirty order members connected with the centre.

Introductory courses on The Noble Eightfold Way, The Tibetan Wheel of Life, The Perfections. Events include meditation courses, special practice days, study groups, retreats, Tara Day, drama and arts events. Weekend retreats are held in the countryside every couple of months, both for newcomers and regular attenders – newcomers need to have learnt the two basic meditation practices (Metta Bhavana and Mindfulness of Breathing) before going on retreat.

Visiting speakers are available for schools, group and institutions. Several communities and Right Livelihood teams are associated with the centre.

Friends of the Western Buddhist Order (FWBO) was established in 1976 in Britain by a London-born Buddhist monk, Sangharakshita. It draws from all the main traditions of Buddhism, not with an attitude of eclecticism, but to take what is useful according to the spiritual needs of Westerners today. Each centre is autonomous, but linked by common practice and friendship between Order members.

Founder/Guru	Sangharakshita
Teachers	Order members
Opening times	For activities in afternoons and evenings
Residents	No
Festivals	Parinirvana Day, FWBO Day, Buddha Day,

	Dharma Day, Padmasambhava Day
Facilities	Shrine room, library of books, tapes and videos, meditation room for individual use, study room
Accommodation	No
Food	No
Booking	In person, phone or post up to day of event
Fees	See programme
Languages	English
Expected behaviour	Normal decent behaviour
How to get there	When entering Cambridge, follow signs to Grafton Centre. Parking is reasonably easy

> I am he who goes his own way;
> I am he who has counsel for every circumstance;
> I am the sage who has no fixed abode.
> I am he is unaffected whatever befall;
> ....
> I am the madman who counts death happiness;
> I am he who has naught and needs naught.
>
> – *The Message of Milarepa*

Cumbria

Manjushri Buddhist Centre (Tibetan – Gelug – New Kadampa Tradition)
Conishead Priory
Ulverston
Cumbria LA12 9QQ
Tel: 01229 584029

Large Victorian mansion set in seventy acres of gardens and woodlands on the shores of Morecambe Bay, close to the Lake District. Principal centre of the New Kadampa Tradition and home of Geshe Kelsang Gyatso Rinpoche. Established 1976.

Visitors welcome on courses or retreats, or to join in the life of the community. Wide variety of courses, both residential and non-residential, ranging from evening classes and daily meditations to one-day courses, one-week courses and retreats. Possibility of working holidays.

The New Kadampa Tradition (NKT) is a Mahayana Buddhist tradition founded by Geshe Kelsang Gyatso, a Tibetan Buddhist Master resident in the UK since 1977. Its main purpose is to preserve and promote the essence of Buddha's teachings in a form that is suited to the modern world and way of life.

All NKT centres form a family spiritually following the same direction and its core is the Three Study Programmes. Of these, this centre offers:

• The General Programme – a basic introduction to Buddhist view, meditation and action in a form that is suitable for beginners. It also includes advanced teachings and practices of both Sutra and Tantra.

• The Foundation Programme to deepen understanding and experience of Buddhism through systematic study of five of Geshe Kelsang's books. It takes about four years to complete.

• The Teacher Training Programme is designed for people who wish to train as authentic Dharma Teachers. This seven-year programme involves studying twelve of Geshe Kelsang's books, observing certain commitments with regard to behaviour and way of life, and completing a number of retreats.

Branch centres at Ambleside, Bangor, Barrow-in-Furness, Carlisle, Colwyn Bay, Glasgow, Kendal, Lancaster, Penrith and Whitehaven.

Founder/Guru	Venerable Geshe Kelsang Gyatso Rinpoche
Teachers	Resident: Venerable Geshe Kelsang Gyatso Rinpoche
Opening times	Office: 9am–5pm
Residents	Ninety people including around twenty ordained Sangha
Festivals	Buddha's Enlightment Day, Turning of the Wheel of Dharma Day, Lha Bab Duchen, Je Tsongkhapa Day and NKT Day
Facilities	Three large meditation rooms, study room with books for visitors, shop
Accommodation	Single, double or dormitory rooms
Food	Three vegetarian meals a day included in accommodation costs

Booking	Contact reception for booking form
Fees	See programme
Languages	Teachings in English, but speakers of other European languages there
Expected behaviour	Five Precepts, no smoking in building
How to get there	Train to Ulverston, taxi from there £2–£2.50 – about two miles

It arises as a thing and into no thing fades,
Having no essence when will it arise again?
Without end or beginning, that which links both is not found.
Stay! The gracious master speaks.

He who clings to the Void
And neglects Compassion,
Does not reach the highest stage,
But he who practises only Compassion
Does not gain release from toils of existence.
He, however, who is strong in practice of both,
Remains neither in Samsara nor in Nirvana.

– Saraha, *Treasury of Songs*

Cheshire

Amitayus Centre (Tibetan – Gelug – New Kadampa Tradition)
173 Ruskin Road
Crewe
Cheshire CW2 7JX
Tel: 01270 664 050
Fax: 01270 655 209
e-mail: dharmabum@netcentral.co.uk.
web site: www.netcentral.co.uk./dharmabum/buddhist/html

Terrace house in town. In Cheshire since 1986, current location since 1990.

Meditation classes Fridays 7.30pm, pujas Fridays 5pm.

All NKT centres form a family spiritually following the same direction. Its core is the Three Study Programmes, of which, this centre offers:

• The General Programme – a basic introduction to Buddhist view, meditation and action in a form that is suitable for beginners. It also includes advanced teachings and practices of both Sutra and Tantra.

• The Foundation Programme – an opportunity to deepen our understanding and experience of Buddhism through systematic study of five of Geshe Kelsang's books. It takes about four years to complete. Classes are on Saturdays.

Also runs classes at other locations locally.

Founder/Guru	Venerable Geshe Kelsang Gyatso Rinpoche
Teachers	Resident teacher: Kelsang Sangye and visiting teachers of NKT
Opening times	Open-house policy, but phone first
Residents	Teacher and five lay people
Festivals	Contact centre
Facilities	Shrine room, library and study room
Accommodation	Contact centre
Food	Lunch on Saturday between the Foundation classes at a cost of £2
Booking	Phone for details
Fees	£3 per session
Languages	English
Expected behaviour	Take off shoes before entering meditation room
How to get there	M6 to Crewe, off the Nantwich Road

May the vision that so many mystic masters of all traditions have had, or a future world free of cruelty and horror, where humanity can live in the ultimate happiness of the nature of mind, come, though all our efforts, to be realized.

– Sogyal Rinpoche, *The Tibetan Book of Living and Dying*

Devon

Gaia House (non-sectarian)
West Ogwell
Newton Abbot
Devon
TQ12 6EN
Tel: 01626 333613

Retreat centre set in just over five acres of peaceful grounds, with large trees, extensive walled garden and views over beautiful countryside. Previously a convent and a retreat centre since 1925 – the atmosphere of silence is tangible. House with fifty-four bedrooms, ample bathroom facilities, indoor walking meditation space, meditation hall, large dining room and spacious meeting rooms. Entire ground floor has wheelchair access. One wing for people undertaking long-term solitary retreats. Founded in 1984 and opening celebration May 1996. Though based in Buddhist teachings, non-sectarian and welcomes people from all backgrounds.

Both beginners and experienced meditators welcome – most group retreats are suitable for beginners. Daily schedule includes work periods and both walking and sitting meditation. Retreats vary in length from a weekend from a month. Topics such as Acceptance and Transformation; Mahamudra: The Primordial Clarity of the Mind; Women in Meditation; Awakening the Heart; Zen and the Art of Working; Dance of Being, Learning to Accept Oneself.

Facilities for people with meditation experience to participate in longer solitary retreats throughout the year – during November and February each year opportunity for month-long solitary retreat. Everyone has their own room. Consent is required from one of the Guiding Teachers at Gaia House. Teachers are available for guidance and interviews.

Three free retreat spaces available for those who undertake work retreats of fourteen nights or more.

Teachers   Resident Guiding Teachers: Christopher Titmuss and Christina Feldman. Visiting teachers from a variety of Buddhist traditions to lead retreats

Opening times	As for events
Residents	Contact centre
Festivals	Contact centre
Facilities	See above
Accommodation	Mostly single or double rooms
Food	Three vegetarian meals per day included in daily rate
Booking	As early as possible, deposit required
Fees	£15 per night
Languages	English
Expected behaviour	Five Precepts and remain silent during retreat
How to get there	Trains and coaches to Newton Abbot. Or A381 towards Totnes, about a mile out of town turn right at the roundabout next to the cemetery and follow the signs to East Ogwell. Go straight through East Ogwell and follow the signs to West Ogwell. Gaia House is on the west side of West Ogwell on the right

The Barn (Non-sectarian)
Lower Sharpham Barton
Ashprington
Totnes
Devon TQ9 7DX
Tel: 01803 732 661

Converted stone barn on the side of the Dart valley about two miles downstream of Totnes. Started in 1986 as part of the Sharpham Trust. A place for people to explore their relationship with others, themselves, the environment and to integrate meditation into their daily lives. Emphasis on working on the land, communication and community.

Do not run courses, retreats, workshops but offer a space where people with an established meditation practice can integrate their practice with mindful work on the land and experience community living.

Daily routine 6.15am meditation, 7.30am breakfast, 8.30am work, 12 noon meditation, 12.45pm lunch, 2.30pm work, 5.15pm meditation. Teachers visit twice weekly for discussions.

Founder/Guru	Maurice Ash and Christopher Titmuss
Teachers	Visiting: Christopher Titmuss, Stephen Batchelor, Martine Batchelor
Opening times	Monday to Friday 9am–5pm
Residents	Two lay people
Festivals	Contact centre
Facilities	Library and meditation room
Accommodation	Seven single rooms from £6 to £9 per night. Minimum stay two nights
Food	Mostly vegan and organic. Take it in turns to cook lunch. Three meals a day
Booking	Write to Managers about six weeks in advance. Deposit when dates are confirmed
Fees	Contact centre
Languages	English
Expected behaviour	Five Precepts and full participation in daily routine
How to get there	Train or coach to Totnes. Then taxi or forty-five minute walk

The Devon Vihara (Theravada – Thai)
Odle Cottage
Uppottery
Honiton
Devon EX14 9QE
Tel & Fax: 01404 891 251

Monastery housed in a farm cottage with land in the Devon countryside. Very small and quiet and in Thai forest tradition. The tranquil rural setting provides an ideal environment for a contemplative life. An adjacent twenty-acre field has been planted with broad-leaf trees, and two meditation huts and a pond have been constructed. Vihara established in 1983, and in 1986 moved to the current location in order to accommodate growing interest.

Daily routine: rising bell at 4am, chanting and meditation at 4.45am, house work 6.45am, tea and gruel at 7.15am, main meal of the day around 11am, evening chanting and meditation at 7.30pm. On Quiet Days (three days a week) there is meditation throughout the day, with a meditation vigil on the weekly Observance Day. On other days there is a study and work period in the afternoon.

Three-week summer retreat at the beginning of August and two-month January/February retreat for monastics. Lay people may join retreat in a helping capacity. Individual retreats are not the usual practice.

Occasional Friday evening guided meditations and Saturday afternoon workshops.

For people who are newcomers to Buddhism or want more formal retreats, it is advisable to contact their two larger centres, **Cittaviveka, Chithurst Buddhist Monastery** (see separate entry on p91) and **Amarvati** (01442 842455).

Founder/Guru	Ajahn Chah
Teachers	Abbot Subbato
Opening times	Monks are around from 7am to 9pm all year round
Residents	Three monks
Festivals	Contact centre
Facilities	Shrine room and library
Accommodation	Up to five women can stay in two caravans, men in the house
Food	One meal a day at 11am
Booking	Write in advance
Fees	By donation rather than fixed fees
Languages	English
Expected behaviour	Eight Precepts, follow the daily routine and join in the Community's activities
How to get there	By road or rail to Honiton BR station and taxi for five miles

> The ultimate standpoint of Zen ... is that we have been led astray through ignorance to find a split in our own being, that there was from the very beginning no need for a struggle between the finite and the infinite, that the peace we are seeking so eagerly after has been there all the time.
>
> – *D.T. Suzuki*

Durham

Atisha Centre (Tibetan – Gelug – New Kadampa Tradition)
9 Milton Street
Darlington
County Durham DL1 4ET
Tel: 01325 365 265
Internet:
:http://www.rmplc.co.uk/eduweb/sites/atisha/index.html

Residential centre in the centre of town. Visitors may go and discuss aspects of Buddhism in a relaxed and friendly way. They can also join in with daily work and daily pujas.

On Thursday evenings self-contained talks, meditations and discussions that emphasise the practical application of Buddha's teachings in modern life. Day courses held regularly, pujas and chanted meditation sessions in English are open to everyone – see programme for details.

The New Kadampa Tradition (NKT) is a Mahayana Buddhist tradition founded by Geshe Kelsang Gyatso, a Tibetan Buddhist Master resident in the UK since 1977. Its main purpose is to preserve and promote the essence of Buddha's teachings in a form that is suited to the modern world and way of life.

All NKT centres form a family spiritually following the same direction and its core is the Three Study Programmes. Of these, this centre offers:

• The General Programme – a basic introduction to Buddhist view, meditation and action in a form that is suitable for beginners. It also includes advanced teachings and practices of both Sutra and Tantra.

• The Foundation Programme to deepen understanding and experience of Buddhism through systematic study of five of Geshe Kelsang's books. It takes about four years to complete.

Runs introductory courses in various towns throughout the North-east of England.

Founder/Guru	Geshe Kelsang Gyatso Rinpoche
Teachers	Nick Gillespie
Opening times	Most days of the year
Residents	Six people

Festivals	Contact centre
Facilities	Shrine room, study room and library
Accommodation	Not available
Food	Three vegetarian meals daily, £1.20 each
Booking	Phone in advance
Fees	£3 per teaching or £60 for a Centre card allowing attendance over a three-month period. Concessions available
Languages	English
Expected behaviour	No smoking, drugs or alcohol. Take off shoes and be reasonably clean and presentable in meditation room
How to get there	Contact centre

> In Buddhism there is no place for using effort. Just be ordinary and nothing special. Eat your food, move your bowels, pass water, and when you're tired go and lie down. The ignorant will laugh at me, but the wise will understand.
>
> – *Lin-chi*

East Sussex

Brighton Bodhisattva Centre (Tibetan – Gelug – New Kadampa Tradition)
11 Vernon Terrace
Brighton BN1 3JG
Tel: 01273 732 917

Five minutes' walk from the beach in the heart of Brighton. Opened by Gen Thubten Gyatso in 1991 as a branch of **Madhyamaka Centre** (see separate entry on p125), it quickly became independent and now has many branches of its own. Rapidly growing residential community of both lay and ordained members. Very friendly and welcoming, enjoy a peaceful atmosphere whether or not interested in becoming a Buddhist.

Daily teachings on a complete range of subjects from Sutra and Tantra, and regular short courses and retreats. Regular classes Mondays and Thursdays at 7.30pm, Guided Meditations

Wednesday lunchtimes, Day Courses and daily pujas daily. Many classes are open to newcomers. Regular retreats, including a four-week Lamrim retreat in January and five day retreats four times a year.

All NKT centres form a family spiritually following the same direction. Its core is the Three Study Programmes, of which, this centre offers:

• The General Programme – a basic introduction to Buddhist view, meditation and action in a form that is suitable for beginners. It also includes advanced teachings and practices of both Sutra and Tantra.

• The Foundation Programme to deepen understanding and experience of Buddhism through systematic study of five of Geshe Kelsang's books. It takes about four years to complete.

• The Teacher Training Programme is designed for people who wish to train as authentic Dharma Teachers. This seven-year programme involves studying twelve of Geshe Kelsang's books, observing certain commitments with regard to behaviour and way of life, and completing a number of retreats.

Run classes in Canterbury, Crawley, Chichester, Dover, Eastbourne, Hastings, Guildford, Lewes, Portsmouth, Reigate and Worthing.

Founder/Guru	Venerable Geshe Kelsang Gyatso Rinpoche
Teachers	Resident: Venerable Kelsang Lodro
Opening times	Phone for details
Residents	Resident teacher
Festivals	Buddha's Enlightenment Day, Dharmachakra Day (Buddha's First teaching), Buddha's return from Heaven day and Je Tsongkhapa Day. Spring and Summer Festivals are celebrated at the NKT's main centre in the UK, Manjushri in Cumbria
Facilities	Shrine room, library and study room
Accommodation	Limited room space £12, floor space in dormitory £8, prices include breakfast
Food	Breakfast self-service, lunch at 1pm and kitchen facilities available for dinner
Booking	Phone for booking form, just drop in for introductory classes

Fees	Some classes are free, some £3. Different prices for longer events
Languages	English
Expected behaviour	To be considerate to others and Five Precepts
How to get there	In the centre of Brighton

Brighton Buddhist Centre (Friends of the Western Buddhist Order)
15 Park Crescent Place
Brighton
East Sussex BN2 3HF
Tel: 01273 698420

Victorian building in the town. Emphasis on friendship. Order members live in various communities around Brighton.

Drop-in classes 1–2pm Tuesdays and Wednesdays and 6.15–7pm Mondays. Day retreats in meditation and Buddhism. Six-week meditation courses for beginners, meditation and study courses for more advanced students. Yoga classes. Associated with **Rivendell Retreat Centre** (see separate entry on p86).

Friends of the Western Buddhist Order (FWBO) was established in 1976 in Britain by a London-born Buddhist monk, Sangharakshita. It draws from all the main traditions of Buddhism, not with an attitude of eclecticism, but to take what is useful according to the spiritual needs of Westerners today. Each centre is autonomous, but linked by common practice and friendship between Order members.

Founder/Guru	Sangharakshita
Teachers	Dharmacharini Kemanandi and others and visiting members of the FWBO
Opening times	Tuesday to Friday during the day
Residents	No
Festivals	Parinirvana Day, Dharma Day, Buddha Day, Sangha Day, FWBO Day
Facilities	Shrine room, small library and study room, Reception room and bookshop
Accommodation	Not usually offered but may be possible by

	arrangement
Food	Lunch included in some day retreats
Booking	One-third deposit in advance
Fees	See programme
Languages	English, French
Expected behaviour	Normal decent behaviour
How to get there	Car or bus to Lewes Road past The Level, Park Crescent Place is a turning to the left by the traffic lights at the bottom of Elm Grove

Rivendell Retreat Centre (Friends of the Western Buddhist Order)
Chillies Lane
High Hurstwood
East Sussex TN22 4AA
Tel: 01825 732 594 or 0181 688 8624 for bookings and enquiries

Rectory built around 1870s, well kept, comfortable, hosting up to twenty-three people. Surrounding countryside is quiet and beautiful with good walks. Beautiful garden. Bought in 1984 and renovated to a high standard. Since 1985 the programme has gradually increased and diversified. Run by Order members and friends – a community well known for their friendliness and helpfulness.

Events include yoga courses, introductory weekends to meditation and Buddhism, week-long open retreats, creativity weekends and work retreats. The programme caters particularly for newcomers, but also for all levels of experience and meets people at their own level of experience. Fully equipped chalet for solitary retreats where food is provided – phone for more details.

Also runs a regular meeting/class in Tunbridge Wells.

Friends of the Western Buddhist Order (FWBO) was established in 1976 in Britain by a London-born Buddhist monk, Sangharakshita. It draws from all the main traditions of Buddhism, not with an attitude of eclecticism, but to take what is useful according to the spiritual needs of Westerners today. Each centre is autonomous, but linked by common practice and friendship between Order members.

Founder/Guru	Sangharakshita
Teachers	Resident and visiting order members
Opening times	According to programme of events
Residents	Currently four order members
Festivals	Celebrated at other FWBO centres
Facilities	Shrine room and small bookshop
Accommodation	For retreat participants
Food	High standard of vegetarian food provided to participants
Booking	Through the Croydon Buddhist centre on 0181 688 8624
Fees	Prices vary but are approximately £10 per night, less for concessions
Languages	English
Expected behaviour	Normal decent behaviour
How to get there	Follow A22 through East Grinstead. Take A26 just before Uckfield. After about a mile, turn right for High Hurstwood. After a mile, turn left into Chillies Lane. Rivendell is on the right after a mile

One in All,
All in One –
If only this is realized,
No more worry about your not being perfect.

– Seng-ts'an, *On Believing in Mind*

Essex

Chos Khor Ling (Tibetan – Karma Kagyu)
Marpa House
Rectory Lane
Ashdon
Saffron Walden
Essex CB10 2HN
Tel: 01799 584 415

Offers residential and retreat accommodation. Ring or write for details.

Founder/Guru	Lama Chime Rinpoche
Teachers	Contact centre
Opening times	All year round
Residents	Contact centre
Festivals	Contact centre
Facilities	Contact centre
Accommodation	Contact centre
Food	Vegetarian
Booking	Contact centre
Fees	Contact centre
Languages	Contact centre
Expected behaviour	Contact centre
How to get there	Train to Saffron Walden from London Liverpool Street Station

Harlow Buddhist Society (Theravada – but embraces all schools)
Dana House
385 Longbanks
Harlow
Essex
Tel: 012979 425 793 and 01279 862 947

House rented from local council in the town. Society formed in 1969 and at present location since 1977. 'We are a down-to-earth group that uses the Buddha's Dhamma as a path to navigate our way through the difficulties of modern life.'
Mondays – Buddhist meeting including chanting, meditation and Dhamma talk
Wednesdays – Self-help group, non-religious for sufferers from anxiety, stress and tension
Thursdays – Beginners' meditation group
Tuesdays – Licensed homeopath
   Short and long retreats for more focused practice.

Founder/Guru	Dhammapalo (Harry G. Knight) 1908–1987, now his disciple Pamutto (Peter Donohoe)

Teachers	Regular visits from **Amaravati Buddhist Monastery** (01442 842455)
Opening times	Mondays, Wednesdays, Thursdays from 8pm onwards. Normally closed on public holidays. Classes start at 8.15pm
Residents	No
Festivals	Contact centre
Facilities	Shrine room, library and study room
Accommodation	During retreats only
Food	Drinks only
Booking	Contact Secretary on 01279 425 793 or President on 01279 862 947
Fees	Classes free with the opportunity to donate according to ability and income
Languages	English
Expected behaviour	Normal decent behaviour
How to get there	Available on request

The Buddha explained that the source of true happiness is living in ease and freedom, fully experiencing the wonders of life. Happiness is being aware of what is going on in the present moment, free from both clinging and aversion.

– Thich Nhat Hanh, *Old Path White Clouds*

Greater Manchester

Manchester Buddhist Centre (Friends of the Western Buddhist Order)
16/20 Turner Street
Manchester M4 1DZ
Tel: 0161 834 9232
Fax: 0161 839 4815
e-mail: mbc@c-vision.demon.co.uk

Five-storey terraced building.
   Open for personal meditation during the daytime. Introductory meditation and Buddhism courses, drop-in classes, day and weekend retreats in the countryside.

Also runs Bodywise centre on site for yoga, massage and acupuncture. Vegetarian cafe planned in basement.

Runs classes at Manchester University.

Friends of the Western Buddhist Order (FWBO) was established in 1976 in Britain by a London-born Buddhist monk, Sangharakshita. It draws from all the main traditions of Buddhism, not with an attitude of eclecticism, but to take what is useful according to the spiritual needs of Westerners today. Each centre is autonomous, but linked by common practice and friendship between Order members.

Founder/Guru	Sangharakshita
Teachers	Members of the Order
Opening times	Approx 9am–5pm – to be extended into the evenings
Residents	Contact centre
Festivals	Padmasambhava, Sangha, Dharma, Parinirvana, Buddha and FWBO Day
Facilities	Large and medium shrine rooms, library, two study rooms, bookshop and reception rooms
Accommodation	When part of event
Food	When part of event
Booking	Phone to book; deposits required for weekend retreats; best to book a few weeks in advance
Fees	See programme
Languages	Contact centre
Expected behaviour	Normal decent behaviour
How to get there	Off the High Street in the city centre

Hampshire

Cittaviveka, Chithurst Buddhist Monastery (Theravada – Thai)
Chithurst
Near Petersfield
Hants GU31 5EU
Tel: 01730 814 986
Fax: 01730 817 334

Large Victorian house set in thirty acres of countryside with a nearby twenty-acre forest belonging to the monastery. Founded in 1979 as a training monastery for new monks and nuns by the Venerable Sumedho Bhikkhu who came to England in response to an invitation from the English Sangha Trust. Follow the Way of Practice of the Thai Forest Tradition as practised and taught by the Venerable Ajahn Chah. Provides opportunity to participate in a quiet and reflective atmosphere that enables the deepening of understanding of the Buddha's teachings.

Newcomers may join in the monastic routine – morning and evening meditation and work around the monastery. Meditations / chanting 5am and 7.30pm daily. Discussions on particular themes on Sunday afternoons. Initial stays of three days, but may be extended with the Abbot's permission. Guidance is available on request for those inexperienced in meditation. Personal interviews with monks and nuns must be arranged prior to a visit.

Accommodation in separate building for nuns and women guests.

Affiliated with the **Amaravati Buddhist Monastery** (01442 842455), **The Devon Vihara** (see separate entry on p80) and **Ratanagiri Harnham Buddhist Monastery** (01661 881612).

Founder/Guru	Venerable Sumedho Bhikku, disciple of the Venerable Ajahn Chah of Thailand
Teachers	Venerable Sucitto Bhikkhu and other senior monks and nuns are resident and occasional visits from other Bhikkus
Opening times	All day except during monastic retreat times in January and February and possibly one month in the summer
Residents	Ten to fifteen monks; three to four nuns and

	one lay person who manages work projects
Festivals	Vesakha Puja in May, Kathina in November
Facilities	Shrine room, small book and tape library, reception room where people can sit, talk or read
Accommodation	For four men and three women sharing, no charge but donations welcome
Food	One meal a day
Booking	Write to guest monk or nun to arrange accommodation
Fees	By donation
Languages	English
Expected behaviour	To follow the Eight Precepts
How to get there	Off the main A3 road from London to Portsmouth. By train from Waterloo to Petersfield

Thekchen Buddhist Centre (Tibetan – Gelug – New Kadampa Tradition)
76 Whitworth Crescent
Bitterne Park
Southampton SO18 1GA
Tel: 01703 557077
Fax: 01703 457092

Large house in residential area, one and a half miles from city centre. Near a large park on the banks of the River Itchen. Residential centre with attached meeting house bought in 1995. Founded after requests from Southampton residents to **Bodhisattva Centre** in Brighton (see separate entry on p83).

Prayers and Lamrim meditation 7.30am and evening teachings every day. Occasional weekend and week retreats and other classes and courses.

The New Kadampa Tradition (NKT) is a Mahayana Buddhist tradition founded by Geshe Kelsang Gyatso, a Tibetan Buddhist Master resident in the UK since 1977. Its main purpose is to preserve and promote the essence of Buddha's teachings in a form that is suited to the modern world and way of life.

All NKT centres form a family spiritually and its core is the

Three Study Programmes. Of these, this centre offers:
- The General Programme – a basic introduction to Buddhist view, meditation and action in a form that is suitable for beginners. It also includes advanced teachings and practices of both Sutra and Tantra.
- The Foundation Programme to deepen understanding and experience of Buddhism through systematic study of five of Geshe Kelsang's books. It takes about four years to complete.

Classes also held at La Sainte Union College of Higher Education.

Founder/Guru	Venerable Geshe Kelsang Gyatso Rinpoche
Teachers	Kelsang Sonam visits from Royal Tunbridge Wells NKT centre
Opening times	7.30am–11pm every day – phone for accessibility
Residents	Nine lay people
Festivals	Contact centre for details
Facilities	Shrine room, lounge and kitchen
Accommodation	Limited and by donation
Food	Macrobiotic vegetarian at £1.50
Booking	By post or phone
Fees	Various for each course or £30 for monthly centre card
Languages	English and German
Expected behaviour	No killing or stealing, no smoking or alcohol in building. Respect for centre, teacher and other people
How to get there	On the banks of the River Itchen by Bitterne triangle and Cobden Bridge

---

As stars, a fault of vision, a mock show, dew drop or a bubble, a dream, a lightning flash, or cloud, so should one view what is conditioned.

– The Diamond Sutra

Humberside

Khedrubje Mahayana Buddhist Centre (Tibetan – Gelug – New Kadampa Tradition)
185 Coltman Street
Anlaby Road
Hull HU3 2SQ
Tel: 01482 324 940

Near the centre of Hull. Originally a branch of **Madhaymaka Centre** in Yorkshire (see separate entry on p125). At present address and given a centre name in 1992. 'A friendly centre offering a warm welcome to anyone. Come and see us!'

Day courses include Transforming Adverse Conditions, Wisdom and Compassion and Introduction to Meditation. Retreats include Lam Rim and Vajrayogini. Special events include Tara Puja by candle light and Chenrezig Puja with flowers.

The New Kadampa Tradition (NKT) is a Mahayana Buddhist tradition founded by Geshe Kelsang Gyatso, a Tibetan Buddhist Master resident in the UK since 1977. Its main purpose is to preserve and promote the essence of Buddha's teachings in a form that is suited to the modern world and way of life.

All NKT centres form a family spiritually following the same direction and its core is the Three Study Programmes. Of these, this centre offers:
• The General Programme – a basic introduction to Buddhist view, meditation and action in a form that is suitable for beginners. It also includes advanced teachings and practices of both Sutra and Tantra.
• The Foundation Programme to deepen understanding and experience of Buddhism through systematic study of five of Geshe Kelsang's books. It takes about four years to complete.

Founder/Guru	Venerable Geshe Kelsang Gyatso Rinpoche
Teachers	Resident: Kelsang Rigma, visiting teacher: Kelsang Khyenrab
Opening times	Monday – Thursday 10am–12 noon; Friday 1–4pm
Residents	Two lay people
Festivals	As other NKT centres

Facilities	Shrine room
Accommodation	No
Food	On day courses, vegetarian lunch at £1.50
Booking	Phone centre
Fees	£3 per class, refreshments provided
Languages	English
Expected behaviour	No smoking, drinking or eating meat. Respectful behaviour especially in the group
How to get there	Contact centre

> Just as, monks, the mighty ocean is of one taste – the taste of salt – so, monks, this Dhamma is of one taste – the taste of freedom.
>
> – The Buddha

Kent

Jangchub Sempa Buddhist Centre (Tibetan – Gelug – New Kadampa Tradition)
Penfro
Sandhurst Road
Royal Tunbridge Wells
Kent TN2 3SR
Tel & Fax: 01892 528279

Large Victorian house with own large semi-woodland garden in a quiet suburb of a spa town. House bought in 1995. Aim to be a place of refuge for all, Buddhist and non-Buddhist.

The New Kadampa Tradition (NKT) is a Mahayana Buddhist tradition founded by Geshe Kelsang Gyatso, a Tibetan Buddhist Master resident in the UK since 1977. Its main purpose is to preserve and promote the essence of Buddha's teachings in a form that is suited to the modern world and way of life.

All NKT centres form a family spiritually following the same direction and its core is the Three Study Programmes. Of these, this centre offers:

• The General Programme provides a basic introduction to Buddhist view, meditation and action in a form that is suitable for beginners. It also includes advanced teachings and practices of both Sutra and Tantra.

• The Foundation Programme to deepen understanding and experience of Buddhism through systematic study of five of Geshe Kelsang's books. It takes about four years to complete.

• The Teacher Training Programme is designed for people who wish to train as authentic Dharma Teachers. This seven-year programme involves studying twelve of Geshe Kelsang's books, observing certain commitments with regard to behaviour and way of life, and completing a number of retreats.

Daily pujas and guided meditations and often a teaching. Newcomers may participate in General Programme, Foundation Programme, most of the pujas and may request a talk individually with lay or ordained members for advice.

Working holidays possible with free board and lodging in return for thirty-five hours work a week.

Kalsang Sonam is English-born monk who has been giving teachings in southern England for three years.

Founder/Guru	Venerable Geshe Kelsang Gyatso Rinpoche
Teachers	Kelsang Sonam and visiting NKT teachers
Opening times	Open all times, best to phone first for accessibility
Residents	One monk and six lay people
Festivals	Contact centre for details
Facilities	Gompa, library, quiet secluded garden suitable for meditation or contemplation, bookshop and Dharma wares shop
Accommodation	From sleeping bag on floor to guest room at £5–15 per night
Food	Vegetarian meals available, cost varies
Booking	By phone, post or in person to Administration Director or Education Programme co-ordinator
Fees	Contact centre
Languages	English
Expected behaviour	To be mindful of others' needs
How to get there	Train to Tunbridge Wells, then taxi or bus, or train to High Brooms and a ten-minute walk

> I wish profoundly that all beings may have peace and happiness, that they may develop love and compassion towards each other and give rise, through Boddhicitta, to enlightenment through to the benefit of all sentient beings.
>
> – Rabjampa Sherab Gyaltsen Amipa

Lancashire

Lancashire Buddhist Centre (Friends of the Western Buddhist Order)
Second Floor, 78/80 King William Street
Blackburn
Lancashire BB1 7DT
Tel: 01254 260 779

Established in 1986, and moved to its current location in 1994.

Beginners' meditation classes Wednesday evenings; other classes and courses by invitation only.

Friends of the Western Buddhist Order (FWBO) was established in 1976 in Britain by a London-born Buddhist monk, Sangharakshita. It draws from all the main traditions of Buddhism, not with an attitude of eclecticism, but to take what is useful according to the spiritual needs of Westerners today. Each centre is autonomous, but linked by common practice and friendship between Order members.

Founder/Guru	Sangharakshita
Teachers	Resident: Dhamachari Pramodana; visiting members of the Order
Opening times	When classes/courses are happening
Residents	No
Festivals	Contact centre
Facilities	Shrine room and study room
Accommodation	No
Food	No
Booking	Contact centre
Fees	Contact centre
Languages	English

Expected behaviour   Normal decent behaviour
How to get there   Short walk from main bus and railway stations

---

More than a million of our compatriots died under the [Chinese] occupation [of Tibet]. Thousands of monasteries have been reduced to ruins. A whole generation has grown up, without any form of education or economic facilities and deprived of their own national identity. Though the present Chinese government has introduced certain reforms . . . the transfer of population continues. . . . Six million Tibetans have been reduced to minority status, in violation of Human Rights in Tibet.

– HH the Dalai Lama speaking to the European Parliament
in 1988

Merseyside

Liverpool Meditation Centre (Friends of the Western Buddhist Order)
37 Hope Street
Liverpool L1 9EA
Tel: 0151 709 5489

Second floor of a Georgian terrace house.

Five-week beginners' courses in meditation and Buddhism, usually Wednesdays or Thursdays at 7.30pm. Meditations taught are Mindfulness of Breathing and Metta Bhavana. Worship or puja takes place during classes for those who have completed beginners' courses and also on festival days. Those who have completed beginners' courses and want to further their interest may attend study classes. Occasional public talks. Occasional day retreats are held at the centre and occasional weekend retreats elsewhere.

Friends of the Western Buddhist Order (FWBO) was established in 1976 in Britain by a London-born Buddhist monk, Sangharakshita. It draws from all the main traditions of Buddhism, not with an attitude of eclecticism, but to take what is useful according to the spiritual needs of Westerners today. Each centre is autonomous, but linked by common practice and friendship between Order members.

Founder/Guru	Sangharakshita; this centre was founded in 1994 by Mangala, a member of the FWBO
Teachers	Mangala and other visiting members of the FWBO
Opening times	For classes several evenings a week throughout the year (may be closed July/August)
Residents	No
Festivals	Wesak, Dharma Day, Sangha Day
Facilities	Shrine room and study room
Accommodation	No
Food	No
Booking	Not usually required
Fees	Courses £30/£20 concessions
Languages	English
Expected behaviour	Normal decent behaviour
How to get there	Easy walking distance from the city centre

> To abstain from evil,
> To do good,
> To purify the mind,
> These are the teachings of all the Buddhas.
>
> – *The Dhammapada*

Norfolk

Kongoryuji Temple (Shingon – British Shingon Association)
London Road
East Dereham NR 19 1AS
Fax: 01362 698 962

Seventeenth-century farmhouses and barns on the edge of town near open countryside. Founded in 1977 to succeed the original Cambridge University Kongoryuji Temple. Dedicated to the study and ritual practices of Chinese and Japanese esoteric

Buddhism. Open to serious practitioners who want to work and study over a length of time. Specialises in anti-commercial courses in healing, physical arts and skills, crafts and traditional Buddhist-only forms of training in a simple and aesthetic environment.

Study, retreats, ritual practices, preparation of Buddhist medicines and the training of healers and teachers. Meditation sessions, study classes, ritual practices and physical exercise each day. Courses include: Teacher Training schemes in natural medicine, remedial yoga, Buddhist medicine and treatments; esoteric mandala studies and painting; Buddhist Kempo (self-defence); physiotherapy; Buddhist psychotherapy; doctrinal history; Study of Yogacara and Shingon texts and analysis; Hermeneutics; Cheirological analysis and diagnosis. Meditations for visitors are three times a month at weekends (write for details). Retreats happen periodically according to training being done – usually twice annually. Daily routine is decided individually for each visitor who is expected to help in basic daily tasks of the temple, such as cleaning.

The British Association is the lay organisation supporting the initiated members of the Order and seeks to encourage studies and reasearch into all the Shingon teachings within both the traditional and contemporary environment. It is part of the little-known Kongo Raiden Ha branch which is not easily penetrated, intense in nature and does not seek disciples.

'When accepted as a visitor, we show you what to do and leave you to practise it – we share all tasks and are non-profit oriented (many courses are free) but we select students. Members are preferred but open to all. We are the only temple of our sect in Europe and offer unique courses and studies unknown elsewhere. We have a network of branch groups and societies in Europe and Eastern bloc countries including Russia. We spread the Dharma whenever possible without publicity, hero-worship or money-making endeavours.'

Founder/Guru	Shifu Nagaboshi
Teachers	Resident teacher is Shifu Nagaboshi, many visiting teachers from all denominations
Opening times	Visitors by appointment only. Members and invitees twenty-four hours a day

Residents	Between one and four monks, and between one and fifty lay people
Festivals	Wesak, O Bon, Gaki and all major feast and anniversary days
Facilities	Shrine room, study room and large library of Chinese, Sanskrit, Japanese, French, Croatian, Tibetan, German, English and Burmese texts and scriptures. Also dispensary, training rooms for physical healings, individual retreat rooms, offices, private study rooms, discussion rooms and Japanese bathrooms
Accommodation	In converted barns, open fires, Agas, sparse Japanese-style traditional decor
Food	Wholefood vegetarian
Booking	Write or fax in the first instance to the Secretary
Fees	For meditations, donations only or free
Languages	English
Expected behaviour	As the Precepts and according to direction of teachers
How to get there	Details sent upon application

Reiyukai Centre (Nichiren – Reiyukai)
Unit 24
Saint Mary's Works
Duke Street
Norwich NR3 1QA
Tel: 01603 630 857
Fax: 01603 760 749

Part of old shoe factory. Founded in 1984 to promote an appreciation of oriental culture and to provide opportunity to participate in a wide range of interesting and educational activities with a common theme of 'Inner Self Development'. Places great emphasis on harmony through mutual understanding and cooperation, which in turn springs from individual spiritual growth.

Variety of classes in the martial, spiritual and healing arts to suit men and women of all ages. Some classes for children. Weekly classes include Ju-Jutsu, Hapkido, Yang Taiji, karate, Chinese yoga, Wing Chun, Choi-Kwang-Do, Choy Lay Fut, Mushindo Kempo, Taoist Qigong and Aikido. Monthly meetings first Sunday of every month for sutras recitation are open to everyone.

Founder/Guru	Contact centre
Teachers	Various
Opening times	10am–11pm Monday–Friday; 10am–4pm weekends
Residents	No
Festivals	Contact centre
Facilities	Shrine room and dojos
Accommodation	Not applicable
Food	Snacks, licensed bar, occasional Japanese food
Booking	Contact centre
Fees	Membership £16 per annum; £8 non-waged and juniors
Languages	English, Japanese, Thai
Expected behaviour	Contact centre
How to get there	See programme

True Zen means sitting quietly in the right posture. Zen means setting the mind at rest, concentrating intuition and reasoning together. Zen is not some special state, it is our normal condition, silent, peaceful, awake, without agitation.

– Taisen Deshimaru

Northumberland

Throssel Hole Priory (Soto Zen – Serene Reflection Meditation Tradition)
Carrshield
Hexham
Northumberland NE47 8AL
Tel: 01434 345 204
Fax: 01434 345 216

In a beautiful valley surrounded by thirty-nine acres of fields and woodland. Monastic buildings, nineteenth-century farmhouse and grounds including Buddhist cemetery, vegetable and fruit gardens. Bright and spacious ceremony hall can sit fifty people for meditation; monastic community and guests also meet there for daily services and ceremonies. Spacious dining room, part of which also serves as a lay common room and small library. The word 'monk' refers to both sexes as men and women train together and receive full and equal ordination in the priesthood. Celibate monastic community. As is usually the case in Buddhism, lay practitioners are also welcome in the monastery to practise as the Buddha recognised lay training as part of the Sangha.

The best way to learn about their particular Buddhist training is to attend a weekend introductory retreat (even if familiar with other Buddhist practices) at which guests are asked to strictly follow monastic routine and behaviour. Thorough instruction in Serene Reflection meditation is given and how it can be applied to all aspects of daily life. Special emphasis is placed on how to continue after leaving the monastery. To those already familiar with their practice, weekend and week retreats are available as well as sesshins, Feeding the Hungry Ghosts and New Year retreats. There is also a Keeping of the Ten Precepts retreat for those who wish to take lay ordination.

To visit for an hour or two, tours can be arranged – phone or write beforehand. Instruction in meditation and private spiritual guidance are usually available at this time, but arrange in advance. Anyone already familiar with their practice is welcome to drop by to meditate.

Senior priests provide spiritual counselling in person or by letter or phone. The Priory also offers names ceremonies for children and traditional Buddhist funeral and memorial services. For details of all these, contact the Guestmaster.

Publish a quarterly journal.

There are over twenty meditation groups affiliated with the Priory in the UK, The Netherlands and Germany, contact the Guestmaster for details.

Founder/Guru   1972 by Reverend Master Jiyu-Kennett
Teachers   Abbot is Reverend Daishin Morgan and

others

Opening times	By appointment only – open throughout the year apart from the two retreat months
Residents	About thirty resident monks, male and female. Numbers of lay people vary
Festivals	Many throughout the year; Lotus Ceremonies first Sunday of every month (unless superseded by a festival)
Facilities	See above, also bookshop
Accommodation	Guests sleep in the ceremony hall, dormitory-style with complete privacy between men and women respected and maintained at night
Food	As for the monks
Booking	One week in advance for weekend retreats, two weeks in advance for week retreats
Fees	No fixed fees, but you are asked to make a donation according to your means
Languages	English, German, Dutch, French, Italian
Expected behaviour	Specific guidelines are available in Guest Information
How to get there	Twenty miles south of Hexham. Details sent with Guest Information

It is said that it is important for a student, prior to making a Dharmic connection with someone as a teacher, to understand what the qualifications of a guru or lama are in accordance with what is set forth in the Vinaya (that's to say, the Discipline), what's set forth in the Discourses [Sutras] and what's set forth in Tantra. Then it's also said that a person who wishes to become a teacher must understand what these qualifications are and work at fulfilling them.

Then in the Mantra [Tantric] system there is a mode of procedure for highly-realised adepts whereby they engage in activities that are not usually allowed. Effectively, this is when they have achieved stability. What is meant by stability? It is when the adept has the capacity to actually overcome in others the loss or lack of faith that such activities might usually cause. . . . However, if a lama does not have this capacity and we think, 'Oh, these are the grand activities of a high lama,' then we are in a difficult situation and must make up our minds as to how to proceed.'

– Love, Altruism, Vegetarianism, Anger and the
Responsibilities of Teachers, HH the Dalai Lama, in *The Middle Way*, Vol 60, No 2, p 68

Nottinghamshire

Akshobya Central (Tibetan – Gelug – New Kadampa Tradition)
52 Mayo Road
Sherwood Rise
Nottingham NG5 1BL
Tel: 0115 985 7356

Close to city in suburban setting. Residential centre in medium-sized house in Sherwood Rise area of Nottingham with easy access by both public and private transport. Very friendly open atmosphere. Started as branch of mother centre (**Madhyamaka** in Yorkshire – see separate entry on p125). Became residential, independent centre in 1994. Open for private meditation and study.

Events range from guided meditation groups and retreats to

day courses and discussion groups. All courses present Buddha's teachings and their practical application through meditation and other Buddhist practices. Monday evening and Tuesday and Friday lunchtime meditations, Introductory talks on Mondays. Topics for day courses e.g. Conquering Hatred and Our Precious Human Life; Retreats – Lam Rim, Vajrayogini, Mandala Offering.

All NKT centres form a family spiritually following the same direction whose core is the Three Study Programmes, and this centre offers all three:

• The General Programme – a basic introduction to Buddhist view, meditation and action in a form that is suitable for beginners. It also includes advanced teachings and practices of both Sutra and Tantra.

• The Foundation Programme – an opportunity to deepen our understanding and experience of Buddhism through systematic study of five of Geshe Kelsang's books. It takes about four years to complete.

• The Teacher Training Programme is designed for people who wish to train as authentic Dharma Teachers. This seven-year programme involves studying twelve of Geshe Kelsang's books, observing certain commitments with regard to behaviour and way of life, and completing a number of retreats.

Attend Summer and Spring Festival at their main centre in the UK, **Manjushri Mahayana Buddhist Centre** in Cumbria (see separate entry on p74).

Have now set up no less than ten branches including Kettering, Peterborough, Nottingham University, Grantham and Norwich.

Founder/Guru	Geshe Kelsang Gyatso Rinpoche
Teachers	Resident: Ani Kelsang Wangchen; visiting: Gelong Thubten Gyatso, Lesang Gyatso, Kelsang Rabga
Opening times	Daily, except Saturdays
Residents	Contact centre
Festivals	Vajrayogini Day, Heruka Day, Buddha's Enlightenment, Turning the Wheel of Dharma Day, Buddha's Return from Heaven Day, Je Tsongkhapa Day
Facilities	Shrine room, library, shop, statue workshop, office

Accommodation	Part of course fee; varies on how full they are; concessions
Food	Vegetarian, prices from £1.00 to £2.50
Booking	Phone or send booking form
Fees	£3 per class, day course £10, £25 per month; concessions available
Languages	English, Slovenian, Hungarian, German, French, Italian, Spanish
Expected behaviour	No offensive behaviour or language, no smoking or drinking alcohol on land or premises; shoes off in shrine room
How to get there	Junction 26 of M1, Follow 610 to city, A60 to Mansfield, A611 to Hucknall, off Hucknall Road

Nottingham Buddhist Centre (Friends of the Western Buddhist Order)
9 St Mary's Place
St Mary's Gate
Nottingham NG1 1PH
Tel: 0115 956 1008 or 0115 950 4649

In centre of town, large renovated warehouse in former lace manufacturing area. Opened February 1996.

Community meditation held 7.15am daily. Introductory meditation courses on Tuesday evenings; seven-fold puja as part of class for regular attendees on Wednesday evenings, Introductory Buddhism talks on Tuesday evenings. Occasional weekend retreats.

Friends of the Western Buddhist Order (FWBO) was established in 1976 in Britain by a London-born Buddhist monk, Sangharakshita. It draws from all the main traditions of Buddhism, not with an attitude of eclecticism, but to take what is useful according to the spiritual needs of Westerners today. Each centre is autonomous, but linked by common practice and friendship between Order members.

Founder/Guru	Sangharakshita
Teachers	Two resident and visiting Order members

Opening times	Phone before as it varies
Residents	No
Festivals	Parinirvana, Buddha, Dharma, Sangha and FWBO Days
Facilities	Shrine room and study room
Accommodation	Occasionally, basic, donation requested to cover costs
Food	Vegetarian and vegan
Booking	Phone before
Fees	See programme
Languages	English, Spanish
Expected behaviour	No smoking or drinking, meditation with the community in the mornings if staying over, the Five Precepts
How to get there	In the centre of town

> It is taught that once one reaches a certain degree of mastery in meditation, it automatically brings great physical and mental comfort.
>
> – from brochure for Thrangu House, Oxford

Oxfordshire

Pure Land Buddhist Fellowship (Pure Land)
Contact address: c/o Jim Pym
3 Field Road
Kingham
Oxfordshire OX7 6YR
Tel: 01608 658425

Founded 1984. Many members follow Jodo Shinshu but essentially non-sectarian. Have contacts with The International Association of Buddhist Culture, The Horaikai, Buddhist Churches of American and many other Pure Land groups worldwide. Informal group, no formal membership or fixed fees. Purpose is communication and anyone who communicates or receives the Newsletter and other mailings is considered a member. Newsletter funded by voluntary donations of around £6 per year. To receive it, send a cheque for what you can afford to Jim Pym at the above address. He is also the editor and contact person and will try to answer any questions. Also have a Network Sangha and circulate names and addresses of those who wish to be in contact with others – currently around thirty Sangha members, both priest and lay. Some books available, including BCA Daily Service Book (£1.25 including post and packing). Organise occasional meetings which all are welcome to attend. Write to be put on the mailing list, saying something about yourself, your interest in Pure Land Buddhism and if willing for name and address to be circulated and if your telephone number is to be included.

The Longchen Foundation (Tibetan)
30 Beechey Avenue
Old Marston
Oxford OX3 0JU
Tel & Fax: 01865 725569
e-mail: lcf@compuserve.com

This is not a centre but the main address for the Foundation which is a circle of teachers and students. Founded in 1975 by Chogyam Trungpa Rinpoche and H.H. Dilgo Khyentse Rinpoche. Entrusted to Rigdzin Shikpo (formerly Michael Hookham) who is the Director.

Ethos is to present Mahayana Buddhism in a way that is appropriate to a Western audience.

Annual programme 'Living the Awakened Heart' is open to newcomers. Run weekend courses. Five-day meditation retreat the week after Easter every year and two-week retreat in August. Distance learning course on The Underlying Principles of Buddhism which involved a short retreat each year.

Local groups meet weekly in Oxford, Worcester, Bristol, London and Leigh-on-Sea.

Publish Longchen Books. Become a Friend of Longchen to receive their quarterly newsletter.

Lama Rigdzin Shikpo has studied and practiced Buddhism for forty years and is a qualified Lama of the Kagyu-Nyingma tradition of Tibetan Buddhism. His main teacher was the late Chogyam

Trungpa Rinpoche.

Founder/Guru	See above
Teachers	Resident: Rigdzin Shikpo; Khenpo Tsultrim Gyamtso Rinpoche visits
Opening times	Not applicable
Residents	Not applicable
Festivals	Not applicable
Facilities	Not applicable
Accommodation	Not applicable
Food	Not applicable
Booking	Write to above address
Fees	Contact centre
Languages	Contact centre
Expected behaviour	Contact centre
How to get there	Not an address for visiting

Thrangu House (Tibetan – Karma Kagyu)
76 Bullingdon Road
Oxford OX4 1QL
Tel: 01865 241 555
Fax: 01865 790 096

Late Victorian semi-detached house in largely Asian neighbour-hood. Opened in 1980. Committed to non-sectarian outlook and have welcomed teachers and students from all traditions of Buddhism. Ani Yeshe Palmo became secretary and director after a four-year meditation retreat in Scotland.

No specific events for newcomers but the opportunity to come and talk with someone. Regular events include weekly meditation classes, Chenrezi and Guru Rinpoche Pujas, monthly Tsok Puja, regular weekend retreats and monthly day of meditation for all Buddhist traditions.

Founder/Guru	Very Venerable Thrangu Rinpoche (who visits at least once a year)
Teachers	Resident: Ani Yeshe Palmo; various visiting Tibetan teachers including Ato Rinpoche, Chime Rigdzin Rinpoche

Opening times	Open every day (not 2–4pm which is practice time), ring before a visit
Residents	Two lay people
Festivals	Contact centre
Facilities	Shrine room and library
Accommodation	Contact centre
Food	Contact centre
Bookings	To be on mailing list, contact the centre
Fees	Contact centre
Languages	English and simple French
Expected behaviour	Officially the Five Precepts, but in practice, consideration of oneself and others
How to get there	By train or bus to Oxford

> When the turbulence of distracting thoughts subsides and our mind becomes still, a deep happiness and contentment arises naturally from within.
>
> – Venerable Geshe Kelsang Gyatso Rinpoche's Introduction to Buddhism

Shropshire

Taraloka Buddhist Retreat Centre (Friends of the Western Buddhist Order)
Bettisfield
Whitchurch
Shropshire SY13 2LD
Tel: 01948 710 646
e-mail: 100073.3502@compuserve.com

Retreat centre for women only (the FWBO also have a men-only retreat centre – see **Vajraloka** in Wales on p134). Set in the soft Welsh countryside in converted barns. Open for about ten years. Originally all work on the property was done by women. Gradually the out-buildings were converted into beautiful modern shrine room, lounge, dining room, bedrooms, etc.

Metta Bhavana and Mindfulness of Breathing meditations, seven-fold pujas and study courses including Introducing

Meditation and Buddhism are offered. Special weekend retreats for beginners and twice a year a one-week retreat. Events offered include Green Tara Visualisation, Tara Festival, arts and intensive meditations retreats some of which are suitable for newcomers and some for Order members only.

Friends of the Western Buddhist Order (FWBO) was established in 1976 in Britain by a London-born Buddhist monk, Sangharakshita. It draws from all the main traditions of Buddhism, not with an attitude of eclecticism, but to take what is useful according to the spiritual needs of Westerners today. Each centre is autonomous, but linked by common practice and friendship between Order members.

Founder/Guru	Sangharakshita
Teachers	Members of the FWBO
Opening times	Retreats run all year. Office hours are 2.30–5pm, Tuesday to Friday
Residents	Contact centre
Festivals	Contact centre
Facilities	Shrine room, library, study room
Accommodation	Dormitories and single rooms. £23 waged, £18 unwaged, £9 guest per night
Food	Vegetarian only included in accommodation costs
Booking	Between 2–12 weeks in advance. Send £20 deposit
Fees	See programme
Languages	English
Expected behaviour	To follow the Five Precepts
How to get there	Trains to Whitchurch, then taxi or drive to Whitchurch (between Shrewsbury and Chester) and follow directions for Ellesmere and take road to Bettisfield

In summary, try to control your mind. If we control our mind, we can solve our problems and then we can help other people.

– Venerable Geshe Kelsang Gyatso Rinpoche

Suffolk

Water Hall Retreat Centre (Friends of the Western Buddhist Order)
c/o The London Buddhist Centre (see p45)

Large isolated farmhouse in Suffolk near Bury St Edmunds which opened in 1988. Used by the London Buddhist Centre for weekend and week-long retreats.

Regular introductory weekend retreats as well as longer retreats for people at all levels of experience. Sessions during retreats include meditation (Metta Bhavana and Mindfulness of Breathing) and seven-fold puja.

Friends of the Western Buddhist Order (FWBO) was established in 1976 in Britain by a London-born Buddhist monk, Sangharakshita. It draws from all the main traditions of Buddhism, not with an attitude of eclecticism, but to take what is useful according to the spiritual needs of Westerners today. Each centre is autonomous, but linked by common practice and friendship between Order members.

Founder/Guru	Sangharakshita
Teachers	Order members of the FWBO
Opening times	Varies according to programme
Residents	Contact centre
Festivals	Contact centre
Facilities	Shrine room, study room and large garden
Accommodation	Sleeps twenty-four in shared rooms
Food	Vegetarian
Booking	Contact **The London Buddhist Centre** (see separate entry on p45)
Fees	Costs vary according to retreat
Languages	English
Expected behaviour	Information from London Buddhist Centre on booking

Unless your work is your meditation, your meditation is not meditation.

– Sangharakshita

Sunderland

Mantra Centre (Tibetan – Gelug – New Kadampa Tradition)
High House
8 South Cliff
Roker
Sunderland SR6 0PH
Tel: 0191 567 5134

On the coast overlooking the sea. Kelsang Chonden from the **Madhyamaka Buddhist Centre** in Yorkshire (see separate entry on p125) has taught a weekly meditation class in Sunderland since 1994. Residential since 1996. Relaxed and informal atmosphere for individual and group meditation.

Daily meditation and puja. Drop-in classes, day retreats and weekend courses. General Programme 4.30pm Thursday and in South Shields 7pm Friday. Stop the Week in South Shields 4.30pm on Friday. Foundation Programme 10–4pm Saturday. Prayers for World Peace 11am Sunday.

The New Kadampa Tradition (NKT) is a Mahayana Buddhist tradition founded by Geshe Kelsang Gyatso, a Tibetan Buddhist Master resident in the UK since 1977. Its main purpose is to preserve and promote the essence of Buddha's teachings in a form that is suited to the modern world and way of life.

All NKT centres form a family spiritually following the same direction and its core is the Three Study Programmes. Of these, this centre offers:

• The General Programme – a basic introduction to Buddhist view, meditation and action in a form that is suitable for beginners. It also includes advanced teachings and practices of both Sutra and Tantra.

• The Foundation Programme to deepen understanding and experience of Buddhism through systematic study of five of Geshe Kelsang's books. It takes about four years to complete.

Working holidays possible, usually for one week, with free dormitory accommodation and vegetarian food in exchange for thirty-five hours work a week.

Run classes in South Shields.

Founder/Guru   Venerable Geshe Kelsang Gyatso Rinpoche

Teachers	Resident: Kelsang Chonden, and visiting NKT teachers
Opening times	See programme times
Residents	One monk, one lay person
Festivals	Buddha's Enlightenment Day, NKT Day, Tsongkhapa Day, Celebration of Buddha's Turning the Wheel of Dharma Day, Celebration of Buddha's Return from Heaven Day
Facilities	Shrine room, library and study room
Accommodation	Dormitory, shared and occasionally single rooms
Food	Vegetarian
Booking	By phone or post. One week in advance
Fees	Around £3 per teaching, concessions available
Languages	English
Expected behaviour	Five Precepts
How to get there	Sunderland railway station, then E1/E3 bus from Sunderland bus station to stop by Bungalow Café on the sea front

> We begin with the recognition that humans cannot create matter. We can, however, create value. Creating value is, in fact, our very humanity. When we praise a person for their 'strength of character', we are really acknowledging their superior ability to create value.
>
> – Tsunesaburo Makiguchi

Tyne & Wear

Amida Quannon (Zen-Therapy – see over)
53 Grosvenor Place
Jesmond
Newcastle upon Tyne NE2 2RD
Tel: 0191 281 5592

Small centre in large terraced house open to all interested people.

Lay practitioners (upasakas). Practice is adherence to the Three Refuges and Five Precepts. Focus is upon the integration of east-west approaches and in particular the integration of Buddhism and psychotherapy – an approach called Zen-Therapy. Offers an atmosphere of respect for personal work and trust in the person and in group process as well as inquiry into important topics in psychotherapy, humanism, spirituality, east-west psychology, creativity and human relations. Practice is still creative and constantly evolving after fourteen years' experience of running a centre.

Daily programme of meditation and other activities which visitors are encouraged to join.

Basic and advanced meditation instruction available in zazen, satipatthana and guided meditations. Retreats and days of mindfulness from time to time, regular Dharma teachings. Private retreats sometimes possible. Offer full professional psychotherapy training and a range of shorter courses on therapy and personal growth topics. Psychotherapy services available in conjunction with Dharma practice. On-going Diploma Programmes or Modular sequences and two-day courses. Topics include Psychodrama, Gegenwelt: the Limits to Self, Feeling Deeply and Hungry Ghosts.

Retreat centre in Cher, Central France, in a converted small farmhouse with eight hectares of land. Now being developed as a non-profit making community on Buddhist principles, offering short and long stays for people interested in finding a quiet spot for retreats, meditation, therapy, Dharma study, developing creative potential and getting close to nature. Visits by arrangement, open from mid-July to mid August. Daily schedule as **Amida** in Newcastle with an outdoors bias. Families are welcome – out of season it may be possible to rent the whole house.

David Brazier and Caroline Beech are psychotherapists and Zen Buddhists. David Brazier is the author of several books. Caroline Beech specialises in working with women, groupwork, and developing community approaches to health. They also lead courses at other venues in the UK.

Founder/Guru	David Brazier and Caroline Beech
Teachers	David Brazier and Caroline Beech
Opening Times	See programme

Residents	Contact centre
Festivals	Various through the year
Facilities	Contact centre
Accommodation	Separate room if possible, if not mattress on floor – contribution according to ability to pay
Food	Vegetarian – £3 per meal
Booking	Contact Amida
Fees	Short courses are £72 / £64
Expected behaviour	The Five Precepts
How to get there	Contact Amida

Newcastle Buddhist Centre (Friends of the Western Buddhist Order)
3rd Floor, The Newe House
12 Pilgrim Street
Newcastle-upon-Tyne NE1 6QG
Tel: 0191 261 1722

Centre of the city. Established 1993. Feel free to drop in and use the facilities.

Introductory and more advanced meditation and Buddhism courses. Classes include drop-in meditations, Yoga classes, day retreats, writing and massage days, women's day retreats and painting weekend. Weekend retreats are held in the countryside.

Friends of the Western Buddhist Order (FWBO) was established in 1976 in Britain by a London-born Buddhist monk, Sangharakshita. It draws from all the main traditions of Buddhism, not with an attitude of eclecticism, but to take what is useful according to the spiritual needs of Westerners today. Each centre is autonomous, but linked by common practice and friendship between Order members.

Also run meditation classes at Newcastle and Durham Universities.

Founder/Guru	Sangharakshita
Teachers	Dharmaghosha, Nandavajra and Subhadassi and visiting teachers
Opening times	12–5pm weekdays

Residents	Contact centre
Festivals	Buddha, Dharma, Sangha, Parinirvana, FWBO and Padmasambhava Day
Facilities	Shrine room, small library, study room and bookshop
Accommodation	No
Food	Tea and biscuits
Booking	Phone in – £20 deposit required for some events
Fees	Concessions available
Languages	English
Expected behaviour	Normal decent behaviour
How to get there	Contact centre. Disabled access

Practise and study to strengthen your faith. Without practice and study, Buddhism cannot exist. To practise and to study are caused by your faith. Follow these yourself and influence others to do the same. Even if only a word or a phrase, spread it to others.

– from Shoho Jisso Sho brochure

Warwickshire

Wat Pah Santidhamma (Theravada – Thai)
The Forest Hermitage
Lower Fulbrook
Near Sherbourne
Warwick CV35 8AS
Tel & *Fax:* 01926 624 385

Small peaceful monastery in the style of the forest monasteries of North-east Thailand. Originally a pair of nineteenth-century cottages now converted into one. Original garden with orchard, ponds and small meditation huts and newly planted woodland. Pagoda in the grounds was a gift from Myanmar devotees. Open to anyone wanting to learn about Buddhist teaching and practice.

Open evenings usually consist of chanting and guided sitting meditation and a talk, followed by a less formal period for tea and questions. Meditation retreats, help days to keep the Hermitage and grounds in good condition and less formal gatherings to allow people to get to know each other. Private retreats can be arranged and the shrine room is always available for meditation. Interested groups such as school parties can be accommodated with advance notice. Plays an increasingly important part in local education.

The Hermitage is also the headquarters of **Angulimala**, the Buddhist Prison Chaplaincy Organisation which, following consultation with the Home Office Prison Service Chaplaincy, was recognised in 1985 as the official representative of Buddhism in all matters concerning the prison service. Has the backing of most major Buddhist organisations in the UK and patrons include Sangharakshita, Venerable Sumedho and Lord Avebury. Objects are to make available facilities for teaching Buddhism in HM prisons, recruiting and advising a team of Buddhist visiting chaplains, to advise and liaise with the Home Office chaplaincy officials and individual chaplains in prisons, and to provide aftercare and advisory service for prisoners after release.

Founder/Guru	Venerable Khemadhammo Mahathera
Teachers	Venerable Khemadhammo Mahathera
Opening times	Open evenings Monday and Friday at 8pm
Residents	Four or more monks and a lay attendant
Festivals	Main Buddhist Festivals
Facilities	As above and a small library for members
Accommodation	Contact centre
Food	Contact centre
Booking	Ask for programme or newsletter
Fees	Contact centre
Languages	Contact centre
Expected behaviour	Contact centre
How to get there	At Junction 15 of the M40, take the A429 towards Cirencester, then first right for Sherbourne and into Fulbrook Lane. On the right set back from the road is a white house amongst the trees. Please use the car park

> The concern of Mahayana Buddhism is with altruistically developing the path to full Buddhahood, absolute perfection of wisdom and compassion, for the benefit not only of human but of all sentient beings.
>
> – from brochure on Lam Rim Buddhist Centre in Wales

West Midlands

Birmingham Buddhist Centre (Friends of the Western Buddhist Order)
135 Salisbury Road
Moseley
Birmingham B13 8LA
Tel: 0121 449 5279

Converted large house in residential area.

Classes most evenings of the week. Beginners and more advanced classes and courses in meditation and Buddhism. Women's, men's, gay men's and arts events as well as weekend retreats held in Worcestershire.

Two Right Livelihood businesses in the city where people can work together. Community above the centre and other groups of friends share houses nearby.

Friends of the Western Buddhist Order (FWBO) was established in 1976 in Britain by a London-born Buddhist monk, Sangharakshita. It draws from all the main traditions of Buddhism, not with an attitude of eclecticism, but to take what is useful according to the spiritual needs of Westerners today. Each centre is autonomous, but linked by common practice and friendship between Order members.

Founder/Guru	Sangharakshita
Teachers	Members of the Order
Opening times	Class times; ring for visits at other times
Residents	See above
Festivals	As usual for FWBO
Facilities	Shrine room, bookshop, tape and video libraries, study facilities

Accommodation	No
Food	No
Booking	Not necessary. Phone for a programme
Fees	Concessions available
Expected behaviour	Shoes off before entering shrine room
How to get there	Five minutes' walk from either Moseley village or the Pershore Road

The Birmingham Buddhist Vihara Trust (Theravada – Myanmar)
47 Carlyle Road
Edgbaston
Birmingham B16 9BH
Tel & Fax: 0121 454 6597

Terrace house. Trust formed 1982 by the Spiritual Director. Supported mostly by the Myanmar community and local native-born Buddhists. Vihara used mainly by local people.

Meditation instruction for beginners Mondays at 7.30pm. Weekend meditation courses every second weekend of the month, starting Friday 8pm till Sunday afternoon. Eight-week courses in Buddhism on Wednesday evenings with a full day of practical experience. Various schools and traditions are introduced on this course. Daily chanting and meditation for the more experienced. Annual ten-day intensive Vipassana retreat in the summer. Special courses run occasionally, e.g. The Abidhamma – The Various Schools of Buddhism.

Open to meditators at virtually any time – phone to make sure someone is available to open the door. Newcomers should write with a brief resume of background and practice and from this appropriate arrangements are made.

Publish a quarterly newsletter.

Founder/Guru	Spiritual Director is Venerable Dr. Rewata Dhamma (senior Myanmar monk)
Teachers	Ven. Dr. Rewata Dhamma assisted by senior layhelpers
Opening times	9am–9pm daily
Residents	One monk, two lay people

Festivals	Kathina, Buddha day – all welcome to join
Facilities	Shrine room, library with study room, bookstall
Accommodation	Room available if someone is attending a period retreat
Food	Confined to retreatants, unless they are bringing their own
Booking	See above
Fees	Contact centre
Languages	Burmese, Hindi, English
Expected behaviour	Please dress decently, talk quietly and move calmly; monks are addressed as Bhante (pronounced Bhantay) which is equivalent to Venerable Sir. Monks and nuns customarily do not shake hands and are prohibited from touching the opposite sex. Generally the Five Precepts, if staying then the basic Eight Precepts
How to get there	Inner city

The mind is fickle and flighty, it flies after fancies wherever it likes: it is difficult indeed to restrain. But it is a great good to control the mind; a mind self-controlled is a source of great joy.

– *The Dhammapada*

Wiltshire

The International Meditation Centre (Theravada – Myanmar – International Meditation Centre)
Splatts House
Heddington
Calne
Wilts SN11 0PE
Tel: 01380 850 238
Fax: 01380 850 833
e-mail: 100330.3304@compuserve.com

Set on the edge of a quiet Wiltshire village with a pagoda as the focal point. Founded in 1979 as a direct offspring of the International Meditation Centre of Yangon, Myanmar (formerly Rangoon, Burma).

Ten-day residential courses with instruction and practice of meditation (Anapana and Vipassana) are held monthly. There are led by Mother Sayamagyi and Sayagyi U Chit Tin or by a regional teacher. First five days involve instruction in Anapana (mindfulness of breathing) and the remaining days are devoted to Vipassana. One should go with the understanding and intention to enter a ten-day retreat. Participants should expect to give up all other spiritual practices and objects and reading materials, although one doesn't have to be a Buddhist, just genuinely interested. Daily interview in which students should give a true and accurate account of their experiences. Timetable very structured, starting at 4am and finishing at 9pm.

Founder/Guru	Sayagyi U Ba Khin
Teachers	Mother Sayamagyi and Sayagyi U Chit Tin
Opening Times	Contact centre
Residents	Contact centre
Festivals	Contact centre
Facilities	Dharma Hall
Accommodation	Shared accommodation in large Queen Anne House
Food	First-class vegetarian with wide selection of dishes
Booking	Pre-registration form included with information sent out by managment. No deposit
Fees	No charge for teachings, but contribution of £150 for ten-day course expected
Languages	Contact centre
Expected behaviour	Five Precepts and observe noble silence
How to get there	Nearby towns of Chippenham, Calne and Devizes are served by public transport from Victoria Coach station and Paddington railway station in London

The House of Inner Tranquility (Theravada)
9 Masons Lane
Bradford-on-Avon
Wiltshire BA15 1QN
Tel: 01225 866 821
Fax: 01225 86 5262

Not open for casual visitors. Fine Bath-stone building overlooking
town with excellent retreat facilities including a Japanese garden
designed for walking meditation. Founded in 1980 and the
growth of the meditation centre has resulted in the formation of
two monasteries for those wishing to train on a full-time basis.
Run by the Aukana Trust which also publishes books on
Buddhism.

Full programme of lectures, evening classes and retreats. Offers
the opportunity for the meditator to follow the Buddha's way to
its conclusion, the emphasis being very much on practice. Anyone
who wishes to learn more should initially read Alan and Jacqui
James' book *A Meditation Retreat* available by post from the same
address. An interview will be arranged before the attendee should
decide whether to join the Introductory Course.

Satellite groups in London, Oxford and Toronto, Canada.

Founder/Guru	Alan and Jacqui James, Alan James now spiritual head
Teachers	As above
Opening times	Not open for casual visits
Residents	Information not given
Festivals	Information not given
Facilities	Information not given
Accommodation	Information not given
Food	Information not given
Booking	See above
Fees	Information not given
Languages	Information not given
Expected behaviour	Five Precepts and to meditate daily
How to get there	Contact centre

> Be a good man;
> Do good deeds;
> Read good books;
> Speak good words.
>
> – Inscription carved on rock near Buddhist monastery of Ku-
> shan, Fuhkien Province, China

Yorkshire – North

Madhyamaka Centre (Tibetan – Gelug – New Kadampa
Tradition)
Kilnwick Percy Hall
Pocklington
York YO4 2UF
Tel: 01759 304832
Fax: 01759 305962
e-mail: madhyama@rmplc.co.uk
website: http://www.rmplc.co.uk/eduweb/sites/madhyama/
index.html

Georgian mansion with forty acres of parkland and woodland.
One of the largest Mahayana Buddhist Colleges in Europe, with a
community of fifty lay and ordained residents. Welcome thousands of visitors of all kinds and all ages each year and also have
a residential centre in York itself. Established 1979.

Visitors may attend courses and retreats or have a peaceful holi-
day. Activities for newcomers include: 11.00am on Sundays –
Prayers for World Peace; 7.30pm Mondays – Introduction to
Buddhism; 6.30pm Fridays – Stop the Week. Day and weekend
courses suitable for beginners and more experienced meditators.
Occasional five-day courses for more experienced practitioners.
Four-week retreat in January and various weekend and five-day
retreats throughout the year.

The New Kadampa Tradition (NKT) is a Mahayana Buddhist
tradition founded by Geshe Kelsang Gyatso, a Tibetan Buddhist
Master resident in the UK since 1977. Its main purpose is to preserve and promote the essence of Buddha's teachings in a form
that is suited to the modern world and way of life.

All NKT centres form a family spiritually following the same direction and its core is the Three Study Programmes. Of these, this centre offers:

• The General Programme – a basic introduction to Buddhist view, meditation and action in a form that is suitable for beginners. It also includes advanced teachings and practices of both Sutra and Tantra.

• The Foundation Programme to deepen understanding and experience of Buddhism through systematic study of five of Geshe Kelsang's books. It takes about four years to complete.

• The Teacher Training Programme is designed for people who wish to train as authentic Dharma Teachers. This seven-year programme involves studying twelve of Geshe Kelsang's books, observing certain commitments with regard to behaviour and way of life, and completing a number of retreats.

Drop in any afternoon between 2 and 5pm for a guided tour and cup of tea or coffee.

Branches in Bedford, Cleethorpes, Driffield, Gateshead, Hartlepool, Hatfield, Ripon, Selby, Scarborough, Stevenage, Thirsk and Whitby. Contact Education Office for details.

Founder/Guru	Venerable Geshe Kelsang Gyatso
Teachers	Ven Khyenrab (the resident teacher); other senior students
Opening times	Contact centre
Residents	See above
Festivals	NKT day and Je Tsongkhapa Day
Facilities	Two shrine rooms, meditation rooms and a study room
Accommodation	Single £20; Twin £17.50 per person; Dormitory £12 (£10 during a course). Prices for full-board
Food	Three vegetarian meals a day at £2.50 each
Booking	Contact centre
Fees	Classes £3.50; Day Courses £13.00 inc. lunch; Weekend Courses £15; Five-day Courses £25; Six-day Courses £30; Retreats £3.50 per day
Languages	English, some German and French
Expected behaviour	Not to eat meat, drink alcohol, smoke or

play loud music on the premises. To wear not-too-revealing clothes

How to get there   Pocklington is midway between York and Hull on the A1079. From there, take the B1246 towards Bridlington. Kilnwick Percy is a small left turning 1 mile outside Pocklington. Buses from York station: 746 to Pocklington, 744 to Kilnwick Percy Hall turn off. Taxis from Pocklington £2.50

All tremble at punishment.
All fear death.
Putting oneself in the place of another,
one should not kill nor cause another to kill.

– The Dhammapada

Yorkshire – South

Buddhist Centre Sheffield (Friends of the Western Buddhist Order)
c/o 354 Crookesmoor Road
Sheffield
South Yorkshire S10 1BH
Tel: 0114 263 7435

Residential house outside city centre. Founded 1989 to house writer/publishers, now home to five men involved in living and teaching Dharma. Plan to open a staffed public centre nearby.

Run morning meditations and various evening classes. Occasional day retreats and weekend retreats at other venues. Women's and men's day and weekend retreats, study days, Introduction to Buddhism eight-week course.

Friends of the Western Buddhist Order (FWBO) was established in 1976 in Britain by a London-born Buddhist monk, Sangharakshita. It draws from all the main traditions of Buddhism, not with an attitude of eclecticism, but to take what is useful according to the spiritual needs of Westerners today. Each centre is autonomous, but linked by common practice and friendship between Order members.

Founder/Guru	Sangharakshita
Teachers	Order members
Opening times	Arrange in advance
Residents	Five male Order members
Festivals	Buddha, Dharma, Sangha, Parinirvana, FWBO and Padmasambhava Days
Facilities	Contact centre
Booking	Contact the secretary
Fees	Classes by donation; weekends £55/£30 concessions; days £12/£6 concessions
Languages	English
Expected behaviour	Normal decent behaviour
How to get there	Phone for details

Gyaltsabje Buddhist Centre (Tibetan – Gelug – New Kadampa Tradition)
11–13 Sharrow View
Nether Edge
Sheffield S7 1ND
Tel & Fax: 0114 250 9663

In leafy part of town in former hotel near to Peak District. Can walk to hills along string of parks which start near the centre. Founded in 1986.

The New Kadampa Tradition (NKT) is a Mahayana Buddhist tradition founded by Geshe Kelsang Gyatso, a Tibetan Buddhist Master resident in the UK since 1977. Its main purpose is to preserve and promote the essence of Buddha's teachings in a form that is suited to the modern world and way of life.

All NKT centres form a family spiritually following the same direction and its core is the Three Study Programmes. Of these, this centre offers:

• The General Programme – a basic introduction to Buddhist view, meditation and action in a form that is suitable for beginners. It also includes advanced teachings and practices of both Sutra and Tantra.

• The Foundation Programme to deepen understanding and

experience of Buddhism through systematic study of five of Geshe Kelsang's books. It takes about four years to complete.
• The Teacher Training Programme is designed for people who wish to train as authentic Dharma teachers. This seven-year programme involves studying twelve of Geshe Kelsang's books, observing certain commitments with regard to behaviour and way of life, and completing a number of retreats.

Pujas daily and on special events. Occasional weekend and day courses and public talks. Course subjects such as In the Footsteps of the Buddha, the Prison of Selfishness, Aspects of Love, Lam Rim and Vajrajyogini. Working holidays also available.

Resident teacher is foremost Thangka painter in the New Kadampa tradition and teaches regular courses for those wishing to either learn or improve their skills.

This centre runs branches at Barnsley, Chesterfield, Doncaster, Lincoln, Rotherham and Scunthorpe.

Founder/Guru	Venerable Geshe Kelsang Gyatso Rinpoche
Teachers	Ani Kelsang Wangchen and visiting NKT teachers
Opening times	2–5pm for visits and as programme
Residents	One monk, two nuns and ten lay people
Festivals	Contact centre
Facilities	Shrine room, library, study room
Accommodation	Dormitory £12.50, double £17.50 and single £25
Food	Three vegetarian meals a day at £1 to £2.50 each, please book in advance
Booking	Contact centre for details
Fees	£3 per class
Languages	English
Expected behaviour	No smoking, drugs, TV, pets or noise outside room. Respect Dharma centre
How to get there	Half mile from inner ring road, between A625 and A621

'Some people,' said Buddha, the master, 'have accused me of uttering these words:

When one attains the release called the Beautiful, and abides therein, at such a time he considers the whole universe as ugly.

But I never said these words. This is what I do say:

When one attains the release called the Beautiful, at such a time he knows in truth what Beauty is'.

– *Samyuta* and *Digha Nikaya*

WALES

Dharmavajra Buddhist Centre (Tibetan – Gelug – New Kadampa Tradition)
13 St. James's Gardens
Uplands
Swansea SA1 6DX
Tel: 01792 458245

Victorian terraced house in quiet area of central Swansea over-looking a park. Local practitioners raised funds to buy the house and it opened as a centre in 1994.

Heart Jewel puja and Lam Rim meditation daily. Day courses every one or two months. Tantric and Lam Rim retreats.

The New Kadampa Tradition (NKT) is a Mahayana Buddhist tradition founded by Geshe Kelsang Gyatso, a Tibetan Buddhist Master resident in the UK since 1977. Its main purpose is to preserve and promote the essence of Buddha's teachings in a form that is suited to the modern world and way of life.

All NKT centres form a family spiritually following the same direction and its core is the Three Study Programmes. Of these, this centre offers:
• The General Programme provides a basic introduction to Buddhist view, meditation and action in a form that is suitable for beginners. It also includes advanced teachings and practices of both Sutra and Tantra.

• The Foundation Programme to deepen understanding and experience of Buddhism through systematic study of five of Geshe Kelsang's books. It takes about four years to complete. Branches in Carmarthen, Bridgend, Cardiff and Abergavenny.

Founder/Guru	Venerable Geshe Kelsang Gyatso Rinpoche
Teachers	Ani La Kelsang Gema
Opening times	By prior arrangement
Residents	One monk part time and 5–6 lay people
Festivals	Lama Choepa twice a month and NKT day
Facilities	Shrine room, bookshop and living room
Accommodation	Single or shared room and floor space at £4–£7 or half-price concessions
Food	Three meals a day £1–£1.50 each or 50p–£1.50 concessions
Booking	Phone for details, usually no need to book in advance
Fees	Various
Languages	English
Expected behaviour	No drinking alcohol or smoking on premises
How to get there	Phone centre for details

Lam Rim Buddhist Centre (Tibetan – Gelug)
Pentwyn Manor
Penrhos
Raglan
Gwent NP5 2LE
Tel: 01600 780 383

In the beautiful countryside of Monmouthshire, South Wales. Mock Tudor house in eight and a half acres of land amid rolling farmland near the Black Mountains.

Morning and evening puja daily. Programme of weekend courses including and extending beyond purely Buddhist themes to include Yoga, Tai Chi and alternative therapies. Meditation training of several types also available. Lam Rim Shiatsu Institute offers courses and trainings.

Short-term individual retreats possible in single rooms. Self-contained accommodation in coachhouse for retreats and study programmes over six months long.

High Lamas sometimes visit to give teachers and inititations. Offer study days for religious education teachers and students and annual teachers' weekend where they can discuss the educational aspect of teaching Buddhism with a university lecturer.

Geshe Damcho mainly in residence and available for interview. Residents also available for assistance.

Founder/Guru	Venerable Geshe Damcho Yonten
Teachers	Resident teacher is founder and visiting teachers from different traditions
Opening times	Phone beforehand. March–July, September–November closed. Silent days Wednesday and Thursday
Residents	One or two monks and three lay people
Festivals	Phone for details
Facilities	Shrine room and library
Accommodation	Dormitory £21, single rooms £27, prices for full-board per day
Food	Vegetarian food, much of it home-grown and home-made. £4–£5.50 per meal
Booking	Telephone or write for programme of events. Prefer one week's notice and 2–3 weeks May to July
Fees	Weekend courses £46 total cost and offering donation
Languages	English, German and Tibetan
Expected behaviour	Five Precepts – have a reputation for being strict. No shoes in centre, no smoking in centre or grounds, wear appropriate clothing at all times. Respect Countryside Code
How to get there	Contact centre for details

Samatha Trust (Theravada – Thai)
Greenstreete
Llangunllo
Near Knighton
Powys LD7 1SP

Tel: 01547 550274

Welsh hill farm bought by the Trust in 1987 and extensively renovated. Surrounded by eighty-eight acres of hills, woods and
streams. Meditation huts for those wanting more solitude. Barn
being converted into a shrine; gardens and woodland being
extended. Samatha meditation technique has its roots in Thai
Theravadin tradition and was brought to England in 1962 by a
Thai meditation teacher. The Samatha Trust was formed in 1973 to
support the teaching in various parts of the country and to establish a national centre. Has also published a number of works on
Buddhist theory and practice.

Practice here involves meditation technique based on attention
to breath combined with mindful work often in gardens or on the
land. Individual retreats available.

Beginners' courses run on the first weekend of each quarter.
Local beginners' classes held throughout the country. For begin-
ners' weekends contact: Graham Murphy, 31 Highville Road,
Liverpool L16 9JE, telephone 0151 722 0893.

Classes and groups are held around the country for beginners
and experienced meditators. Contact this centre for groups in
Altrincham, Bolton, Bristol/Bath, Cambridge, Chester,
Durham/Sunderland, Ipswich, Liverpool, Llangunllo, London,
Manchester, Oldham, Oxford, Pembrokeshire, Peterborough,
Rossendale and Stockport.

Founder/Guru	From Thai tradition
Teachers	From local groups
Opening times	As programme
Residents	No
Festivals	Contact centre
Facilities	Contact centre
Accommodation	In farmhouse or meditation huts – cost included in course fee
Food	Vegetarian/non-vegetarian
Booking	Contact centre
Fees	Around £30 full-board for weekend course
Languages	English
Expected behaviour	No alcohol or drugs. Consult teacher before bringing reading material

How to get there   Train to Llangunllo station and fifteen minutes walk from station

Vajraloka Buddhist Meditation Centre for Men (Friends of the Western Buddhist Order)
Tyn-y-Ddol
Corwen
Clwyd LL21 0EN
Tel: 01490 460 406

Restored Welsh stone farmhouse and outbuildings in North Wales countryside. Started in late seventies initially as a place for meditation which has expanded into teaching meditation and holding retreats.

Main meditation centre of the FWBO and in the forefront of the development of meditation in the movement. Follows the basic systems for meditation developed in the FWBO (Metta Bhavana and Mindfulness of Breathing).

All retreats are for men only (occasionally a special retreat for women) – see **Taraloka** in Shropshire for the FWBO women-only retreat centre on p111. Retreats involve periods of meditation, talks, ritual and devotion, meditation interviews and work sessions. Retreats geared to every level of experience.

Open day to the public about once every two years.

Friends of the Western Buddhist Order (FWBO) was established in 1976 in Britain by a London-born Buddhist monk, Sangharakshita. It draws from all the main traditions of Buddhism, not with an attitude of eclecticism, but to take what is useful according to the spiritual needs of Westerners today. Each centre is autonomous, but linked by common practice and friendship between Order members.

Founder/Guru	Sangharakshita, Founder this centre Dharmachari Kamalashila
Teachers	Resident and occasionally visiting members of the FWBO
Opening times	For retreats only
Residents	4–6 members of the FWBO
Festivals	Given special emphasis when falling during

	a retreat
Facilities	Contact centre
Accommodation	Single, double or triple rooms or dormitory. £22 per night or £18 concession. Cheaper rates for long-term guests
Food	Three vegetarian meals a day included in accommodation rates
Booking	Shrine room, lounge and reading room
Fees	Contact centre for details
Languages	English
Expected behaviour	As suitable for retreats, consideration for others
How to get there	Two miles past Corwen on A5 and turn off at old creamery. Second left and follow this farm road for two miles

> In reality Buddhism is neither pessimistic nor optimistic. If compelled to label it in this way at all we should borrow a word from George Eliot and call it melioristic, for though asserting that conditioned existence is suffering it also maintains, as the Third Aryan Truth teaches, that suffering can be transcended.
>
> – Sangharakshita, *The Three Jewels*

SCOTLAND

Edinburgh Buddhist Centre (Friends of the Western Buddhist Order)
55a Grange Road
Edinburgh EH9 1TX
Tel & Fax: 0131 662 4945

Large sandstone semi-detached residential house. Use of garden for some events in summer. Resident community of five men, two of whom are members of the FWBO. At this address since August 1994.

Friends of the Western Buddhist Order (FWBO) was established in 1976 in Britain by a London-born Buddhist monk,

Sangharakshita. It draws from all the main traditions of Buddhism, not with an attitude of eclecticism, but to take what is useful according to the spiritual needs of Westerners today. Each centre is autonomous, but linked by common practice and friendship between Order members.

Events include six-week introductory evening courses in Buddhism and meditation, day retreats, and topics include creative dance and movement, Yoga and meditation, assertiveness training, Alexander technique, Heart Sutra study day, Introduction to Buddhist symbols and ritual.

Founder/Guru	Sangharakshita
Teachers	Resident and visiting members of the Order
Opening times	Weekdays 5pm for Yoga, 7pm for classes; Weekends 10am for day events. At other times, phone to arrange beforehand. Closed two weeks over Christmas.
Residents	See above
Festivals	Buddha Day, Dharma Day, Sangha Day, Parinirvana Day
Facilities	Two shrine rooms, small reference library, study room, bookshop and yoga room
Accommodation	No
Food	Bring food to share on day events
Booking	Two weeks in advance by sending £10 deposit
Fees	Various suggested donations according to event
Languages	English and Gaelic
Expected behaviour	Respecting the quiet especially if people are meditating, removing shoes before entering shrine room
How to get there	By foot or bus, twenty minutes' walk from city centre

Mahakaruna Centre (Tibetan – Gelug – New Kadampa Tradition)
1st Floor
28 Mardale Crescent
Edinburgh EH10 5AG

Tel: 0131 229 2204

Residential flat twenty minutes' walk from town centre. Branch of
Madhyamaka Centre in Yorkshire (see separate entry on p125)
and initiated in 1993, at present property since 1995 and currently
looking for larger premises.

The New Kadampa Tradition (NKT) is a Mahayana Buddhist
tradition founded by Geshe Kelsang Gyatso, a Tibetan Buddhist
Master resident in the UK since 1977. Its main purpose is to preserve and promote the essence of Buddha's teachings in a form
that is suited to the modern world and way of life.

All NKT centres form a family spiritually following the same
direction and its core is the Three Study Programmes. Of these,
this centre offers:

• The General Programme – a basic introduction to Buddhist
view, meditation and action in a form that is suitable for beginners. It also includes advanced teachings and practices of both
Sutra and Tantra.

• The Foundation Programme to deepen understanding and
experience of Buddhism through systematic study of five of
Geshe Kelsang's books. It takes about four years to complete.

Avalokiteshara Puja Mondays and Tuesdays 7.30pm.
Thursdays General Programme 7.30pm, Saturdays Vajrayogini
Puja 7.30pm (for initiates only). Sundays Foundation Programme.
Day courses held every couple of months for beginners and
advanced practitioners on the range of subjects from the Sutras
and Tantras.

Founder/Guru	Venerable Geshe Kelsang Gyatso Rinpoche
Teachers	Resident: Kelsang Zopa, other NKT teach-ers occasionally visit
Opening times	10am–10pm
Residents	Two monks and two lay people
Festivals	Contact centre
Facilities	Shrine room, library and sitting room
Accommodation	No at present
Food	Only during day courses and Foundation Programme days
Booking	By phone – booking needed for day courses only

Fees	See programme
Languages	Contact centre
Expected behaviour	Five Precepts and not to play loud music or use television
How to get there	Many buses or twenty minutes' walk from town centre

Glasgow Buddhist Centre (Friends of the Western Buddhist Order)
329 Sauchiehall Street
Glasgow G2 3HW
Tel & Fax: 0141 333 0524

Located in city centre. Opened in 1972. Centre is spacious and atmosphere relaxed. During opening hours people are available to discuss the centre's activities, Buddhism and meditation. Meditations taught are mindfulness of breathing and Metta Bhavana (loving-kindness).

Friends of the Western Buddhist Order (FWBO) was established in 1976 in Britain by a London-born Buddhist monk, Sangharakshita. It draws from all the main traditions of Buddhism, not with an attitude of eclecticism, but to take what is useful according to the spiritual needs of Westerners today. Each centre is autonomous, but linked by common practice and friendship between Order members.

All meditation classes are open to newcomers as are some weekend introductory events. Pujas are performed once a month and Thursday mornings after the meditation class and festival days. Events include Introductory Classes, Open Day, free public talks, Massage and Meditation Weekends, Yoga, Awareness through Art and Creative Writing and Meditation. Retreats are held at **Dhanakosa Retreat Centre** (see separate entry on p142) and last between two to ten days. Topics for these include Singing and Meditation, Introduction to Buddhism, Hillwalking and Meditation, Introduction to Meditation.

Founder/Guru	Sangharakshita
Teachers	Resident: Dharmacharya Jinavamsa, Dharmacharya Vimalavajra, Dharma-

	charya Amoghangra and visiting members of FWBO
Opening times	Monday to Friday 11.30am to 5pm
Residents	No
Festivals	Buddha Day, Dharma Day, Sangha Day, Parinirvana Day, Padmasambhava Day
Facilities	Shrine room, reference library, study room, bookshop and reception room
Accommodation	Contact centre
Food	On weekend events and festival days, people are asked to bring vegetarian food
Booking	£5 non-returnable deposit
Fees	All prices are suggested donations and concessions are available
Languages	English
Expected behaviour	Normal decent behaviour
How to get there	Charing Cross end of Sauchihall Street, opposite School of Dentistry – door entry system, on first floor

Samye Ling Tibetan Centre (Tibetan – Kagyu)
Eskdalemuir
Langholm
Dumfriesshire DG13 0QL
Tel: 013873 73232
Fax: 013873 73223

On the Scottish borders – wet weather. Wooded grounds surrounded by hills with riverside walks. Founded 1967 and was the first Tibetan centre in Europe. Specialisation is oral transmission of Kagyu Lineage. Practice wisdom through kindness and compassion for all sentient beings. Tibetan-style temple finished in 1988 and at time of writing were building Samye College, Library and Museum. Driving force behind the purchase of Holy Island near the Isle of Arran in the West of Scotland as a natural haven of peace to be used for retreats and for the Centre for Peace, Reconciliation and Retreat.

Samye Ling is a key focus for the preservation of Tibetan religion, culture, medicine, art, architecture and handicrafts; a highly respected international centre of Buddhist training; hub of a network of international humanitarian activities which feed the needy in cities worldwide; mother centre for its branch centres; a voice in interfaith understanding and a college of Tibetan medicine.

To stay you don't need to be a Buddhist and you are free to follow your own timetable. You are welcome to join in courses, daily prayers, meditations and to help with daily chores. Meditations are daily at 8am and 5pm in the temple; mornings there is Tara Puja, afternoons Mahakala Puja, evenings Amitabha and Chenrezig Puja. Retreats include the Nunghey Retreat, one-year and three-year, three-month and three-day retreats. Weekend workshops and courses on range of subjects including Buddhism, meditation, therapy, storytelling, Yoga, alternative medicines and Tibetan arts and culture.

Branch centres are in Glasgow, Edinburgh, Norfolk, Birmingham, Isle of Arran, Belgium and Spain.

Founder/Guru	Akong Rinpoche and late Trungpa Rinpoche
Teachers	Resident: Akong Rinpoche and Lama Yeshe Losal Ringu Tulku among others and visiting teachers including The XIIth Tai Situpa
Opening times	9am to 6pm for day visitors
Residents	Forty monks and nuns, about fifty lay people
Festivals	Mahayana and Vajrayana Buddhist Festivals
Facilities	See above
Accommodation	Single room £20 per night, twin bed room £25 per night, dormitory £12 per night, camping in own tent £10.50 per night
Food	Vegetarian full-board included in accommodation prices or £3 for lunch
Booking	Telephone or write, deposit of £15 per person
Fees	All weekend workshops are £35
Languages	English, Tibetan, French, German, Italian and Spanish
Expected behaviour	Kindness to and respect for others. No

smoking, drugs, alcohol or fishing anywhere on the property. No pets. Children should be supervised at all times

How to get there   By road from Langholm take the B709 to Eskdalemuir or follow Eskdalemuir signs from Lockerbie. By train, go to Lockerbie and phone in advance to book a taxi to pick you up

Vajrasattva Buddhist Centre (Tibetan – Gelug – New Kadampa Tradition)
4 Kingholm Road
Dumfries DG1 4AX
Tel: 01387 263 821

Semi-detached four-bedroomed house on the outskirts of town overlooking a park, river and cemetery. Developed from a meditation group into a centre in 1992. Growing community.

The New Kadampa Tradition (NKT) is a Mahayana Buddhist tradition founded by Geshe Kelsang Gyatso, a Tibetan Buddhist Master resident in the UK since 1977. Its main purpose is to preserve and promote the essence of Buddha's teachings in a form that is suited to the modern world and way of life.

All NKT centres form a family spiritually following the same direction and its core is the Three Study Programmes. Of these, this centre offers:

• The General Programme – a basic introduction to Buddhist view, meditation and action in a form that is suitable for beginners. It also includes advanced teachings and practices of both Sutra and Tantra.

• The Foundation Programme to deepen understanding and experience of Buddhism through systematic study of five of Geshe Kelsang's books. It takes about four years to complete.

Evening classes and day courses on different topics including Entering the Bodhisattva's Way of Life and Tara Empowerment and Commentary.

Meditation classes held at George Street Community Centre on Friday evenings.

Founder/Guru	Venerable Geshe Kelsang Gyatso Rinpoche
Teachers	Venerable Ani Kelsang Montam and visiting teachers
Opening times	Open for enquiries at all times
Residents	One monk and three lay people
Festivals	Buddhist festivals and Spring and Summer Festivals at **Manjushri** in Cumbria (see separate entry on p74)
Facilities	Shrine room, library and bookshop
Accommodation	Single room £25 per week and any additional costs
Food	Self-catering
Booking	Contact centre in advance with 25% deposit
Fees	Sessions £3, day courses £12.30 with lunch, £10 without lunch
Languages	English and basic German and Spanish if needed
Expected behaviour	Respect of Dharma centre and others' spiritual and mundane needs
How to get there	Twenty minutes' walk from railway station. Contact centre for details

Dhanakosa Retreat Centre (Friends of the Western Buddhist Order)
Ledcreich House
Balquhidder
Lochearnhead FK19 8PQ
Tel: 0187 384 213

The FWBO's retreat centre in Scotland. No previous experience of meditation or Buddhism is needed. By the shores of Loch Voil and surrounded by mountains and forests.

Friends of the Western Buddhist Order (FWBO) was established in 1976 in Britain by a London-born Buddhist monk, Sangharakshita. It draws from all the main traditions of Buddhism, not with an attitude of eclecticism, but to take what is useful according to the spiritual needs of Westerners today. Each centre is autonomous, but linked by common practice and friendship between Order members.

Approximately one-third of participants are committed FWBO Buddhists, the rest are either interested in Buddhism, meditation or a particular activity run at the centre. All events apart from the Open Day are residential and full-board. Daily routine depends on the retreat but most have three periods of meditation per day as well as any specialist activity such as Yoga or massage. Usually a few hours of free time in the afternoon. Topics for retreats include introductions to Buddhism and Meditation, alternative health retreats such as reflexology, massage, Alexander Technique, Yoga and shiatsu and arts retreats such as painting and drawing, singing, writing and language. Annual gay men's retreats and Working and Mindfulness Retreats. All are open to newcomers, for more advanced topics, please ask for a separate programme.

Founder/Guru	Sangharakshita
Teachers	Various visiting teachers
Opening times	Contact centre
Residents	Contact centre
Festivals	Contact centre
Facilities	Contact centre
Accommodation	Very comfortable, most rooms have en-suite bathrooms.
Food	Part of accommodation cost – all vegan and vegetarian. Special diets can be catered for by prior arrangement
Booking	By phone or post with deposit of £15 weekend, £30 week
Fees	Suggested donation of £160 per week (£130 low waged and £90 unwaged)
Languages	English.
Expected behaviour	No alcohol, no smoking in the building and grounds, to follow a vegetarian diet
How to get there	Sixteen miles from Callander and one and a half hour's drive from Glasgow and Edinburgh

Tharpaland Retreat Centre (Tibetan – Gelug – New Kadampa Tradition)
Parkgate
Dumfries DG1 3LY
Tel: 01387 860298

Retreat centre for the New Kadampa Tradition in the UK. Situated in the Forest of Ae. Panoramic views over forests and hills and to the Cumbrian coastline. Formerly a large farmhouse with out-houses and barns.

The New Kadampa Tradition (NKT) is a Mahayana Buddhist tradition founded by Geshe Kelsang Gyatso, a Tibetan Buddhist Master resident in the UK since 1977. Its main purpose is to pre-serve and promote the essence of Buddha's teachings in a form that is suited to the modern world and way of life. All NKT cen-tres form a family spiritually following the same direction.

Twenty rooms, mostly with private facilities and central heat-ing, many with private access. Additional bedrooms and dormi-tory space also available for group retreats and short stay visitors. Various scheduled retreats thoughout year. Facilities for both long and short stay private retreats. Special rates for long stay retreatants. Facilities open for group retreats of up to forty people.

Founder/Guru	Venerable Geshe Kelsang Gyatso
Teachers	Resident: Venerable Ani Kelsang Monlam
Opening times	By prior arrangement only
Residents	Contact centre
Festivals	Contact centre
Facilities	See above
Accommodation	See above
Food	Vegetarian
Booking	Well in advance
Fees	Various – contact centre for details
Languages	Contact centre
Expected behaviour	Five Precepts and silence during parts of the day
How to get there	Detailed instructions sent with confirma-tion of booking

It has been recognized even in the West (by Schopenhauer) that all great Art contains an element of self-transcendence akin to that which constitutes the quintessence of religion. When this element of self-transcendence is consciously cultivated in poetry, in music, or in painting and sculpture, instead of the element·of mere sensuous appeal, Art ceases to be a form of sensuous indulgence and becomes a kind of spiritual discipline, and the highest stages of aesthetic contemplation become spiritual experiences.

– Sangharakshita, *The Path of the Inner Life*

NORTHERN IRELAND

Tilopa Buddhist Centre (Tibetan – Gelug – New Kadampa Tradition)
3 Iona Terrace
Derry BT47 1EY
Tel: 01504 42232

Four-bedroom house in quiet area with easy access to countryside. Established 1994 when classes were first offered in Derry. Fully residential centre established in 1996.

Pujas held weekly. Evening meditation with study classes. Lam Rim retreats.

The New Kadampa Tradition (NKT) is a Mahayana Buddhist tradition founded by Geshe Kelsang Gyatso, a Tibetan Buddhist Master resident in the UK since 1977. Its main purpose is to preserve and promote the essence of Buddha's teachings in a form that is suited to the modern world and way of life.

All NKT centres form a family spiritually following the same direction and its core is the Three Study Programmes. Of these, this centre offers:

• The General Programme – a basic introduction to Buddhist view, meditation and action in a form that is suitable for beginners. It also includes advanced teachings and practices of both Sutra and Tantra.

• The Foundation Programme to deepen understanding and experience of Buddhism through systematic study of five of

Geshe Kelsang's books. It takes about four years to complete.

Resident nun also teaches in Belfast where both General and Foundation Programmes are offered.

Founder/Guru	Geshe Kelsang Gyatso
Teachers	Ani Kelsang Drolkar
Opening times	By arrangement
Residents	One nun
Festivals	Buddhist festivals and Je Tsongkapa and Tara Day
Facilities	Shrine and study rooms
Accommodation	Possible by arrangement
Food	Can be arranged
Booking	Contact centre for specific information
Fees	Contact centre
Languages	Contact centre
Expected behaviour	To be respectful and harmonious
How to get there	On waterside area of city. At bottom of Limavady Road

> Heaven, the ultimate goal of so many faiths, since it is a mode of contingent and hence of transitory existence, is accounted no more than a pleasant interlude in a pilgrimage fundamentally of more serious import.
>
> — Sangharakshita, *The Three Jewels*

REPUBLIC OF IRELAND

Dublin Meditation Centre (Friends of the Western Buddhist Order)
23 South Frederick Street
Dublin 4
Tel: +353 (0)1 671 3187

Georgian building in the centre of town near Trinity College. Activities began in 1991, centre acquired in 1993.

Classes Mondays to Fridays and workshops most weekends on massage, chanting and communication as well as meditation and yoga. Weekend retreats every six weeks and regular day retreats usually specialising in either Sati or Metta Bhavana. Six-week Meditation Foundation course with free introductory night to see if you would like to participate.

Friends of the Western Buddhist Order (FWBO) was established in 1976 in Britain by a London-born Buddhist monk, Sangharakshita. It draws from all the main traditions of Buddhism, not with an attitude of eclecticism, but to take what is useful according to the spiritual needs of Westerners today. Each centre is autonomous, but linked by common practice and friendship between Order members.

New calendar with details of events every six weeks – let them know if you want to be on the mailing list.

Founder/Guru	Sangharakshita
Teachers	Sanghapala and Ratnabhandu and visiting FWBO members
Opening times	10am–5pm for drop-in; 6–10pm for courses and classes
Residents	Two
Festivals	Usual Buddhist calendar
Facilities	Shrine room
Accommodation	No
Food	No
Booking	Phone in and send deposit three days in advance
Fees	Daytime meditations 50p, six-week yoga course £30, other courses £50–60. Concessions available
Languages	English and Irish
Expected behaviour	Normal decent behaviour
How to get there	Town centre

Samyedzong Buddhist Centre (Tibetan – Karma Kagyu)
Kilmainham Well House
56 Inchicore Road
Kilmainham
Dublin 8
Tel: +353 (0)1 453 7427

Fax: +353 (0)1 453 7304

Large Edwardian house and gardens located in the oldest part of Dublin. Three museums, river Liffey and 'largest city park in European (including a wild deer herd) within a few minutes' walk. First Buddhist Centre to be established in Ireland when started in 1977. Named after Samye – first Buddhist monastery in Tibet.

Constantly changing programme, including meditations, Green Tara and Chenrizig pujas. Introductory session most Tuesdays 8–9.30pm – check current programme for other times. Occasional non-residential retreats.

Back to Beginnings, Taming the Tiger and other therapeutic programmes developed by Akong Rinpoche also available under qualified guidance. These were developed over many years in consultation with therapists of various disciplines, drawing on his knowledge of meditation, Tibetan medicine and thirty years' work with people in the West. Modern culture strongly encourages intellectual growth, sometimes at the expense of emotional maturity and these methods help redress this balance.

Apart from catering for its supporting community's interests, it also serves as an information resource for schools, etc. and the general public.

Founder/Guru	Spiritual Director: Akong Rinpoche
Teachers	Visiting from all traditions but chiefly from Kagyu tradition
Opening times	As per courses, etc., in progress
Residents	Not continuously – one or more monks or nuns for extended stays; two or three lay residents
Festivals	Contact centre
Facilities	Shrine room, therapy and reception rooms, books for sale
Accommodation	Not on premises, but many guest houses, hostels, etc. nearby
Food	Vegetarian meals occasionally during weekend events
Booking	Varies – see programme
Fees	Mostly by donation

Languages   Contact centre
Expected behaviour   No smoking on premises
How to get there   Two miles west of city centre, almost oppo-
site Kilmainham Gaol Museum

Dzogchen Beara Retreat and Conference Centre (Tibetan –
Nyingma – Rigpa)
Garranes
Allihies
West Cork
Tel: +353 (0)27 73032
Fax: +353 (0)27 73177
e-mail: 100727,1504@compuserve.com
Garranes Farmhouse Hostel *Tel:* +353 (0)27 73147

Dramatic cliff-top location in one of the most beautiful and
unspoiled parts of Europe. Outstanding panoramic views across
Bantry Bay and the Atlantic Ocean. Main house has accommodation for long-term retreatants and a spacious meditation room,
four self-catering cottages and a traditional farmhouse building
for dormitory accommodation which functions as a hostel.

Environment conducive to spiritual practice whether in the
Tibetan Buddhist tradition or otherwise. Offer retreats, courses
and instruction in Tibetan Buddhism. During the summer daily
open meditation with instruction for beginners. Saturday evening
open meditation throughout the year. Instruction generally available at other times on request. Some separate practice sessions for
students familiar with the particular meditation being practised.
Introductory weekends about six times a year focusing on meditation as taught by Sogyal Rinpoche in *The Tibetan Book of Living
and Dying*. Five or six weekends a year, retreats are led by visiting
teachers. Normally a retreat or course over the St. Patrick's Day
holiday weekend in March and the holiday weekend at the end of
October. Normally one- or two-week retreats during the summer
and around Christmas. Nearly all courses and retreats are open to
newcomers, some with specific sessions for more experienced students. Study courses for those wishing to pursue Sogyal
Rinpoche's teachings more thoroughly.

Centre can be booked by outside groups – ideal environment

for workshops, offering an inspiring atmosphere, accommodation and excellent catering service.

Rigpa centres also in Dublin, Limerick and Cork – phone for details.

Founder/Guru	Sogyal Rinpoche
Teachers	Senior students give basic instruction and teachers and masters including Sogyal Rinpoche visit
Opening times	Office hours 10.30am–1pm and 2.30–5.30pm Monday to Friday
Residents	Six lay people and eleven one–year retreatants
Festivals	Contact centre
Facilities	Shrine room and well stocked shop
Accommodation	Self-catering cottages and hostel at Dzogchen Beara and other options in the local area. Prices from £6–£20 per person per night
Food	Vegetarian for some retreats and courses, rest self-catering
Booking	See details in programme
Fees	Various
Expected behaviour	No specific rules, but to be considerate of others and respectful of the centre
How to get there	Nearest airport, train station and ferry port are in Cork, 100 miles away. Nearest town is Castletownbere, five miles away. Minibuses run from Cork to Castletownbere, from there take a taxi

Centres in Europe

> For Buddhism, no less than for modern physics and psychology,
> all the apparently stable and solid material and mental objects
> in the universe are in reality temporary condensations of energy.
> — Sangharakshita, *The Three Jewels*

AUSTRIA

Arranged according to postcode

Buddhistisches Zentrum (All traditions)
Fleischmarkt 16
1010 Vienna
Tel & *Fax:* +43 (0)222 512 37 19

The Österreichische Buddhistische Religionsgesellschaft is based here and is the umbrella organisation for Buddhist activities in Austria. Contact this address for information on all Buddhist activities in Austria as well as other Buddhist organisations at this address.

Ten different Buddhist traditions hold events here and run their programmes individually. Austria accepts Buddhism as a religion officially which gives it a different status than in other countries, for example, there are Buddhist children's schools.

Among others at this address are: **Bodhidharma Zendo** (see separate entry on p152), **Drikung Kagyu Orden, Karma Kagyu Österreich, Theravada Schule** (see separate entry on p153), and **Koreanische Son-Gemeinschaft**. There is also information able here on **Dhamma Zentrum Nyanaponika**, Haeckelstrasse 31/2, 1235 Vienna, **Bildungszentrum Sanghamitta**, Biberstraße 9/2, 1010 Vienna and **Dharmadhatu**, Westbahnstrasse 32-34/22, 1070 Vienna.

Founder/Guru	As per different schools based here
Teachers	Various from all traditions
Opening times	Office: Monday to Thursday 3–7pm and Friday 9am–1pm
Residents	No
Festivals	As per different schools based here
Facilities	Shrine rooms, library and secretariat
Accommodation	Will help people to find private accommodation
Food	Vegetarian restaurant on premises
Booking	As per different schools based here
Fees	As per different schools based here
Languages	As per different schools based here
Expected behaviour	Normal decent behaviour
How to get there	Nearest underground station Schwedenplatz

Bodhidharma Zendo (Zen – Rinzai)
Fleischmarkt 16
1010 Vienna
Tel: +43 (0)222 513 38 80
Fax: +43 (0)1 512 37 19
e-mail: genro@magnet.at

Building in the centre of Vienna. Rinzai in the transmission line of Myoshin-ji. Open to all including non-Buddhists and Buddhists of other traditions.

Introductory courses approximately six times a year or phone in advance and arrive an hour before usual session time. Session times are Monday 7–9pm, Wednesdays and Fridays 6.30pm, Tuesdays and Thursdays 6–7.30am. Sessions involve Zazen and sutra recitation. Dharma study every last Saturday of the month at 2.30pm. Sesshins four times a year, Zen weekends, Yaza (night meditations).

Ikuro Grassmück is the Shaku – the monk responsible for administration and answering enquiries.

Founder/Guru	Genro Seiun Koudela Osho
Teachers	Resident: Genro Seiun Koudela Osho and visiting teachers
Opening times	See session times above
Residents	No
Festivals	Hanamatsuri (Buddha's Birthday) and Rohatsu (Buddha's Enlightenment)
Facilities	Zendo, library and meeting room
Accommodation	Speak to Shaku
Food	Breakfast after morning Zazen on Tuesday and Thursday. Meals during Zazen weekends and sesshins. Vegetarian restaurant in building
Booking	Needed for sesshins and Zazen weekends only – by post
Fees	Contact centre
Languages	German, English and phone in advance for French
Expected behaviour	No special rules, but expected to be aware of traditional form of Zazen
How to get there	Nearest underground station Schwedenplatz

Theravada Schule (Theravada – Sri Lankan)
Fleischmarkt 16
1010 Vienna
Tel & Fax: +43 (0)222 512 23719 or 8653491

Old building in the inner city. Led by Sinhalese monks for last twenty years. Open for people from all religions and for dialogue between religions, sciences and philosophies e.g. in March 1996 talk on Islam and Buddhism.

Meditation nearly every day. Study of Buddhism, Pali, Sanskrit and Sinhala. Regular introductions to Buddhism and Meditation. Various yoga courses. Regular meditation Monday 7–9pm and Wednesdays 7–8am. One-day and weekend retreats. Classes for school children. Classes most Saturdays and Sundays including meditation and Yoga, and Qi Gong and many others.

Founder/Guru	Contact centre
Teachers	Resident: Bhikkhu W. Seelawansa and various visiting teachers
Opening times	Monday to Thursday 3–7pm, Fridays 9am – 1pm
Residents	Two monks at a separate residence
Festivals	Uposatha puja (full moons) and Vesakh
Facilities	Shrine room, library and study room
Accommodation	Only for monks
Food	No
Booking	Check with centre
Fees	Most activities based on donation
Languages	German, English, Sinhala
Expected behaviour	Contact centre
How to get there	Underground station Schwedenplatz

Buddhistisches Zentrum Scheibbs (three main traditions but mainly Zen and Theravada)
Ginselberg 12
3272 Scheibbs/Neustift
Tel & Fax: +43 (0)7482 424 12

400-year-old building, formerly part of a castle on the edge of a small town, near meadows, forests and mountains. Founded in 1975 and ceremony with the Karmapa in 1978. Zen is the tradition mostly followed by the residents. Centre is a teaching institute of the Austrian Buddhist community which is recognised as a religion by the state, so their emphasis is to represent the three main Buddhist traditions in their seminars.

Daily meditations with meditation at 5am and 5pm daily for one and a half hours each. Five week-long Zen retreats a year. Introductory Zen courses twice a year. Yoga and Vipassana courses ten times a year. Events include children's meditation weekends, Introduction to Buddhist Psychology, Health and Healing, Eightfold Path Meditation weekends, Family Weekends, Dai Sesshins, Tao-Yoga and the Art of Presence.

Publish quarterly magazine *Ursache und Wirkung*.

Founder/Guru	Group of Austrian Buddhists
Teachers	Visiting teachers of different traditions
Opening times	Year round
Residents	One monk and up to seven lay people
Festivals	Contact centre
Facilities	Two shrine rooms, library and study room
Accommodation	For up to forty guests. Some one and two bed rooms at 100 AS extra
Food	Three lacto-vegetarian meals a day included in accommodation price of 370 AS per day
Booking	Call or write then 50% deposit
Fees	See programme for details
Languages	German and English
Expected behaviour	Participation in the daily meditation, one hour's help in house and mindfulness
How to get there	Train or car to Scheibbs

Buddhistische Gemeinschaft Jodo-Shinshu Österreich (Pure Land – Jodo Shinshu)
Merianstrasse 29-4-52
5020 Salzburg
Tel: +43 (0)662 87 99 51

In the home of the resident teacher. Jodo Shinshu's main temple in Europe is **EKO** in Düsseldorf, Germany (see separate entry on p231).

Service 4pm Sundays involving ritual, Dharma talks, meditation and sutra chanting. Study is of the three Amida Sutras and the scriptures of Shinran Shonin who was the founder of Shin Buddhism. Meditation is Seiza meditation (silent sitting) and meditation on Amida Buddha, gratitude, etc. Introductory courses in Buddhism generally and Shin Buddhism. 3–4 day retreats are with Shin Buddhists from Germany 2–3 times a year. As is usual for Jodo Shinshu, they are also involved in charitable works – Buddhist hospital chaplaincy, Buddhist adviser to Salzburg hospice movement.

Publish a quarterly magazine and brochures on Shin Buddhism. Videos on Buddhist topics available.

Founder/Guru	H.E. Lord Patriarch emeritus Kosho Ohtani of Nishi Honganji, Kyoto, Japan, Reverend Shogon Hoshi H. Piper
Teachers	Resident: Shaku Myoshin (Friedrich Fenzl) and occasional visiting teacher from Japan or USA
Opening times	Services and teachings every Sunday 4pm
Residents	No
Festivals	Jodo Shinsu festival days
Facilities	Shrine room and library
Accommodation	No
Food	Tea and biscuits after Sunday service for small donation
Booking	Contact centre
Fees	Contact centre
Languages	German, English and Japanese
Expected behaviour	Contact centre
How to get there	Five minutes' walk from the Salzburg central railway station

Puregg – Ökumenisches Haus der Stille (Zen mainly)
Berg 12
5652 Dienten
Tel: +43 (0)663 86 97 54

Two old houses at the highest altitude in Salzburg Country for a farm, at about 1300m altitude. Pretty location overlooking the valley of Dienten. The farmhouse has been converted into living accommodation and the stable and hayloft into a Japanese-style Zendo, two dormitories and other accommodation for participants. Associated with **Kannon-Do** (see separate entry on p158). Founded 1989 by Zen monk and Benedictine monk as an ecumenical centre for meditation and spiritual encounter. Small community of mostly Zen monks.

Seminars and retreats of all kinds, but mostly Zen and Christian. Samu (manual work) every day. Groups of up to thirty people.

People are welcome to join in the life of a western Zen monastery after making contact. Special programmes for beginners.

Founder/Guru	Vanya Palmers Sensei and Brother David Steindl-Rast
Teachers	Kobun Chino Roshi (Abbot of two Soto temples in USA), Vanya Palmers Sensei and Genju Oda Sensei (resident monk) and many visiting teachers
Opening times	Contact centre
Residents	Occasionally a monk and between one and three lay people
Festivals	Contact centre
Facilities	Shrine room and library with study room
Accommodation	Dormitories and individual rooms at 200 AS per night full-board
Food	Three vegetarian meals a day
Booking	Preferably by mail or phone
Fees	Contact centre
Languages	German and some English
Expected behaviour	Follow the daily schedule of Zazen, work periods and study
How to get there	Train to Saalfelden, then fifteen minutes' walk

Dharma Group Innsbruck (Tibetan – Karma Kagyu)
Begegnunszentrum
Zollerstrasse 3
6020 Innsbruck
Tel: +43 (0)512 579 048
Postal Address: c/o Dr. D.W. Rossboth, Staffler Strasse 3, 6020 Innsbruck

In the city, founded 1994.
   Meditations Monday evenings at 7.30–10pm. Practices include Karmapa and Chenrezig meditations, Phowa preparation, Gampopa, Paramitas and Buddhist philosophy and practice. Programme can be found in the Saturday edition of the local newspapers.

All Karma Kagyu centres in Austria are part of Karma Kagyu Österreich. Contact Mag. Alexander Draszczyk, Auhofstr 39, 1130 Vienna, telephone +43 (0)222 8765434.

Founder/Guru	Lama Ole Nydahl
Teachers	Visiting teachers from all over Europe
Opening times	See meditation times above
Residents	One lay person
Festivals	According to Tibetan and Gregorian calendar
Facilities	Contact centre
Accommodation	Not in centre, but private pensions in and around Innsbruck
Food	No
Booking	Call about fourteen days before arrival
Fees	Contact centre
Languages	German and English
Expected behaviour	No freaks
How to get there	Near University Hospital

Zen Gemeinschaft Kannon-do (Zen – Soto)
An der Furt 18/II
6020 Innsbruck
Tel & Fax: +43 (0)512 367113
e-mail: aldo.deutsch@uibk.ac.at or wolfgang.i.waas@uibk.ac.at

Blue tenement building in park-like surroundings. Founded in 1986 as a non-denominational group which later split into two Zen, two Tibetan and a Theravada group. Loosely Soto Zen centre with strong Ch'an roots and a policy of being open to other groups. Main practice is Zazen where the resident teachers see themselves as more experienced co-practitioners rather than masters and welcome people finding their own spiritual teacher from any source.

Zazen once a week, with teachings once a month. Twice monthly Buddhist lecture. Occasional sesshin, Zazenkai or study week mainly at **Puregg** (see separate entry on p156). Their main connection is to Kobun Chino Roshi, Abbot of two Soto temples in the USA. Tai-san also has pastoral duties at local university, hospital and jail.

Publish a newsletter *GraswurZEN*.

Founder/Guru	Reverend Tai-San Osho
Teachers	Reverend Tai-San Osho and Wolfgang I. Waas
Opening times	10am–6pm daily
Residents	One monk
Festivals	Hanamatsuri, Buddha's Paranirvana, Bodhidharma Day, Kannon Day, O Bon and Rohatsu
Facilities	Shrine room and library in Tai-San's sitting room
Accommodation	No
Food	Tea and biscuits only
Booking	Thirty days in advance for retreats and seminars, everything else, call in advance, but not necessary
Fees	Contact centre; zazen sessions no charge, but donation welcome
Languages	German, English
Expected behaviour	Contact centre
How to get there	From Innsbruck railway station, bus line R or O to Mitterhoferstrasse stop

Rinzai Ji (Zen – Rinzai)
Herzog-Friedrich-Strasse 22, IV Stock
6020 Innsbruck
Tel: +43 (0)512 277297 – private telephone number of Peter Schrom

Seminar room at the top of house in the old part of the city. Open for people of all philosophies or religious denominations who want to practise Zen meditation. Founded 1986. People at all levels of experience welcome.

Zen sessions involve Rinzai-style meditation in combination with Sutra recitation and are at 8–10.30pm on Mondays except during school holidays. For more experienced practitioners practice weekends are arranged according to individual requirements. Tea ceremony.

Founder/Guru	Founder is Dokuro Roland Jaeckel (a student of Joshu Sasaki Roshi of Mt. Baldy Zen Center, USA)
Teachers	Ko-un Ken P. Whilligis Jäger (from Zen centre, Würzburg, Germany)
Opening times	See session times above
Residents	No
Festivals	Contact centre
Facilities	Contact centre
Accommodation	No
Food	No
Booking	Contact centre
Fees	Contact centre
Expected behaviour	To wear dark or discreet neutral clothes
How to get there	Contact centre

International Meditation Centre (IMC) Austria (Theravada – Myanmar – International Meditation Centre)
Gurk 6
9064 St Michael
Tel: +43 (0)4224 2820
Fax: +43 (0)4224 28204
e-mail: 10425.3423@compuserve.imc-austria

In the countryside near a small village. Two local-style farmhouses with a pagoda and a Myanmar-style Dhamma Hall. An offshoot of the IMC centres in Myanmar and the UK.

Practice of the Eightfold Path which is divided into Sila (morality), Samadhi (concentration) and Panna (wisdom). Emphasis is on direct experience through practice. Daily meditation hours and 4–5 ten-day Vispasana courses a year involving morning and evening discourses and daily interviews with teachers. Monthly weekend courses.

Other than for courses, visitors may feel free to visit any time.

Founder/Guru	Sayagyi U Ba Khin International Meditation Centres
Teachers	Four regional teachers, others visit
Opening times	See above

Residents	One caretaker
Festivals	Usual Myanmar Theravada dates
Facilities	Pagoda and Dhamma Hall
Accommodation	No
Food	Only during residential courses
Booking	Contact centre
Fees	Contact centre

The well-informed holy disciples do not take delight in the senses and their objects, are not impressed by them, are not attached to them, and in consequence their craving ceases; the cessation of craving leads successively to that of grasping, of becoming, of birth, of old age and death, of grief, lamentation, pain, sadness, and despair – that is to say to the cessation of all this mass of ill. It is thus that cessation is Nirvana.

– *Questions of King Milina*, translated by Edward Conze

Languages	German and English
Expected behaviour	Normal decent behaviour
How to get there	Train or plane to Klagenfurt and then twenty minute taxi ride

BELGIUM

Arranged according to postcode

Association Zen de Belgique (Zen – Soto – Association Zen Internationale)
11 Rue Cattoir
1050 Bruxelles
Tel & Fax: +32 (0)2 648 64 08

Traditional Zen teaching according to Master Deshimaru.
Zazen times: Monday to Friday 6.30–7.30am; Monday, Thursday, Friday 8–9pm; Tuesday, Wednesday and Friday 7–8.30pm; Thursday 12.30–1.30pm. Newcomers should arrive half an hour before session.
Study of Zen masters and patriarchs. Introductory class with video on Saturdays. Courses in sewing of traditional Zen clothing, Chinese calligraphy, Do-In (Zen massage) and shiatsu and voice workshops.
One-day sesshins once a month and longer sesshins three times a year.
Contact this centre for addresses of other AZI dojos in Belgium.

Founder/Guru	Taisen Deshimaru's disciple Nicole de Merkline
Teachers	Roland Rech visits
Opening times	See session times above
Residents	No
Festivals	Contact centre
Facilities	Dojo and library
Accommodation	During sesshins – cost included in course fee
Food	During sesshins – cost included in course fee
Booking	Contact centre
Fees	150 BF for one hour meditation; 500 BF for a day (including lunch)
Languages	French, Flemish and English
Expected behaviour	To be silent and not disturb Zazen practice
How to get there	Contact centre

Samye Dzong (Tibetan – Karma Kagyu)
Centre d'Etude Tibetain
33 rue Capouillet
1060 Bruxelles
Tel: +32 (0)33 2 537 5417

Large four-storey house with garden in city centre. Tara puja mornings and Shine meditation evenings and different puja every day. Tara, Chenrizig, Guru Rinpoche pujas and Tsog pujas on festival days. Daily Shine meditation is suitable for newcomers, who may learn rituals, etc., with resident nun. Individual retreats on request. Programme of events includes teachings and ceremonies with visiting Tibetan teachers.
Publish quarterly magazine *Samye Tribune*.

Founder/Guru	H.H. 16th Karmapa, Chodje Akong Rinpoche
Teachers	Visiting Tibetan teachers
Opening times	Daily 7–8.10am and 6–9pm; weekends 9-10am and on appointment. Closed during summer holidays
Residents	One nun and ten lay people
Festivals	New and full moons and New Year
Facilities	Shrine room, library and study room
Accommodation	5–8 single rooms at 850 BF per night; dormitory with three double beds 500 BF per night
Food	Self-catering possible
Booking	By phone or letter as far ahead as possible as places are limited
Fees	Contact centre
Languages	French, English, Dutch
Expected behaviour	Normal decent behaviour; respect for others; no alcohol or drugs
How to get there	Near Avenue Louise, Chaussée de Charleroi

Institut Tibetain (Tibetan – Kagyu)
Avenue du Paepedelle 91/4G
1160 Brussels
Tel & Fax: +32 (0)2 675 3805

Large apartment in the city. Connected to **Yeunten Ling** (see separate entry on p166). Teachings Wednesdays at 8pm. Topics include Death, the Intermediate State and Reincarnation, Chenrezig, Practice of Compassion, Bodhisattvas and Lodjong. Each teaching is preceded by a meditation. Teachings for newcomers once a month. Personal interview with a lama by appointment.

Founder/Guru	Lama Karta, Kongtrul Rinpoche
Teachers	Visiting teachers from **Yeunten Ling**
Opening times	Wednesdays at 8pm
Residents	No
Festivals	Contact centre
Facilities	Shrine room, library and study room
Accommodation	No
Food	No
Booking	Pay on arrival
Fees	120 BF members, 150 BF non-members
Languages	French
Expected behaviour	Contact centre
How to get there	Metro to Hankar or car to near Chaussée de Wavre

Centrum voor Shin-Boeddhisme (Pure Land – Jodo Shinshu)
Jikoji – Temple of the Light of Compassion
Pretoriastraat 68
2600 Berchem-Antwerpen
Tel: +32 (0)3 218 7363
Fax: +32 (0)3 281 6333

Terraced house. Centre founded 1976, temple 1979, moved to current location 1984.

Services Tuesday evenings, lectures Friday evenings. Meditations and devotional services. At least two series of approximately fifteen lectures – one for beginners and one for advanced students. Visits and interviews by appointment.

Founder/Guru	Reverend Shitoku A. Peel (sponsored by H. E. Kosho Ohtani)
Teachers	Founder is resident teacher and sometimes other teachers visit
Opening times	See event times above
Residents	No
Festivals	Year-round, held on Saturdays or Sundays
Facilities	Shrine room, library and study room
Accommodation	No
Food	No
Booking	Contact centre
Fees	Contact centre
Languages	Dutch, French, English and German
Expected behaviour	Contact centre
How to get there	Car: Ring exit Borgerhout. Train to Berchem-Antwerp then ten minutes walk

Tibetan Institute (Tibetan – Kagyu)
Karma Sonam Gyamtso Ling
Kruispadstraat 33
2900 Schoten
Tel: +32 (0)3 685 09 19
Fax: +32 (0)3 685 09 91

Four-storey house in quiet area of city. Authentic teachings on Buddhism by Tibetan teachers. Established in 1976 by H.H. the Karmapa and has since become one of the main Buddhist Institutes in the Flandres. Famous documentation centre with books and magazines on Buddhism.

Weekly teachings and meditations. Regular courses on Buddhism in collaboration with the Ministry of Education for teachers and students. Classes on such topics as mantra, mudra and mandala, samsara and nirvana, Chenrezig, Tibetan Yoga, Mahakala meditation and Manjushri. Introductory event once every three months. Tibetan language course every week.

Have published *Principles of Tibetan Art* by Gega Lama and a

book on Buddhist iconometry.
Connected to **Yeunten Ling** (see separate entry on p166).

Founder/Guru	H.H. the Karmapa and Kalu Rinpoche
Teachers	Lama Karta and visiting teachers mostly from **Yeunten Ling** (see separate entry)
Opening times	Wednesdays 2–6pm, Thursday 4–8pm and some weekends
Residents	Two lay people
Festivals	Contact centre
Facilities	Shrine room, library, study room and documentation centre
Accommodation	No
Food	No
Booking	Pay on arrival
Fees	Contact centre
Languages	Dutch, French, English, German and Tibetan
Expected behaviour	Contact centre
How to get there	Few hundred yards from main market place

Institut Yeunten Ling (Tibetan – Kagyu)
Château de Fond L'Evêque
St. Jean l'Agneau 4
4500 Huy
Tel: +32 (0)85 21 48 20
Fax: +32 (0)85 23 66 58

Château set in twenty-six acres of forested grounds and surrounded by a nature conservation area. Founded in 1983 with the aim of preserving and making known all aspects of Tibetan culture – artistic, historical and ethnological as well as philosophical and religious. Includes Tibetan Institute of Performing Arts. Stupa built in 1988.

Meditation and retreat centre. Offers guided tours, courses, seminars, retreats, lectures, courses on Tibetan language and texts, book publication (Kunchab editions), personal interviews with Tibetan Lamas and the organisation of cultural evenings.

Continous programme of retreats and other events. Traditional teachings on Buddhist philosophy, meditation practice and Buddhist art. Daily meditation sessions at 7am, 6pm and 8pm.

Three resident lamas who also give lectures at the invitation of cultural groups and schools. Dalai Lama has visited twice to give teachings.

Guided tours for tourists 2.30pm on Sundays.

Publications include a special Tibetan language course using books and cassettes in German, French and Dutch, an introduction to Buddhism used in schools also in German, French and Dutch and a cassette of Tibetan chants for Buddhist meditation which has been distributed worldwide.

Founder/Guru	Kalu Rinpoche
Teachers	Resident: Lama Karta, Lama Zeupa, Lama Tashi Nyima and many visiting teachers
Opening times	Year round; guided tours 2.30pm Sundays
Residents	Three monks and ten lay people
Festivals	Contact centre for details
Facilities	Two shrine rooms, library, study room, studios for up to 150 people, and stupa
Accommodation	Retreat cells, rooms, 700 BF per day full-board
Food	Vegetarian and non-vegetarian – three meals a day
Booking	Phone or write, no deposit needed
Fees	200 BF per day
Languages	English, French, German, Dutch, Tibetan, etc.
Expected behaviour	Arrive before 9pm, no animals, respect for peaceful atmosphere during retreats
How to get there	Highway Brussels – Namur. Near Namur, take the Liège direction, then exit for Huy. In the town of Huy, go towards Hamoin and the Institut Tibetain is signposted

Bouddha Dhamma (Theravada)
Bruggestwg 82
8755 Ruiselede
Tel & Fax: +32 (0)51 689 582

Between Bruges and Ghent in country house. Emphasises integration of Dhamma in daily life for lay people.

Offers intensive contemplative practice of Vipassana, deep study based on the Four Noble Truths and Ahlidhamma psychology (which includes modern depth psychology) and individual guidance.

Anapanasati – Vipassana – Metta Bhavana weekends once every two months. Ten-day retreats once a year. Self-retreats to meditate and study alone or in contact with a teacher. Possible for participation in Dhutanga Nidessa (traditional ascetic practice in Forest Tradition).

Weekly meditation and teachings in Brussels on Tuesdays 1.45–4pm and 6.45–9pm at Rue J. B. Colyns, 1050 Brussels (telephone +32 (0)2 345 55 71, fax +32 (0)2 343 11 50).

Eole Daniel Stevens has practiced Vipassana meditation for twenty years and also studied contemporary psychology and comparative mythology.

Founder/Guru	Eole Daniel Stevens
Teachers	Founder and John E. Coleman visits
Opening times	Contact centre
Residents	No
Festivals	Contact centre
Facilities	Meditation house, library and study room
Accommodation	Single and double room and private apartment
Food	Vegetarian food during retreats – self-catering other times
Booking	By fax or letter only at least two weeks in advance
Fees	Contact centre
Languages	French, Flemish and English
Expected behaviour	Five Precepts, being vegetarian, no smoking, drugs or TV
How to get there	Map sent on booking

Nichiren Shu Hokkeji (Nichiren Shu)
Knaagreepstraat 8a
8890 Moorslede
Tel: +32 (0)51 779434
Fax: +32 (0)51 701346

Big country house in a rural area. Founded in 1991 by Japanese Nichiren Shu priests.

Nichiren Shu practice is centred around chanting of the Lotus Sutra. Worship at 6am and 8pm daily. Meditations at 3pm on Sundays. Study by request. Retreats held in Japan.

Founder/Guru	Founder is Professor Senchu Murano
Teachers	Resident: Senkei Pieters and visiting Japanese priests
Opening times	Every day after 7pm
Residents	Two or three lay people
Festivals	All festivals days of Japanese Mahayana
Facilities	Shrine room, library and study room
Accommodation	No
Food	No
Booking	No need to book

> When one attains the release called the Beautiful, at such a time he knows in truth what Beauty is.
>
> – *Samyuta* and *Digha Nikaya*

Fees	Contact centre
Languages	Dutch, French and English
Expected behaviour	No smoking, no shoes
How to get there	From Roeselare city take a bus to Moorslede

DENMARK

Sangye Tashi Chö Ling (Tibetan – Karma Kagyu)
Vesterbrogade 37
1620 Copenhagen
Tel: +45 (0)31 21 26 17

Established in 1992 in a large apartment in the city.

Founder/Guru	H. H. the 17th Karmapa Urgyen Trinley Dorje
Teachers	Various visiting Lamas
Opening times	Contact centre
Residents	Four lay people
Festivals	Contact centre
Facilities	Shrine room
Accommodation	No
Food	No
Booking	Contact centre
Fees	Contact centre
Languages	Danish and English
Expected behaviour	Normal decent behaviour
How to get there	500m from Central Station

Karma Wangchuk Ling (The Powerful Place) (Tibetan – Karma Kagyu)
Konsholmvej 178
9631 Gedsted
Tel: +45 (0) 98 64 56 55
Fax: +45 (0) 98 64 59 99

Set in a country house. Various meditations, chanting, study and Guru Yoga for experienced practitioners. Introductory activities on Sundays.

Founder/Guru	Lama Ole Nydahl
Teachers	Resident teacher Claus Hermansen and visiting teachers

Opening times	All the time
Residents	Varying numbers of resident lay people
Festivals	Contact centre
Facilities	Shrine room, library in Danish, study room and videos in Danish
Accommodation	Different kinds – contact centre for details
Food	Vegetarian
Booking	Phone in advance
Fees	Contact centre
Languages	Danish, German and English
Expected behaviour	Abide by the rules
How to get there	Bus to Gedsted

Karma Geleg Dardje Ling (Tibetan – Kagyu)
Dronningensgade 16, 1
5000 Odense C
Tel: +45 (0)65 91 28 95

Three-storey building in the middle of town. Four people have been running this centre since about 1980. About fifty people are connected with the centre.

No fixed programme, phone for details of current activities. Describe themselves as down-to-earth. 'We are a small centre and we are not bound by any big organisation or community. We are very ordinary and we do what is necessary in that manner.'

Founder/Guru	Tenga Rinpoche
Teachers	Tenga Rinpoche
Opening times	Phone in advance
Residents	Two lay people
Facilities	Shrine room and library
Accommodation	Accommodation during seminars only at dormitory cost
Food	Tea and coffee available
Booking	Not necessary
Fees	Contact centre
Languages	Danish, English, German, Greek and a little Tibetan

Expected behaviour	Normal decent behaviour
How to get there	Walking distance from railway station (less than a mile)

Tarab Ladrung Institute – Denmark (Tibetan – Tarab Ladrung Institute)
Stor Søhøj
Hørsholm Kongevej 40
2970 Hørsholm
Tel / Fax: +45 (0) 45 76 00 44 and +45 (0) 42 86 20 27

Large turn of the century house in the rolling countryside of North Zeeland. Established fifteen years ago. Visitors are usually mature students. 'A relaxed atmosphere in one of the most laid back countries in the world.' Very down to earth.

Weekly meditations very suitable for beginners. Meditations are held weekly and on full moons. Teachings on interpreting Buddhism for daily Western life and how to use the psychological and psychotherapeutic tools developed by Tarab Tulku. Tarab Rinpoche advises as to what is suitable for each individual. Weekend and week-long retreats and very much on an individual basis. Courses include: Lucid Dream, Gate of Death and Dzong-chen (using the mind to reach Rigpa) and a university level course in Tibetan Psychology, Psychotherapy and Self-Development.

There are Tarab Ladrung Institutes in Denmark, France, Belgium, Germany and Austria.

Founder/Guru	Tarab Tulku Rinpoche
Teachers	Resident teacher is Tarab Tulku Rinpoche and visiting teacher are Tibetan Rinpoches who visit Scandinavia – members and affiliates are advised
Opening times	No set times – call before visiting
Residents	Tarab Tulku Rinpoche and a Danish family
Festivals	Tibetan New Year held in Copenhagen and a Tibetan picnic in August at Store Søhøj
Facilities	Shrine room and library
Accommodation	Apartment available in the house for retreats

Food	Generally food is brought in for visitors or they share meals and cooking with residents
Booking	By telephone. Deposit required for courses but not for retreats
Fees	See programme
Languages	Danish, English, Tibetan and most major European languages
Expected behaviour	Respect for other residents
How to get there	Motorway to Helsingør. Turn off at Horsholm S. Turn towards Hørsholm. Very large white house 100m on the left side

Thai Buddhist Temple (Theravada – Thai)
H. P. Hansensvej 3
3660 Stenløse
Tel: +45 (0) 42 17 11 80

Converted old farm in the countryside. Temple started when the Buddhist Society of the local Thai community invited Phra Soodthibongse Soodthiwungso (the Abbot) to stay in Denmark in 1990. Cultural centre for Thais in Denmark, but in response to others' interest in Buddhism, the monks have opened their doors for all.

Meditation and chanting session mornings and afternoons. Visitors who have received the Eight Precepts follow the meditation and chanting schedule, other visitors may please themselves. Resident monks teach meditation, Dhamma and the Pali language. No special arrangements for retreats, but individuals or groups are welcome to come and receive the Eight Precepts and practice meditation.

Founder/Guru	Phra Soodthibongse Soodthiwungso (Abbot)
Teachers	Resident monks
Opening times	5am–8pm every day
Residents	Four monks
Facilities	Shrine room, Thai and English library which is also the study room

Accommodation	Visitor's rooms with beds, mattresses and blankets are free
Food	Meals available
Booking	Phone the temple to make an appointment with a monk
Fees	Contact centre
Languagues	Mostly Thai spoken in the temple, but also Danish and English
Expected behaviour	Everyone sits on the floor, shoes are left in the hall and decent behaviour is expected; women should be aware not to touch the monks. Please note that for Thai people, it is disrespectful to point the feet or show the soles to other people or images of the Buddha
How to get there	S-train from Copenhagen Central to Frederikssund, getting off at Stenløse. From there two minutes walk, ask local people for help with directions. Temple is orange, so easily spotted!

Danish Buddhist Forum (All traditions)
c/o Lakha Lama
Niels Bohrs Alle 21
2860 Søborg
Tel: +45 (0)31 56 34 42

Rent rooms for lectures and courses. Started 1991 as an association of individuals and groups from different Buddhist traditions. Works for more understanding between these traditions and between Buddhism and the wider society. Arrange courses and lectures with teachers and master from many traditions.

Publish a magazine twice a year and members receive a newsletter quarterly.

Founder/Guru	Lakha Lama
Teachers	Visiting teachers from all traditions
Opening times	Contact address only
Residents	No

Festivals	Contact centre
Facilities	Rented accommodation
Accommodation	No
Food	Contact centre
Booking	Contact centre
Fees	Contact centre
Languages	Danish
Expected behaviour	Contact centre
How to get there	Contact centre

Fred Er Vejen (Zen)
c/o Vinkelvej 16C
3200 Helsinge
Tel: +45 (0)4879 62 88
Fax: +45 (0)4879 62 88

Not a centre, but a Sangha who meet regularly to meditate and study. Meetings take place at the private address above which is a family home in the town. Study and practice of the five Wonderful Precepts as presented by Thich Nhat Hahn.

Weekly evening meetings with awareness meditations. Transmission of the Three Refuges and the Five Wonderful Precepts on request. Basic Buddhism as presented by Thich Nhat Hahn. Regular retreats with disciples of Thich Nhat Hahn.

Founder/Guru	Jørgen Hannibal
Teachers	Resident: Jørgen Hannibal and visiting teachers from **Plum Village** in France (see separate entry on p180)
Opening times	Private home – for meetings only
Residents	Two lay people
Festivals	Contact centre
Facilities	Contact centre
Accommodation	No
Food	Contact centre
Booking	Contact centre
Fees	Contact centre
Languages	Danish
Expected behaviour	Contact centre

How to get there   Train from Copenhagen to Hillerod. Train
from Hillerod to Helsinge

The mighty sea, unmeasured mighty lake,
The fearsome home of multitudes of pearls –
As rivers, serving countless hosts of men,
Flow widely forth and to that ocean come:–

Just so, on him that giveth food, drink, clothes,
Who bed and seat and coverlet provides,
Torrents of merit flood that mortal wise,
As rivers, bearing water, reach the main.

– *Samyutta Nikaya*, v. 400, translated by F. L. Woodward, in
Some Sayings of the Buddha

FINLAND

Helsingin Buddhalainen Keskus (Friends of the Western
Buddhist Order)
Punavuorenkatu 16
00150 Helsinki
(*Postal address:* FWBO Finland, P O Box 288, 00121 Helsinki)
Tel: +358 (0)90 66 38 92
e-mail: fwbo@cute.fi

In central Helsinki. Established in 1973.

Friends of the Western Buddhist Order (FWBO) was established in 1976 in Britain by a London-born Buddhist monk,
Sangharakshita. It draws from all the main traditions of
Buddhism, not with an attitude of eclecticism, but to take what is
useful according to the spiritual needs of Westerners today. Each
centre is autonomous, but linked by common practice and friendship between Order members.

Meditation class for experienced meditators on Tuesday
evenings at 6pm. Introductory meditation class on Monday nights
at 6pm. Separate retreat centre in the countryside with a varied
programme from beginners onwards.

Founder/Guru	Sangharakshita
Teachers	Order members
Opening times	Monday – Thursday 4–6pm September to May (not during the summer)
Residents	Contact centre
Festivals	Buddha Day, Dharma Day, Sangha Day, Parinirvana Day and Padmasambhava Day are usually held on the nearest convenient Sunday
Facilities	Shrine room and reception/bookshop area
Accommodation	No
Food	Tea and biscuits only
Booking	Contact centre
Fees	Contact centre
Languages	Contact centre
Expected behaviour	Normal decent behaviour
How to get there	Contact centre

Finnish–Tibetan Cultural Association (Tibetan)
Pirkankatu 1 B PL 24
33230 Tampere
Tel: +358 (0)31 229877

Plan to get a resident teacher and a centre in the future.

Meditations Mondays 6–8pm suitable for newcomers and more experienced practitioners. Visits by teaching lamas, Tibetan language course, Tibetan psychology, etc. Retreats when lamas visit.

Founder/Guru	Contact centre
Teachers	Various Nyingma and Kagyu teachers from France and Copenhagen
Opening times	As per programme of events
Residents	No
Festivals	Contact centre
Facilities	Meditation room
Accommodation	No
Food	No
Booking	Contact centre
Fees	Contact centre
Languages	Finnish
Expected behaviour	Quiet and courteous
How to get there	Contact centre

To keep the body in good health is a duty, for otherwise we shall not be able to trim the lamp of wisdom, and keep our mind strong and clear. Water surrounds the lotus flower, but does not wet its petals.

– The Buddha

FRANCE

Arranged by district

Alsace

Sakya Tsechen Ling (Tibetan – Sakya)
5 Rond-Point du Vignoble
67520 Kuttolsheim
Tel: +33 (0)88 87 73 80 or Secretary 88 60 74 52
Fax: +33 (0)88 60 74 52

Big house in a village. Temple has capacity for 100 people. Headquarters of the Sakya school in Europe. Founded in 1978 following the growth of followers after H.H. Dalai Lama and H.H. Sakya Trizin sent the Venerable Geshe Sherab Gyaltsen Amipa to Switzerland. Has been visited by Dalai Lama, H.H. Sakya Dagchen Rinpoche and H.H. Sakya Trizin.

Visitors generally come for the monthly sessions by Venerable Geshe Sherab Gyaltsen Amipa or at the weekend for puja. Tara puja takes place every morning and Mehokala puja every afternoon. Buddha Hevajra meditation every Saturday afternoon 3.30–5.30pm. Study of Boddhicaryavatara of Shantideva and Tibetan courses. Retreats twice a year (in summer and December) e.g. Vajrasattava in August. Lectures on Tibetan root texts and studies such as Zempa–Zidel. Monthly sessions of three days with meditations, study of root texts and initiations. Vajrayana Yoga.

Founder/Guru	Venerable Geshe Sherab Gyaltsen Amipa
Teachers	Teacher visits once a month, resident monk for regular puja and teachings
Opening times	According to programme
Residents	One monk and two lay people
Festivals	Tibetan New Year and all other auspicious Buddhist days
Facilities	Shrine room, library and study room
Accommodation	Two single and four double rooms (30 FF per night). There is also a hostel with 100 beds 3km away at 40 FF per night

Food	Generally vegetarian at 35 FF per meal organised by members
Booking	Phone secretary or write
Fees	Contact centre
Languages	French, English, German
Expected behaviour	No cigarettes, alcohol or drugs
How to get there	Approx 20km from Strasbourg; buses from Strasbourg

Aquitaine

Plum Village – Village des Pruniers (Zen – Vietnamese)
Meyrace
47120 Loubes-Bernac
Tel: +33 (0)16 53 96 75 40 and +33 (0)16 53 58 48 58
Fax: +33 (0)16 53 94 75 90
e-mail: parapress@aol.com

Founded in 1982. Home to an international and interdenominational sangha who are members of the Order of Interbeing. Practice mindfulness in daily life. Receive about 1,000 visitors and guests every year. All welcome but especially those who would like to practice Zen meditation and are familiar with Thich Nhat Hanh's books. Ethos is mindfulness in daily life.

Summer opening from 15 July to 15 August for family practice. Children over six years old may participate and those with under sixes must be completely responsible for them, although sometimes retreatants coordinate childcare among themselves to allow adults to participate. Sample daily schedule: 6am wake up bell, 6.30am sitting meditation and Precepts recitation, 8am breakfast, 9.15am community meeting, 9.30am Dharma talk, 12 noon Outdoor walking meditation, 1.30pm lunch, 1.30–4.30pm personal time, 4.30pm deep relaxation, 5.30pm question and answer session and tea meditation, 6.30pm dinner, 7.30pm orientation, dharma practice discussion, etc., 9pm sitting meditation and 10pm bedtime.

Three-month winter retreat with sutra study and daily practice. Spring or Autumn retreat. For the art of mindful living to take root during your stay and become a vital part of daily life, visitors are requested to stay for a minimum of one week.

Visitors should participate in all scheduled activities – sitting and walking meditations, work and Dharma talks.

Founder/Guru	Thich Nhat Hanh who is based here
Teachers	Resident: Thich Nhat Hanh and many visiting teachers from Vietnam and USA
Opening times	Year round
Residents	About sixty monks and nuns; about twenty lay people
Festivals	Christmas, New Year and Chinese New Year. Once a week during summer retreat
Facilities	Zendo and library
Accommodation	Very simple in shared rooms. Camping possible during summer
Food	Vegetarian
Booking	At least two months in advance for summer retreat, £30 deposit
Fees	1,200 FF for one week including full board and tuition during summer opening
Languages	English, French, German and Vietnamese
Expected behaviour	To fully participate in all scheduled activities and observe Five Precepts
How to get there	Train to Sainte Foy La Grande railway station. Phone centre from there when you arrive

Centre d'Etudes de Chanteloube (Tibetan – Rime)
La Bicanderie
24290 St Léon-sur-Vézère
Tel: +33 (0)53 50 75 24
Fax: +33 (0)53 51 02 44

Ancient farmhouse on the Côte de Jor, in attractive grounds with stupa, on a wooded ridge in the heart of the Dordogne region, surrounded by ancient prehistoric sites. Grouped around the family of a great Tibetan teacher, Kangyur Rinpoche, the centre has an intimate, personal atmosphere. Draws its inspiration from Tibet's nonsectarian (Rime) movement and open to all Buddhist traditions. Retreat centre where major holders of the various lineages, including the Dalai Lama have transmitted their teachings. Most visitors are French but also other Europeans and Americans. Some group leaders are English.

Seminars are held in the spring, summer and Christmas holidays combining teaching and the practice of meditation. Summer seminar takes place at La Sonnerie, the residence of Dilgo Khyentse Rinpoche, in a big tent under the trees. Frequent short retreats combining group and individual meditation practice. Individual retreats also possible. Basic Buddhism retreat for newcomers includes guided group and individual meditation sessions.

Other activities on the site include Padmakara which produces high quality translations of Tibetan texts and oral teachings in English, French, German and Spanish; Siddhartha for the support of Tibetan children, and Songtsen Development for cultural and economic development of Tibetan communites.

Affiliated groups around France, England, Holland, Switzerland and the USA.

Founder/Guru	Kangyur Rinpoche
Teachers	Spiritual Director Pema Wangyal Rinpoche, his brothers, Jigme Khyentse Rinpoche, Rangdrol Rinpoche, and his mother and three sisters. Also visiting teachers
Opening times	During seminars and retreats – outside this, contact centre
Residents	Members live independently in houses in the area. Most are lay, but some monks and nuns
Festivals	Yes
Facilities	Contact centre
Accommodation	Simple for those taking part in programmes. Individual retreats at 80 FF per day
Food	Vegetarian food during seminars and retreat programmes
Booking	Contact centre
Fees	According to activity, e.g. 700 FF for three-day retreat including teaching, food and

	accommodation
Languages	French, English and possibility of help with other languages. Group leaders often speak French and English fluently
Expected behaviour	Train to Les Eyzies and taxi, or car via Brive or Perigueux

Dhagpo Kagyu Ling (Tibetan – Kagyu)
24290 St Léon-sur-Vézère
Tel: +33 (0)53 50 70 75
Fax: +33 (0)53 50 80 54

Courses and retreats include: The Science of Enlightenment, Intensive Lodjong Retreat, Tantrism or the path of the secret mantra, self-confidence, faith in one's master and trust in others, developing mind and body awareness and preparing one's death, helping the dying. Possibility of translating programme teachings into English if sufficient demand – let them know in advance.

Founder/Guru	XVIth Gyalwa Karmapa
Teachers	The Gyalwa Karmapa, Gendun Rinpoche (spiritual director), Lama Jigme Rinpoche, Lama Purtsela and many other visiting teachers
Opening times	As for course times
Residents	Yes, including Tibetan New Year
Festivals	Contact centre
Facilities	Contact centre
Accommodation	Individual rooms, dormitory or camping, prices vary according to visitors' monthly income after tax
Food	Three meals a day offered
Booking	At least one month in advance with 200 FF deposit
Fees	Membership required plus 50 FF per day for most courses and 100 FF for intensive courses by two teachers jointly
Languages	French and English
Expected behaviour	Suitable conduct

How to get there	Train to Les Eyzies and phone for collection at 40 FF or take a taxi. If driving nearest village is Le Moustier

Urgyen Samye Chöling (Tibetan – Nyingma)
Laugeral
St Léon-sur-Vézère
Tel: +33 (0)53 50 75 29
Fax: +33 (0)53 50 56 85

Founded in 1977. Includes traditional Nyingma Vajrayana Temple with magnificent statues and a wall of prayer-wheels.

Short courses throughout the year. Longer, retreat-style courses usually in the summer. Emphasis is on intensive practice, according to the nine-yana system of Nyingma. Personal instruction, oral transmission, initiation, daily practice and retreats are considered essential. Transmission and practice of the inner tantras of Nyingma (Mahayaga, Anuyoga and Dzogchen) are authentic and rigorous.

Affiliated centres in Spain, England, Switzerland and the USA. Contact this centre for details.

Founder/Guru	H.H. the late Dudjom Rinpoche
Teachers	Spiritual director: H.E. Shenphen Dawa Rinpoche and other visiting teachers
Opening times	Contact centre for details
Residents	Contact centre for details
Festivals	Contact centre for details
Facilities	Contact centre for details
Accommodation	Rooms for two or three people, dormitories and camping (in summer)
Food	Available
Booking	Contact centre for details
Fees	Contact centre for details
Languages	Working languages are French and English
Expected behaviour	No smoking anywhere on the property and no making of any kind of fire (offerings are in temple only). Parents should take total responsibility for their children

How to get there   Train to Les Eyzies station from Paris, then taxi

Kadam Tcheuling Centre Bouddhiste Tibetain (Tibetan – Gelug)
4 rue Bergeret
33000 Bordeaux
Tel: +33 (0)56 92 63 38 (after 6pm) or 56 80 43 81 (before 6pm)

In town centre. Founded 1991. Monthly information session for the public wanting to have some information on the teachings of the Buddha. Green Tara sessions once a month. Meditation, rituals and Lam Rim (study) twice a week. Exhibition on Buddhism. Books and cassettes available. Association to help young Tibetan refugees at Dogpo Trasang monastery in India.

Founder/Guru	Dagpo Rimpoche
Teachers	Dagpo Rimpoche four times a year
Opening times	6–9pm, closed in June, July and August
Residents	Two lay people
Festivals	Contact centre
Facilities	Shrine room, library and study room
Accommodation	No
Food	No
Booking	Contact centre
Fees	Contact centre
Languages	French
Expected behaviour	Contact centre
How to get there	Contact centre

> Withdrawing into meditation, and then advancing and handling affairs – this advancing and withdrawing, movement and rest, together, must be Zen.
> – Sessan Amakuki, *Zen Meditation* translated by R. Legget

Auvergne

La Demeure sans Limites (Zen – Soto)
Riou la Selle
07320 St Agreve
Tel & Fax: +33 (0)75 30 13 62

Set in an old farm among fields and forests – very peaceful and beautiful, rather cold too as at 1000m altitude! Founded in 1992 by Reverend Joshin, a French Buddhist nun and teacher who is the disciple and unique Dharma Successor of Moriyama Roshi, a Japanese Zen Master. Aims to offer an introduction and to Zen Buddhism involving meditation, study and manual work.

Temple for ten to fifteen people at a time so that everyone can have the time and attention needed. Reverend Joshin shares all activities with the guests and is willing to answer any questions or give guidance. To practice zazen in daily life, they live simply, based on silence and an open mind, where all daily activities can be performed in harmony. Dharma lectures are given by Reverend Joshin or senior disciples. First week of the month silent retreat and no newcomers are received. Visitors can decide for themselves when and for how long they want to stay. Activities are zazen and Samu with meals in silence in accordance with Japanese Zen tradition. There are also more informal times which allow communication between practitioners. Day usually starts at 5am and goes on till 9.30pm.

Founder/Guru	Reverend Joshin Bachoux
Teachers	Reverend Joshin Bachoux and senior disciples
Opening times	April to October, open every day
Residents	Reverend Joshin Bachoux and guests
Festivals	Contact centre
Facilities	Large meditation hall, library for study
Accommodation	Two four-bed rooms and a dormitory
Food	Vegetarian, three meals a day, price included in cost of stay
Booking	By letter at least one week in advance, deposit welcome
Fees	200 FF per day, 1200 FF per week, 2200 FF

	two weeks, 3500 FF per month
Languages	French, English, Spanish, Japanese
Expected behaviour	To comply with the daily routine which can change due to circumstances
How to get there	Train to Valence or St Etienne, then bus to St Agreve, from there one hour walk or taxi

Bourgogne

Kagyu Ling (Temple of a Thousand Buddhas) (Tibetan – Kagyu)
Plaige
71320 La Boulaye
Tel: +33 (0)85 79 43 41
Fax: +33 (0)85 79 43 09

Set in a beautiful region of Burgundy, with several religious sites nearby. This is the first monastery in Europe to house a Himalayan temple and is unique in Europe for its size and beauty. Temple was built between 1982 and 1987, with its design based on the Temple of Samye, the first Buddhist monastery to be built in Tibet, but draws its inspiration from the culture of Bhutan, the sovereign kingdom perched along the lofty ridges of the eastern Himalayas. The temple is decorated inside and outside with ornate Buddhist artwork, carvings, statues, etc. The monastery is devoted to meditation and study of the scriptures, and the Marpa Institute was built here to be used for study programmes and courses in the Tibetan language and for visiting instructors to teach courses in yoga, sophrology, astrology and Buddhist medicine.

Centre was built with the aim of receiving as many visitors and participants in courses from different backgrounds as possible. It is not so much a monastery as a Tibetan centre as monastic life happens only in the retreat centres. The two daily offices in the temple at 7am and 6 or 7pm are open to the public.

Weekend meditation courses happen once a month, longer ones in July and August. Shine meditation is for beginners, others for more advanced practitioners. Yoga courses with different tutors once a month thoughout the year. Retreats lasting six months, one year or three years, plus short individual retreats. As well as the usual Tibetan practices, courses in sophrology, Chinese and Tibetan medicine, astrology, relaxation, ikebana, etc.

Founder/Guru	Kalu Rinpoche
Teachers	Four resident Lamas: Lama Sharab, Lama Seunam, Lama Orgyen and Lama Tenpa; also visiting teachers
Opening times	For visits: In the winter – Wednesday, Saturday, Sunday and public holidays from 2.30 to 6pm. In the summer every afternoon from 3pm to 7pm. The temple may be temporarily closed for some ceremonies
Residents	Eight monks and six nuns in retreat, three nuns not in retreat, about 25–30 lay people
Festivals	Tibetan New Year, Commemoration of Inauguration of the Temple in August
Facilities	See above
Accommodation	Camping, wooden huts, dormitories, rooms or apartments. Prices vary from 25 FF to 240 FF per night
Food	Fixed menu at fixed times, mostly vegetarian, three meals a day, 20 FF to 40 FF
Booking	To visit, book ahead if a group, otherwise turn up. Otherwise by phone or letter. Book as far ahead as possible for July, August and for Festivals and visiting Rinpoches. Deposit usually required
Fees	Visits 10 FF donation is requested. See programme for other events
Languages	French and English
Expected behaviour	To leave rooms clean and tidy, not to take anything from restaurant or kitchen, to behave calmly and to respect the place and residents
How to get there	By car or train and taxi (the nearest station is 15km away)

> If there is joy in meditation upon the mountain,
> the fruit-trees are the magic creation of the mountain;
> make thyself like the mountain itself.
>
> – The Message of Milarepa

Bretagne

Drouk Toupten Tcheukhor Ling (Tibetan – Drukpa Kagyu)
Bel Avenir
56770 Plouray
Tel: +33 (0)97 34 82 65
Fax: +33 (0)97 34 84 09

In the Black Mountains – a very green place of hills and farm land. Moderate temperatures all year round with much rain. Many local walks. Currently building a retreat centre and expect it to be ready in 1997. Created in 1985 by Very Venerable Khenpo Yeshe Tcheudar and in 1989, H.H. 12th Gyalwang Drukchen Rinpoche, became spiritual director. Reputation for its cordial and family welcome and simplicity.

Daily morning and evening Tara and Chenrezig mantra recitations. Study of Tibetan language. Teachings for newcomers by Venerable Lama Tcheuten every two or three weeks at weekends. Periodic higher level teachings by other Lamas.

Founder/Guru	His Holiness the 12th Gyalwang Drukchen Rinpoche
Teachers	Resident: Venerable Lama Nawang Tenzin and Venerable Lama Tchurten Dorje and visiting Lamas
Opening times	Visitors welcome all day, but afternoons preferred
Residents	Two lamas, one monk, one Anila and one lay person
Festivals	Losar and His Holiness' Birthday (around February)
Facilities	Temple, stupa, library and study room.
Accommodation	Bedrooms 50 FF to 90 FF per night, dormi-

	tory 30 FF per night, campsite 20 FF per night
Food	Three meals a day at 20–45 FF each
Booking	In writing one or two months in advance
Fees	Between 50–130 FF per day of teachings and accommodation
Languages	French, Tibetan, English and German
Expected behaviour	No drinking or smoking in the centre, no pets, take care of your children and to respect Buddhist people. Everyone should come to mealtimes, but are not obliged to atttend religious practice if not Buddhists
How to get there	By car via Paris, Rennes, Pontivy to Plouray. By train to Lorient and then a bus

Centre

Temple Zen la Gendronnière (Zen – Soto – Association Zen Internationale)
Commune de Valaire
41120 Les Montils
Tel: +33 (0)54 44 04 86
e-mail: 41120 Les Montils

On the edge of the Sologne region with meadows, lakes and forests to help create a calm, atmosphere making it easy to concentrate. First Zen temple in Europe. Attracts practitioners from all over the world. Dojo for 350 persons with corresponding accommodation and restaurant.

Summer camps held each year from July to start of September following the Buddha's tradition of rains retreats. Visitors to sesshins practice the daily schedule of two to four periods of zazen and physical work (Samu) every day. Other activities include Zen massage, calligraphy, martial arts, ikebana (Japanese floral art), Qi Gong and relaxation.

Zazen meditation, Hannya Shin Gyo worship/chanting. Monthly sessions at weekends and summer sesshins (six times over nine days).

Founder/Guru	Taisen Deshimaru in 1980
Teachers	Resident: Guy Mercier, visiting elder disciples of Master Deshimaru
Opening times	All year
Residents	5–10 monks; 5–10 lay people
Festivals	Contact centre
Facilities	Shrine room, library, study room and dojo for Zazen, fields for working in
Accommodation	Dormitory, rooms for 3–6, double rooms and communal tent during summer camps
Food	Included in accommodation costs
Booking	One week in advance, no deposit needed
Fees	According to type of accommodation
Languages	French with some teachings translated into English, German and Spanish
Expected behaviour	Contact centre
How to get there	Train to Blois (200km southwest of Paris). Shuttle service from here or arrange in advance to be met

> Fortunately we live in a time when all over the world many people are becoming familiar with meditation. It is being increasingly accepted as a practice that cuts through and soars above cultural and religious barriers, and enables those who pursue it to establish a direct contact with the truth of their being. It is a practice that at once transcends the dogma of religions and is the essence of religions.
>
> – Sogyal Rinpoche, *The Tibetan Book of Living and Dying*

Franche-Comté

Kagyu Dashang Tcheu Ling (Tibetan – Changpa Kagyu)
Rue du Reservoir
39800 Le Fied
Tel: +33 (0)84 85 32 66

Old house in the countryside on the Jura plateau, established January 1992 by Lama Sherab Dorje, director of **Kagyu Ling** (see separate entry on p187). Weekend courses on such subjects as Chenrezig, Guru Yoga, Tara Practice and The Six Bardos. Individual retreats possible. Homeopathic treatments and courses and sweat lodges.

Founder/Guru	Kalu Rinpoche
Teachers	Visting lamas from Kagyu Ling
Opening times	Contact centre
Residents	A lay couple
Festivals	No
Facilities	Shrine room, study room in temple, bookshop
Accommodation	No
Food	No
Booking	Not needed
Fees	30 FF per session
Languages	French
Expected behaviour	Contact centre
How to get there	Contact centre

Ile de France

Heruka Centre (Tibetan – Gelug)
c/o Francis Coutant
32 Rue Pasteur
91120 Palaiseau
Tel & Fax: +33 (0)1 60 14 61 54

House in a quiet residential street near the town centre. Organised two tours in Europe of 'Sacred Dance and Music'; organised H.E. Kyabje Gosok Rinpoche to raise funds for Sera Med Monastery in India.

Tuesday evenings Sangye Menla ritual (prayers for sick people) and Vajrasattva mantra, once a month Green Tara ritual and Sangye Menla, on the tenth and twenty-fifth day of the lunar month Vajrayogini Tsok. Dharma teachings on such subjects as Lam Rim, Death, Peace of Mind, The Three Principles and Tantra. Tibetan courses. Occasional retreats.

In 1996, formed Aid Project for Tibetans to develop cultural and humanitarian projects. It aims to raise funds to improve the conditions of refugees, especially monks.

Founder/Guru	H.E. Kyabje Gosok Rinpoche
Teachers	Founder visits
Opening times	See event times above
Residents	No
Festivals	No
Facilities	Shrine room and small library
Accommodation	No
Food	No
Booking	By phone or post
Fees	Contact centre
Languages	French, some English and some Tibetan
Expected behaviour	Respect for the Dalai Lama
How to get there	Train to Palaiseau station

Centre Bouddhiste Bodhichitta (Tibetan – Gelug – New Kadampa Tradition)
13 rue de l'Epée de Bois
75005 Paris
Tel & Fax: +33 (0)1 43 36 20 20
e-mail: bodhi@worldnet.fr

Quiet flat in the Quartier Latin, a friendly, attractive area in the heart of Paris with a village atmosphere. Established December 1995 and expanding rapidly. Aim is not to convert people to Buddhism but to help them overcome problems and find the happiness they seek. Relaxed, friendly atmosphere open to all, especially those new to Buddhism and meditation.

Meditations at no charge daily at 5pm, except weekends when times vary. Teachings Tuesdays and Fridays 7–9pm and Sundays 10.30–12.30am. These teachings and all meditations are suitable for newcomers. Friday evenings, there is a meditation followed by supper for about 60 FF. Other sessions cost about 30 FF. Frequent retreats on the preliminary practices, Tara Six session retreats once a month, extensive Lam Rim retreats in January and Vajrayogini retreat in January for those empowered. Also occasional day courses.

All NKT centres form a family spiritually following the same direction. Its core is the Three Study Programmes, of which, this centre offers:

• The General Programme provides a basic introduction to Buddhist view, meditation and action in a form that is suitable for beginners. It also includes advanced teachings and practices of both Sutra and Tantra.

• The Foundation Programme provides an opportunity to deepen understanding and experience of Buddhism through systematic study of five of Geshe Kelsang's books. This programme takes about four years to complete.

Working holiday sometimes possible – free food, lodging and teachings in exchange for thirty-five hour week of work.

Phone for details of your local NKT branch.

Founder/Guru	Venerable Geshe Kelsang Gyatso
Teachers	Resident: Gen Kelsang Lhamo (nun). Venerable Geshe Kelsang, Venerable Gen Thubten and other occasional NKT teachers visit
Opening times	Daily midday to 9pm, except August
Residents	Nun who teaches and one lay person
Festivals	NKT day, Buddha's Enlightenment Day, Buddha's Descent from Heaven Day, Je Tsongkahapa Day and Buddha's first turning of the wheel of Dharma Day
Facilities	Meditation room, library, study room and sitting room
Accommodation	Can suggest cheap accommodation nearby and plan to offer accommodation when they move to large premises
Food	See above
Booking	Varies according to activity – check with centre
Fees	See above
Languages	French, English, Spanish – all classes are in French
Expected behaviour	Five Precepts, not to eat meat or fish while at centre
How to get there	Metro to Censier Dauberton

> To the Awakened One for Refuge I go,
> To the Sangha for Refuge I go,
> To the Dharma for Refuge I go.
> – *The Three Great Refuges*

Languedoc Roussillon

Karma Toksum Tcheuling (KTT) Centre d'Etude et de Meditation (Tibetan – Karma Kagyu)
2 rue des Abreuvoirs
66000 Perpignan
Tel: +33 (0)68 64 52 33
Fax: +33 (0)68 34 30 47

Situated in the heart of the city in a small street near the cathedral. Founded in 1983 by Lama Namgyal (a student of Lama Gendun Rinpoche) in a private home and moved to current address in 1988. Stable team of practitioners. Branch of **Dhagpo Kagyu Ling** (see separate entry on p183) and so has a strong connection with that school of Buddhism, but all honest practitioners are of course most welcome.

Prostrations daily at 6.30am. Meditations Mondays at 2.30pm, Tuesdays at 9am and Wednesdays at 8pm. Other activities are held when Lamas are visiting for teachings. Short retreats once or twice a year. Yoga courses.

Founder/Guru	Lama Gundun Rinpoche
Teachers	Visiting lamas from **Dhagpo Kagyu Ling** (see separate entry) about once a month
Opening times	See practice times above
Residents	No
Festivals	Contact centre
Facilities	Shrine room, library, study room
Accommodation	No
Food	Tea and coffee
Booking	Write or call for retreats or special event, no booking for teachings
Fees	Contact centre

Languages	French and English
Expected behaviour	Be polite and smiling if possible
How to get there	Leave the highway at Perpignan-nord, go to Centre Ville, and park near the Castillet, a local landmark

Limousin

Dechen Chöling (Tibetan – Kagyu and Nyingma – Shambhala)
Mas Marvent
87700 Saint Yrieix-sous-Aixe
Tel: +33 (0)55 03 55 52

Purchased in 1994 as rural centre for European Shambhala community in central France, near Limoges. Small château and a number of farm buildings in fifty-six hectares of grounds. Part of Shambhala International (see *Schools of Buddhism*).

Courses include Shambhala Level I, Buddhist Introductory Programme and Family Camp which are open to all. Shambhala Training Teachers Academy, Dathün, Shambhala Level I, Vajrayana Programme and Intensive Training Session are open to more experienced members.

Founder/Guru	Chogyam Trungpa Rinpoche and now son Sakyong Mipham Rinpoche
Teachers	Various visiting
Opening times	Contact centre
Residents	Contact centre
Festivals	Contact centre
Facilities	Contact centre
Accommodation	Forty people in château (shared bedrooms) and thirty places in camping site
Food	Contact centre
Booking	Contact centre for details
Fees	Varies according to course – from 800 FF to 4,900 FF
Languages	Most teachings will be in English; introductory programmes in both French and English. Hope to be able to provide transla-

Expected behaviour   tion where needed if request made in
advance
Contact centre
How to get there   Twenty minutes by car from Limoges
which accessible by train, car or plane. Also
train service to Saint Victurnien which is ten
minutes' drive away. Pick-up can be
arranged from either of these stations

> Whether a man remains deluded or gains Illumination depends
> upon himself, not upon differences or similarity of doctrine.
>
> *– The Zen Teachings of Hui Hai*

Midi Pyrenees

Institute Vajra Yogini (Tibetan – Gelug)
Chateau d'en Clauzades
Marzens
81500 Lavaur
Tel: +33 (0)63 58 17 22
Fax: +33 (0)63 58 03 48

Set in the countryside, in a château with outbuildings and stables,
5km from Lavaur, a medium-sized town. Lay community of
single people, couples and families with children. Founded in
1980, spiritual heads Lama Thubten Yeshe and Lama Thubten
Zopa Rinpoche. Aim is to study and practise as a part of everyday
life and to reach and be there for as many people as possible.

Cater for beginners through to advanced students and people
needing rest, and/or contact and communication with others.
Study cycles that run over one or two years either on weekdays or
weekends. Families with children are welcome – parents should
take responsibility for their children.

Courses in Tibetan practices, teachings by Venerable Lati
Rimpoche, Tibetan culture including medicine and Thangka
painting, Vipassana meditation, Reiki, Yoga, Tai Chi and Qi Gong,
dance and voice workshops.

There is also a monastery for monks 10km away founded by the same Lamas.

Founder/Guru	Lama Thubten Yeshe and Lama Thubten Zopa Rinpoche
Teachers	Resident–Venerable Geshe Lobsang Tengye and many other visiting Tibetan Lamas
Opening times	March to December except September when no visitors are accepted at all. January and February is the retreat period when only retreatants may visit
Residents	The resident Lama, two monks, sixteen lay people and seven children
Festivals	Tibetan New Year and other Buddhist festivals
Facilities	Shrine room, library, study room, video library, cassettes and Walkman for hire. Simultaneous translation of teaching in French and English
Accommodation	Camping, dormitory, single and double rooms. Prices from 120 FF to 200 FF per night per person, meals included
Food	Three usually vegetarian meals per day, from 20 FF to 45 FF per meal
Booking	Write with 200 FF deposit, latest one week in advance. Book early for rooms and dorm accommodation
Fees	Vary according to length of course and teacher
Languages	French, English, German, Tibetan, Nepalese
Expected behaviour	Smoking only in car park. Repect for park and buildings, Five Precepts (refraining from killing includes insects)
How to get there	From Toulouse by train or bus to Lavaur. A car will pick you up from there at a cost of 10 FF, call 63 58 17 22 or if before 10am or after 6pm call 63 58 29 61

Dojo Zen of Toulouse (Zen – Soto – Association Zen Internationale)
51 rue Bayard
31000 Toulouse
Tel: +33 (0)61 99 27 37

In a quiet part of town. Founded by a disciple of Master Taisan Deshimaru in 1969 for people to practice zazen (Shikantaza – simple quiet and silent sitting) a few hours a day. Since 1976 under the responsibility of J.C. Vendetti, a Zen monk. About twenty-five monks, about twenty-five bodhisattvas and as many lay people use the Dojo to practice.

Practice times: Monday 12.30–1.30pm, Tuesday 7–8am, Wednesday 7–8am and 7.30–9pm, Thursday 7–8am and 12.30–1.30pm, Friday 7–8am and 7.30–9pm, Saturday 8–9am. Visitors should arrive a few minutes early for sessions for practices and behaviour in the Dojo to be explained. Samu (work in concentration) is part of Soto Zen practice. Teaching is given as a part of the meditation session. Special sessions are held for newcomers on Monday and Thursday at noon. Every second month sesshin of one or two days held. Shiatsu and traditional sewing of Kesa, Rakusu and Zagu (Zen monk garments) also take place. The Dojo is modest and absolutely authentic.

Founder/Guru	Taisen Deshimaru Roshi
Teachers	Jean Claude Vendetti, resident Zen monk and visiting French Zen teachers
Opening times	As practice times above
Residents	No residents, but twelve monks hold centre in common
Festivals	Contact centre
Facilities	Dojo and library
Accommodation	No
Food	Traditional rice soup (Guen Mai) after the morning Zazen
Booking	Contact centre
Fees	Contact centre
Languages	French and English
Expected behaviour	Contact centre

How to get there   100m from main railway station of
Matabiau

Nord Pas De Calais

Kagyu Rinchen Djoungne Ling (Tibetan – Kagyu)
24 rue Thiers
59110 La Madeleine
Tel: +33 (0)20 55 76 59

House in city centre. Founded by the Most Venerable Gyabab
Rinpoche in 1989. In 1990, a couple offered the centre use of their
house which was blessed by the Most Venerable Bokar Rinpoche
and placed under his protection. Since then, it has invited various
lamas from Belgium and France. Aims to promote wellbeing
through study and meditation practice. Offers a place of exchange
and dialogues for practitioners. Warm and friendly atmosphere.

Meditations Tuesdays 8pm, Fridays 8pm, full moon nights 8pm
and weekends when lamas are present. Study once a month on
weekends. Possible to borrow from library. Chenrezig practice on
Tuesdays open to newcomers. Members may meditate whenever
they wish.

Founder/Guru	The Most Venerable Bokar Rinpoche
Teachers	Visit once a month, mostly Lama Lodreu from Paris or Lama Sonam from Montpellier
Opening times	See meditation times above
Residents	Two lay people
Festivals	Tibetan New Year
Facilities	Shrine room, library, meeting room
Accommodation	Not usually
Food	During weekends. Lunch 40 FF, supper 35 FF
Booking	For weekends book two or three days in advance
Fees	80 FF per weekend
Languages	French, Tibetan, English
Expected behaviour	No smoking in the house, Five Precepts

How to get there Located in the suburb of Loille. Access by bus from city centre

---

Faith is, above all, open-ness – an act of trust in the unknown.
  – Alan Watts, *On the Taboo Against Knowing Who You Are*

Normandy

Centre de Yoga – Dharma (Tibetan – Kagyu)
Hameau de Babylone
76430 La Remuée
Tel: +33 (0)35 20 65 28
Fax: +33 (0)35 30 65 77

In Normandy, close to forest of Tancarville. Two brick and stone traditional-style buildings. Alain Duhayon met Lama Tunsang in 1977 and set up a centre in town. Needing a quiet place for practice and courses, his students helped him find this centre in the countryside, 20km from Le Havre. Temple, dormitory, yoga room, sauna, shop, eating room, small library.

Generally, newcomers have practices explained to them, but no difference made between beginners and experienced practitioners. An extremely wide programme of Buddhist and yoga practices. First temple in Western Europe with 1000 brass Buddha statues, consecrated according to tradition using earth from holy places in Nepal, India and Tibet. Statues include a metre-high Medicine Buddha. Temple painted by a Tibetan artist in 1993.

Due to Alain Duhayon's nineteen years of work with Lama Teunsang and Kalu Rinpoche on Mahamudra, the centre's specialities are meditation practice for the good of all sentient beings, and also work on negative emotions through Dream yoga. Courses run year round and are led by different Lamas based in Europe and other teachers. Course subjects such as: massage, baby massage, traditional purifications (Kriyas Yoga) and restoration of energy, personal development (emotional work), relaxation, reflexology, dream Yoga, integral Yoga, Tibetan Yoga of Kalu Rinpoche, Yoga Nadopasana. Individual retreats are possible and several group retreats are organised during the year.

Tuesday and Friday Shine teaching and practice 7–8pm, Tea 8pm, 8.30–9.30pm Chenrezig practice. Saturday 7–8am Recitation of 10,000 mantras, 9–10.30am Tara.

During courses, visitors are expected to participate in a session before breakfast and help with the daily chores.

A small group in the town undertake Tibetan language classes.

Founder/Guru	Lama Teunsang
Teachers	Resident: Alain Duhayon (Karma Puntso Gyaltsen) and visiting teachers
Opening times	Inform centre in advance of your arrival
Residents	Two families
Festivals	Occasionally
Facilities	See above
Accommodation	Dormitory for twelve people; camping possible, during Dream Yoga courses sixteen people can sleep in the work room. Full-board 110 FF
Food	Vegetarian and non-vegetarian, only by booking in advance
Booking	For a stay, fifteen days in advance by post
Fees	Annual fee of 120 FF to be paid on arrival
Languages	French, and translation of teachings and practices into English when advance notice given
Expected behaviour	No smoking, no animals, no musical instruments
How to get there	Easy access from Paris

Provence

Le Jardin du Dharma Très Bon (Tibetan – Kagyu)
180 Chemin de la Capelasse
13080 Luynes
Tel: +33 (0)42 24 08 96

Centre for practice and meditation in an old converted garage in the countryside. Established in 1974. Meditations Thursday evenings and one Sunday afternoon a month. Tibetan language classes once a week.

Founder/Guru	Founded by Kalu Rinpoche and now under the authority of Bokar Rinpoche
Teachers	Lama Tcheuky visits for teachings
Opening times	Thursday at 7pm and on every first Sunday of the month
Residents	No
Festivals	Yes
Facilities	Contact centre
Accommodation	No
Food	No
Booking	Contact centre
Fees	Annual membership 200FF, monthly participation 110 FF
Languages	French
Expected behaviour	Contact centre
How to get there	Between Aix en Provence (5km) and Marseille (25km)

I had lost a head and gained a world. . . it felt like a sudden waking from the sleep of ordinary life, an end to dreaming. . . *It was the revelation, at long last, of the perfectly obvious.*

– Douglas Harding, *On Having No Head*

Rhone Alpes

Centre de la Falaise Verte (Zen – Rinzai)
La Riaille
07800 St Laurent du Pape
Tel: +33 (0)75 85 10 39
Fax: +33 (0)75 85 39 49

A retreat centre for those who sincerely wish to practice Zen Buddhism. Sesshins are either weekend or seven days and may involve Chado (Japanese tea ceremony), Kyudo (Japanese Zen archery), zazen (sitting meditation), Kin-Hin (walking meditation), Hitsouzendo (Zen calligraphy) and Samu (manual work).

Weekend sesshins about once a month.

Founder	Taikan Jyoji
Teachers	Taikan Jyoji
Opening times	All year round, permanently open
Residents	Monks occasionally, between two and four lay people
Festivals	No
Facilities	Zen ·Dojo, shrine room, study room and swimming pool
Accommodation	One, two or four person rooms in Japanese Zen-style
Food	Three vegetarian meals a day, wholefood cereals
Booking	Write in advance
Fees	Between 540 FF and 1950 FF depending on length of sesshin
Languages	French, English, Japanese
Expected behaviour	No smoking and to follow the schedule
How to get there	20km south of Valence, on the right hand side of the Rhone river

Centre d'Etudes Bouddhiques (Tibetan and Zen)
16 rue Thiers
38000 Grenoble
Tel: +33 (0)76 46 70 16

Old house in the centre of town.

Offers zazen, talks for beginners and meditations, talks on topics such as paramitas, lodjong, yanas and mantras. Chenrezig and Samatha-Vipassana. Weekends for intensive practice. Indian singing lessons and Yoga.

Founder/Guru	Kalu Rinpoche
Teachers	Visiting Tibetan and Zen teachers
Opening times	See programme
Residents	No
Festivals	No
Facilities	Shrine room and library

Accommodation	No
Food	No
Booking	Not necessary
Fees	Monthly fee of 100FF and/or donations
Languages	French
Expected behaviour	No smoking, no drugs, show respect for the place and people
How to get there	In the centre of town

Tachi Tcheu Ling (Tibetan – Kagyu)
5 rue des Marronniers
69002 Lyon – Bellecour
Tel: +33 (0)78 42 81 59

Flat in the centre of town. Branch of **Karma Ling** in Arvillard (see separate entry on p207). Meditations include Shamatha-Vipassana and Chenrezig for more experienced practitioners. Tibetan and Dharma texts are studied. Several instructors are available to teach newcomers meditation practice.

Founder/Guru	Kalu Rinpoche
Teachers	Lama Neldjorpa Sherab is the centre's teacher, but does not reside there. Ven Lama Denys Teundroup and other **Karma Ling** teachers visit
Opening times	September to June: Monday and Friday evenings, Saturday morning and some Tuesdays in the afternoon
Residents	No
Festivals	See Karma Ling
Facilities	Shrine room, small library, study room and room for personal instructions with the Lama
Accommodation	No
Food	No
Booking	Contact centre
Fees	Contact centre
Languages	French
Expected behaviour	Contact centre

How to get there   In the centre of town

Sakya Tashi Choling Association Humanitaire (Tibetan – Sakya)
14 rue de l'Ancien Champ de Mars
38000 Grenoble
Tel: +33 (0)76 87 68 14
Fax: +33 (0)76 46 35 18

Centre of town on the first floor of a small house – quiet. Branch of Sakya Centre in Rajpur, India where H.H. Sakya Trizin is based. Founded in 1988 by Daniel Telmont, yoga teacher and psychotherapist, disciple of H.H. Sakya Trizin since 1973 who asked him to open this Institute. Daniel spends one or two months a year with H.H. Daniel seeks to adapt the external presentation of Tibetan Buddhism to the Western mind without transforming the basics.

Sponsoring of Tibetan children, readings and exchanges about Buddhist philosophy, meditation and videos, lessons in spoken Tibetan.

Meditations second and fourth Thursday of each month at 8.30pm. Practices include Chenrezig, Vajrasattva and Tara. Study includes Zempa Zidel, Triple vision and all subjects of philosophy which can help in daily life. Gom-takh Tibetan Yoga.

Founder/Guru	H.H. Sakya Trizin
Teachers	Resident: Daniel Telmont; visiting: Lama Gendung Gyatso from Rikon, Switzerland
Opening times	Year round, except August
Residents	No
Festivals	Contact centre
Facilities	Meditation and yoga room, library and video
Accommodation	No
Food	Only occasionally
Booking	Newcomers should arrange an interview before attending
Fees	Annual subscription: 300 FF; per session 60 FF
Languages	French, English, Tibetan

Expected behaviour   No cigarettes or drugs, dress decently
How to get there   Behind cinema 'Pathé Gambetta'

Institut Karma Ling (Tibetan – Kagyu)
Hameau de Saint Hugon
73110 Arvillard
Tel: +33 (0)79 65 64 62
Fax: +33 (0)79 25 78 08

In an alpine forest at 800m altitude. Twelfth-century Chartreux monastery, bought in 1979 and renovated. Emphasis on integration of teaching and practice into the Western lifestyle and on being non-dogmatic. For this reason, teachings and some practice texts have been translated into French. Lama Denys Teundrop is French and Kalu Rinpoche asked him to teach as appropriate to the Western environment.

A wide variety of practices from different disciplines are offered in an eclectic approach which seeks to unite mind, body and spirit. As well as more traditional Buddhist practices, these include walking meditation or mountain climbing, Bach Flower remedies, Western relaxation techniques, Gestalt therapy, Ayurvedic massage, Reiki, Qi Gong, Tai Chi Chuan, dance, voice work, various kinds of Yoga, meditation techniques and Tibetan and Western astrology. Sessions for children.

Meditation courses last from one weekend to one week and are open to all. For newcomers to Buddhism there is a course 'Voie du Bouddha'.

Two programmes for advanced students: Chedra, three years or more of one weekend a month study and practice and Droupdra with the possibility of a six-month or traditional three-year retreat. Summer University during the month of July.

Daily routine for residents consists of 7–8am meditation, followed by work time and 8–9pm meditation.

Guided tours at 4pm every Tuesday and every day from 1 July to 31 August except Wednesdays.

Ask for list of affiliated centres in Europe.

Founder/Guru   Kalu Rimpoche
Teachers   Resident: Lama Denys Teundrop and visit-

ing lamas from **Longchen Foundation** in England (see separate entry on p109)

Opening Times	See programme of events
Residents	Two monks and twelve people in three-year retreat plus twenty-five lay people
Festivals	Lossar and Summer Festival over a weekend in late July
Facilities	See above
Accommodation	112 beds in rooms, dormitories and bungalows from 113 FF to 310 FF depending on accommodation and salary
Food	Price included in accommodation costs
Booking	By post, with deposit of 50 FF per day as far in advance as possible
Fees	Varies according to option chosen
Languages	French, English and Tibetan
Expected behaviour	Contact centre
How to get there	30km from Chambéry (Savoie). Car or train to Chambéry or Grenoble, then taxi from Pontcharra sur Bréda station

European Buddhist Union
For lack of a permanent secretariat, the following addresses can be used:
Ven. Lama Denys Teundroup, President
Congrégation Dachang Rimé
Institut Karma Ling
Hameau de Saint Hugon
73100 Arvillard
France
Tel: Institut +33 (0)79 65 64 62
Fax: +33 (0)79 25 78 08

Aad Verboom, Vice-President
EBU c/o SJBN
P O Box 1519
3500 BM Utrecht
The Netherlands
Tel: +31 (0)30 2888 655

Fax: +31 (0)30 2898 294
e-mail: averboom@knoware.nl

The European Buddhist Directory Project:
EBU c/o BUN
P O Box 17286
1001 JG Amsterdam
The Netherlands

An umbrella organisation of Buddhist organisations, centres and groups in Europe. As a union, it is broad, impartial and open to Buddhists of all schools and traditions. Its principal aims are to promote the fellowship of, and encourage co-operation between, Buddhists in Europe, to promote Buddhists in Europe to meet and to get acquainted, to promote the development of friendly relations between Buddhist organisations and consequently to promote co-operation on matters that are of interest to all. As such the EBU supports and promotes a natural growth of Buddhism in Europe.

Founded in 1975, its activities include the organisation of Annual General Meetings and International Congresses. They are considering participating in international and national events organised by other Buddhist organisations. They are also engaged in two projects: the compilation of a European Buddhist Directory which will list Buddhist organisations, centres and groups in Europe and Buddhism and Education to make available good educational material throughout Europe. A newsletter will appear once a year. They also represent Buddhism in Europe to other Buddhist and non-Buddhist organisations such as the European Parliament, UNESCO and organisations involved in interreligious dialogue.

I don't believe that there is anyone to wake up! Sentient beings are not *there* at all as such – as the Buddha pointed out in the Diamond Sutra, so how can they wake up? And *what* is there to wake up?

— Wei Wu Wei, *Open Secret*

GERMANY

Kongo-An (Zen – Rinzai)
Marienstrasse 30
03046 Cottbus
Tel: +49 (0)355 70 28 52

Zendo opened in 1989 as a branch of **Kin-Mo-Zendo** in Berlin. Room in a rented flat with space for twelve people to do Zazen together. Zazen practice on Tuesdays at 8pm and Thursdays at 7pm. Newcomers should come at the start of opening time for instruction and there is also a special introductory session once a year.

The group have seven members, three of whom practice Tai Chi Chuan once a fortnight. Also making a protest vigil in the city for Liberty for Tibet.

Founder/Guru	Sotetsu Yuzen Sensei (Dr. Klaus Zernickow)
Teachers	Founder visits
Opening times	Tuesdays 7–9.30pm and Thursdays 6–9.30pm
Residents	Two lay people
Festivals	Contact Zendo
Facilities	Dojo
Accommodation	In private home possible with notice
Food	No
Booking	Contact Zendo
Fees	Contact Zendo
Languages	German, Polish, English, Spanish and Portugese
Expected behaviour	No special rules
How to get there	Five minutes from railway station – turn left at railway bridge, then second right

Buddhistisches Zentrum Berlin (Tibetan – Karma Kagyu)
c/o Mentzel
Bundes Allee 32
10717 Berlin
Tel: +49 (0)30 861 39 21

Fax: +49 (0)30 862 23 42
e-mail: paldroen@zedat.fu-berlin.de

Meditations are Guru Yoga and Chenrezig, both guided in German. Irregular study classes with teachings given by advanced practitioners.

Founder/Guru	17th Karmapa, Thaye Dorje, directed by Lama Ole Nydahl
Teachers	Several lay teachers from centres directed by Lama Ole Nydahl
Opening times	Monday, Tuesday and Thursday 8–11pm, Sunday 11am to 3pm
Residents	No
Festivals	Contact centre
Facilities	Shrine room, book and tape library and shop and tea room
Accommodation	No
Food	No
Booking	By phone or fax
Fees	Contact centre
Languages	German and English
Expected behaviour	Contact centre
How to get there	U-Bahn U7 to Berliner Strasse or U9 to Güntzelstrasse

Zen Dojo Berlin (Zen – Soto – Association Zen Internationale)
Mehringdamm 57
10961 Berlin
Tel: +49 (0)30 693 99 55
Fax: +49 (0)30 694 73 18

Situated in Berlin Kreutzberg. Founded in 1974 by a disciple of Taisen Deshimaru. Open to all interested in the practice. Consider it of major importance that spirituality takes more place in ordinary life. They also host occasional visits from schools and adult institutions for two-hour demonstration and talk on the Dojo's activities.

Zazen is held Thursday and Friday 7.15am and 7.15pm,

Saturday 5.45pm and Sunday 10.45am. After the Saturday session, there is the opportunity to ask questions of the teacher and after the Sunday session there is a breakfast. Morning sessions are closed by a short ceremony and evening sessions by chanting of the Prajna Paramita Sutra. Teaching is given during the meditation. Much the same practice is open to newcomers and more experienced practitioners. Three-day retreats are organised in February, at Easter, June and November in the countryside near Berlin. There is also a nine-day retreat held in the Swiss mountains in October. From the beginning of July to the beginning of September, ten-day retreats are held at the AZI's temple in the Loire valley of France.

Founder/Guru	Taisen Deshimaru, currently led by Bernard Poirier, a monk and disciple of Master Deshimaru
Teachers	Resident: Bernard Poirier and many visiting teachers
Opening times	Expect during retreats, as for Zazen times above
Residents	Seven monks, one nun, about ten who have received first ordination and about thirty lay people are associated with the Dojo
Festivals	Several held during the summer retreat
Facilities	Dojo and library
Accommodation	No
Food	No
Booking	Contact centre
Fees	Either 50 or 60 DM a month or 5 DM per session for Zazen; 120 to 200 DM for three-day retreats plus a donation to the teacher
Languages	German, French and English
Expected behaviour	Not to disturb others, follow the rules of the Dojo and vigilance.
How to get there	U-Bahn 6 or 7 to Mehringdamm station. Walk towards Tempelhof airport on the left side of the street. Through a gateway, on the first floor of the second stairway from the right building in the court.

Shogozan Zenkoji (Zen – Soto – Association Zen Internationale)
Zen Temple
Rheinstrasse 45, Eing. C
12161 Berlin
Tel: +49 (0)30 851 20 73

German Zen Association was founded 1984 to give opportunity
for people to deepen their Zazen practice. In the tradition of
Dogen-Zenji's Soto Zen brought to Europe by Taisen Deshimaru
Roshi and here presented by L. Tenryu Tenbreul.
  Practice times Tuesday 7am and 7pm, Wednesday 7am and
7.30pm, Thursday 7am and 7.30pm, Friday 7am, Saturday 6pm
with Introduction for Beginners at 5pm and Sunday at 9.30am.
Daily teachings by Master Tenryu. Recital of sutras and Buddhist
ceremony. Introduction into formal behaviour in the Dojo, but
apart from that the practice is the same for beginners and
advanced students.
  Their sesshin centre is **Mokushozan Jakkoji** in Schönböken (see
separate entry on p220).

Founder/Guru	Taisen Deshimaru Roshi, led by Zen Master L. Tenryu Tenbreul
Teachers	Resident: Zen Master L. Tenryu Tenbreul
Opening times	See practice times above
Residents	No
Festivals	Check with Dojo
Facilities	Dojo, tea room, office, Shiatsu room, room for other activities like sewing, small library
Accommodation	No
Food	Gen-Mai (Traditional rice soup eaten after morning Zazen)
Booking	Not necessary
Fees	Check with Dojo
Languages	German, English and French
Expected behaviour	Ask centre
How to get there	Take subway to Walter Schreiber Platz, direction Berlin-Steglitz or Bus 186 or 148

Zen Zentrum Mumon-Kai (Zen – Rinzai)
Frohnauer Strasse 148
13465 Berlin
Tel: +49 (0)30 401 30 69

Zendo with garden. Founded in 1971 by the German Dharma successor of Seki Yuho Roshi, Abbot of Eigen-Ji in Japan to offer the opportunity of practising Zen under an authorised Rinzai Zen master.
Zazen daily at 7–7.30am, 8–9.30pm on Tuesdays, 7–9.30pm on Thursdays (Dokusan) and 8–11.30am on first and third Sunday of the month (Taiwa). Also Weekend zazen, zazen trainings and sesshins (one week, Dai-Sesshin and Rohatsu-Sesshin). Introduction to Zazen and the Zendo rules for newcomers. Other activities include Tai Chi Chuan, ka-do (flower arranging), tea ceremony and bamboo flute playing.
Run a vegetarian restaurant in Berlin where they practice Zen in daily life – Hakuin, Martin-Luther-Str 1/1a, 10777 Berlin, *Tel:* +49 (0)30 218 20 27. The centre also runs nine branches in Germany, Austria and Poland – contact Zendo for more details.

Founder/Guru	Sotetsu Yuzen Sensei (Dr Klaus Zernickow)
Teachers	Sotetsu Yuzen Sensei
Opening times	At practice times – see above
Residents	No
Festivals	Dharma-Chakra-Pravartana, Kaisan-Ki, Nehan-E, Kambutsu-E, Ski-Yuho-Ki, Kannon-Ki, Daruma-Ki, Jodo-E and Hakuin's Birthday
Facilities	Zendo
Accommodation	Guestroom for invited guests only
Food	Check with Zendo
Booking	Write at least five weeks in advance and full information will be sent
Fees	Daily Zazen no charge, weekend Zazen 180 DM, two and a half-day Zazen training 200 DM and one week sesshin 450 DM
Languages	German and English
Expected behaviour	Zendo rules
How to get there	By S-Bahn from Zoologischer Garten or bus 125 from Alt Tegel

Karma Tengyal Ling (Tibetan – Karma Kagyu)
Neuruppinerstrasse 6
16775 Menz
Tel: +49 (0)33082 50 289
Fax: +49 (0)33082 51 437

Isolated location about 90km north of Berlin, 2km from nearest villages and surrounded by fields and forests. Was a children's holiday resort in DDR times. Founded in 1987 in Berlin, moved to Menz in 1992.

Daily 7am Green Tara Puja and 7.30pm Guru Yoga and Chenrezig Puja. Shrine room also available for individual practice. Various courses by various teachers. Visitors expected to help with daily chores for one hour daily.

Open to all Buddhist schools which may arrange to use the facilities for courses.

Dedicated to H.H. the Seventeenth Gyalwa Karmapa Urgyen Trinley Dorje.

Founder/Guru	H.H. the Sixteenth Gyalwa Karmapa – Rangschung Rigpa Dorje
Teachers	Visiting Karma Kagyu teachers
Opening times	Always open – phone before to make sure someone home
Residents	Three lay people
Festivals	Check with centre
Facilities	Two shrine rooms, library and study room
Accommodation	Simple – single room 42 DM, double room 23 DM per person, dormitory 14 DM, camping 12 DM; all prices per night – reduced rates for members
Food	Vegetarian food available – let them know in advance
Booking	For courses – two weeks in advance with 30 DM deposit
Fees	Varies with course
Languages	German and English
Expected behaviour	Decently and quietly so as not to disturb meditations. Smoking only in Smokers Corner

How to get there By car: North from Berlin on B76 to Gransee, then first left towards Rheinsberg, then right to Menz. By train to Gransee and then bus to Menz.

Tibetisches Zentrum (Tibetan – as expressed by patronage of H.H. the 14th Dalai Lama)
Hermann-Balk-Strasse 106
22147 Hamburg
Tel: +49 (0)40 644 3585
Fax: +49 (0)40 644 3515
e-mail: +z-hh% link-hh@comlink.de
Bookshop Tel: +49 (0)40 644 9828

Small house in surburban area with temple, Maitreya shrine and stupa in garden. Aim is to provide facilities for people to get to know Tibetan Buddhist study and practice and all other aspects of Tibetan culture including staging art exhibitions, etc. Open to all Tibetan Buddhist traditions expressed by patronage of H.H. Dalai Lama and also to keep up interreligious dialogue with religions of West to demonstrate value of spiritual life.

Offers courses throughout the year: Introduction to Buddhism, seminars and retreats lasting several days, weekly meditation classes, daily prayers, systematic study courses lasting several years, traditional Tibetan academic education in Buddhist philosophy and Tibetan language courses which are open to all. Well- stocked library with audio and video tapes and a shop selling Buddhist books and articles. Library and temple can be used by non-members for reading or meditation by arrangement. Meditation and retreat centre is **Semkye Ling** (see separate entry on p225).

Studies and seminars take place in March to July and September to January with retreat times in February and August (may vary slightly according to Buddhist calendar).

Extensive aid programme for Tibetan refugees. Own publishing department 'Dharma Edition' and quarterly magazine, *Tibet und Buddhismus.*

Founder/Guru H.H. the Dalai Lama, Geshe Rabten, Geshe Ugyen Tseten, Geshe Thubten Ngawang

Teachers	Resident: Geshe Thubten Ngawang and Geshe Tenpa Choephel, visiting many others
Opening times	Bookshop: Monday–Friday 2–6pm all year round; Library and temple during seminars and by arrangement; Office: Tuesday–Friday 1–4pm and Thursday 1–6.30pm
Residents	Three monks and four nuns
Festivals	Vesakh, Je Tsongkapa Day, Dalai Lama's Birthday, First Turning of the Wheel of Dharma Day, Descent from Heaven Day and Losar
Facilities	Shrine room, library, study room, stupa and Maitreya shrine and shop
Accommodation	No
Food	No
Booking	Write six weeks in advance, deposit sometimes required
Fees	Check with centre
Expected behaviour	Five Precepts
How to get there	Take U1 towards Großhansdorf as far as Berne. Turn left out of the station and cross market square to Hermann-Balk-Strasse and centre is on left-hand side

---

Learned Audience, the illimitable Void of the universe is capable of holding myriads of things of various shape and form, such as the sun, the moon, stars, mountains, rivers, worlds, springs, rivulets, bushes, woods, good men, bad men, Dharmas pertaining to goodness or badness . . . hells, great oceans. . . . Space takes in all these, and so does the voidness of our nature. We say that the Essence of Mind is great because it embraces all things, since all things are within our nature. When we see the goodness or the badness of other people we are not attracted by it, nor repelled by it, nor attached to it; so that our attitude of mind is as void as space. In this way we say our mind is great. . . .

– *The Sutra of Wei Lang (or Hui Neng)*, translated from the Chinese by Wong Mou-Lam

Buddhistische Gesellschaft Hamburg (Theravada, Zen and Tibetan Traditions)
Beisserstrasse 23
22337 Hamburg
Tel: +49 (0)(0)40 631 36 96
Fax: +49 (0)(0)40 631 36 90

Large 100-year-old house on the edge of town. Specialisation is Theravada. Strive for openness and try to do work on a donation basis so rely heavily on voluntary work.

Regular classes include Sundays 10am–12 noon Gacchama – Theravada teaching; Monday 7–9.30pm Zazen for advanced students; Tuesday 7.30–9pm Thich-Nhat-Hanh meditation and Stillness and Movement; Thursdays 7.30–9pm Zazen for beginners; Saturdays 3.30–6pm Korean study and meditation group and alternate Saturdays study of sutras. Weekend retreats on different topics and in different traditions starting on Fridays with a public lecture.

Organise meetings of Buddhist groups on a broad scale including a convention in Hamburg in 1996 with other Hamburg groups.

Some translation work and publication. Bi-monthly magazine *Buddhistische Monatsblätter.*

Founder/Guru	Venerable Narada Mahathera
Teachers	Many visiting teachers of different Buddhist traditions
Opening times	Office: Monday, Tuesday and Thursday 9.30am–1pm, Wednesday 4–7pm. Library: office hours and Sunday 9.30–10am
Residents	Four lay people
Festivals	Vesakh, Full moon Thai Buddhist celebrations, open and close of rains retreat if monk in residence
Facilities	Two shrine rooms, library with study room, office and meeting rooms
Accommodation	No
Food	No
Booking	In advance, pay on arrival, no deposit.
Fees	By donation as much as possible; 100 DM

	weekend retreat
Languages	German and English
Expected bhaviour	Five Precepts, no shoes in some rooms, don't point feet at Buddha statue or nun, be punctual
How to get there	Good access by U-Bahn, S-Bahn and bus

Buddhistisches Zentrum Hamburg (Tibetan – Karma Kagyu)
der Karma-Kagyü-Linie
Karma Drub Gjy Ling
Stahltwiete 20
22761 Hamburg
Tel: +49 (0)(0)40 389 3631
Fax: +49 (0)(0)40 389 8702

In the western part of the city. Founded in the 1970s. Teachings are offered in a yogi/lay style suited to modern life.

Daily Karmapa meditation (Guru yoga on the 16th Karmapa) at 7pm, Thursdays at 8pm. Monday, Tuesday and Wednesdays other guided meditations, for example Tara, Loving Eyes, Refuge. Tara Puja Sundays at 10.30am. Phowa Puja twice a year. Medicine Buddha Puja monthly. Ngondro practice (four foundation practices) offered irregularly and introductory courses 2–3 times a year. Newcomers are welcome to go to the Thursday evening meditation which is followed by questions and answers. Yidam or Guru Yoga practice initiations and teachings are available to more advanced students. Retreats are held occasionally at a rural meditation centre in Denmark not far from Hamburg.

Founder/Guru	H.H. the 16th Karmapa under the name of Karma Drub Gjy Ling
Teachers	Visiting: Sharmapa Rinpoche, Lopon Tsechu Rinpoche, Lama Ole Nydahl
Opening times	Every evening and Sunday mornings
Residents	No
Festivals	Milarepa Tsok Puja on full moons
Facilities	Shrine room, library, study room
Accommodation	Only on exceptional occasions
Food	Light lunch during seminars that go

	through the whole day
Booking	Phone, fax or write
Fees	Contact centre
Languages	German and English
Expected behaviour	A genuine interest in Buddhism
How to get there	Freeway No. 7, exit 'Bahrenfeld', turn left coming from north or right from south. On Stresemannstrasse turn right into Stahltwiete

Mokushozan Jakkoji (Zen – Soto – Association Zen Internationale)
Zen Centre
Hauptstrasse 1
24601 Schönböken
Tel: +49 (0)4323 7104

Situated in the Schleswig-Holstein countryside. Nineteenth-century New Gothic style manor house with large archway building surrounded by five acres of parkland with lakes, bridges, and many old trees at the edge of a village. Sesshin centre for **Shogozan Zenkoji** in Berlin (see separate entry on p213) and used by other Zen centres.

Two and a half day sesshins most months and also longer training periods – up to four weeks in spring and summer. Sesshins consist of Zazen, Buddhist ceremonies and Samu (manual work).

Founder/Guru	Deshimaru Roshi, led by Zen Master L. Tenryu Tenbreul
Teachers	Zen Master L. Tenryu Tenbreul and visiting guests from other Zen centres
Opening times	As for sesshins and weekly practice
Residents	Two monks
Festivals	Check with Zen Centre or Zen Temple Berlin
Facilities	Check with Zen Centre or Zen Temple Berlin
Accommodation	Yes
Food	Vegetarian

Booking	Phone or write to Berlin Temple – **Shogozan Zenkoji** (see separate entry)
Fees	For two and a half-day sesshins DM 150 members, 170 DM non-members including accommodation and meals, deposit at least two weeks in advance
Languages	German, English and French
Expected behaviour	To follow sesshin/training programme according to Soto Zen rules
How to get there	Train to Neumünster, then bus to Schönböken

Buddhistisches Zentrum Auenbüttel (Tibetan – Karma Kagyu)
Auenbüttel 8
25724 Schmedeswurth
Tel: +49 (0)4851 85130
Fax: +49 (0)4851 2071
e-mail: 048512071@btxgate.de

Small centre 100km west of Hamburg on land reclaimed from the North Sea, situated in a small village. Private house which will be given to the Karmapa and the German Trust. Founded in 1980 by Lama Ole Nydahl, who is a disciple of the Karmapa. Lay tradition, not monastic, in centres guided by Ole. Stupa being built by Tsechoo Rinpoche in front of the centre during 1996. Plans for retreat houses in future.

Karmapa Meditation is held every Thursday and is followed by an introduction for newcomers. Occasional retreats.

Founder/Guru	Lama Ole Nydahl
Teachers	Visiting: Tsechoo Rinpoche and other Karma Kagyu teachers
Opening times	Contact centre
Residents	Two lay people
Festivals	No
Facilities	Shrine room and small library
Accommodation	Not as yet
Food	No
Booking	Contact centre

Fees	Contact centre
Languages	German and English
Expected behaviour	Nothing special
How to get there	100km west of Hamburg near Brunsbüttel and Marne

Buddhistisches Zentrum (Tibetan – Karma Kagyu)
Nordfriesland
Dorfstrasse 124
25842 Langenhorn
Tel: +49 (0)46 72 1515
Fax: +49 (0)46 72 7028

30km from the Danish border in the north-west of Germany. Old house (sixteenth-century) which was a farm house in a village. Founded in 1991. Practice of Dharma in daily life 'nothing exotic but freshness here and now'.

Karmapa meditation every Wednesday at 8.30pm, Tara Puja Sundays at 10am. Possibility of individual retreats. Phone for programme.

Founder/Guru	Karmapa Lodro Thaye represented by Lama Ole Nydahl
Teachers	Visting lamas and their students
Opening times	Always contactable
Residents	Two adults and their three children
Festivals	Milarepa Tsok Puja on full and half moon days
Facilities	Shrine room, small library and garden
Accommodation	For retreatants: 10 DM per night and one hour's housework
Food	Normal family cooking at 10 DM per meal
Booking	Fax or phone
Fees	Contact centre
Languages	German and English
Expected behaviour	Usual behaviour for family life
How to get there	By car: A1 Hamburg to Flensburg

Zen Kreis Wilhelmshaven (Zen)
Kai In Zendo
Schellingstrasse 21
26384 Wilhelmshaven
Tel: +49 (0)4421 85615

Founded in 1984.
Zazen sessions Mondays and Thursdays at 7.30–9.30pm.
Weekend sesshins every month and seven-day sesshins twice a
year.

Founder/Guru	Founder: Oi Saidan Roshi, Abbot of Hokoji monastery in Japan
Teachers	Resident: Eckhart Reitetsu Gattermann Sensei and visiting Japanese teachers
Opening times	See event times above
Residents	No
Festivals	Contact centre
Facilities	Contact centre
Accommodation	During sesshins
Food	During sesshins
Booking	By post or phone one week in advance for weekend sesshins, one month in advance for seven-day sesshins. No deposit required
Fees	Between 30 and 240 DM depending on event and whether you are a member
Languages	German and English
Expected behaviour	Contact centre
How to get there	Contact centre

> Over the years and over many meetings with scientists of all
> kinds, I have become increasingly struck by the richness of the
> parallels between the teachings of Buddha and the discoveries
> of modern physics.
>
> – Sogyal Rinpoche, *The Tibetan Book of Living and Dying*

Zen Dojo Bremen (Zen – Soto)
Mathildenstrasse 18
28203 Bremen
Tel: +49 (0)421 77623

Founded in 1989.
Zazen times: Tuesday 7.30am, Wednesday 7pm, Thursday 7.30am, Friday 7.00pm, Saturday 10am and Sunday 11am. Hannya Shingyo practice. Sesshins are two or three times a year. Introduction for newcomers.

Founder/Guru	Master Kosen Thibant of Amsterdam
Teachers	Resident: Will Gmehling, and visiting Master Kosen Thibant and disciples
Opening times	See Zazen times above
Residents	No
Festivals	No
Facilities	Dojo and library
Accommodation	Possible to stay in the Dojo for 10 DM per night
Food	No
Booking	Contact centre
Fees	Contact centre
Languages	German, English, French
Expected behaviour	No special behaviour asked
How to get there	Trams No. 10 or 1 or bus No. 25

Zen Kreis Bremen (Zen – Rinzai)
Ji-Kai-Zen-Kutsu
Atrium Hof
Vor dem Steintor 34
28203 Bremen
Tel: +49 (0)421 381985 or 2182771

Meditations: Zazen, Shikantaza, Kanna-Zen. Introductory sessions: Wednesday 8–9.30pm and Sunday 9–10.30am. Regular sessions: Monday to Saturday 7–7.45am, Monday, Tuesday and Wednesday 8–9.30pm, Thursday 7.30–10pm and Sunday 9–10.30pm.

Sessions include personal question and answer sessions, Buddhist talks or koan teaching.
Weekend and seven-day sesshins. Rohatsu sesshin first week of January.
Rei Shin Sensei trained with Oi Saidan Roshi, Rinzai Zen Patriarch and Abbot of Hojo-Ji in Japan.
Contact centre for other meditation groups around Germany.

Founder/Guru	Rei Shin Sensei (Wolf-Dieter Nolting)
Teachers	Founder and two other Zen monks from the Hoko-Ji monasteries
Opening times	See session times above
Residents	No
Festivals	Contact centre
Facilities	Dojo
Accommodation	No
Food	No
Booking	Contact centre
Fees	40 DM per month or 5 DM per session
Languages	German and English mainly
Expected behaviour	Practising mindfulness
How to get there	Contact centre

Semkye Ling (Tibetan – as expressed by patronage of H.H. the 14th Dalai Lama)
Buddhistisches Meditationshaus des Tibetisches Zentrums
Lünzener Strasse 4
29640 Schneverdingen
Tel & Fax: +49 (0)5193 52511

Meditation and retreat centre connected to **Tibetisches Zentrum** in Hamburg (see separate entry on p216). Quiet house on edge of Lüneburger Heide National Park. Opened in August 1996.
 Offers group and individual retreats of short or long duration. One-week meditation courses and teachings. Daily routine runs from 6.30am till 10.30pm unless a specific seminar or retreat programme is different.
 Contact Tibetisches Zentrum for more information and programme.

Founder/Guru	As for Tibetisches Zentrum
Teachers	As for Tibetisches Zentrum
Opening times	Contact Tibetisches Zentrum
Residents	Contact Tibetisches Zentrum
Festivals	Contact Tibetisches Zentrum
Facilities	Meditation house, shrine room, library and study room
Accommodation	Yes
Food	Vegetarian
Booking	Contact Tibetisches Zentrum
Fees	Contact Tibetisches Zentrum
Languages	German
Expected behaviour	Five Precepts
How to get there	Contact Tibetisches Zentrum

Buddhisticher Bund Hannover (All traditions including Theravada and Soto Zen)
Drostestrasse 8
30161 Hannover
Tel & Fax: +49 (0)511 3 94 17 56

First-floor flat in a block of flats. Founded 1963, current location since 1988. Purpose is practice and explanation of Buddhist teachings, looking at different traditions for people seriously looking for a change of consciousness and attitude in daily life and inter-religious dialogue.

Regular evening events: Zen practice Wednesday, Friday and Sundays, talk and discussion of Buddhist practice Tuesdays, meditation and Dhamma teachings Mondays, meditation and yoga Thursdays, puja Sunday morning. Afternoon tea with readings and discussion last Saturday of month. Introduction to Meditation class once a month. Newcomers welcome to Hatha Yoga classes also. One-day and weekend retreats and seminars. Subjects include Lam Rim, Zen sesshins, Karma and rebirth, Vipassana Bhavana, Mindfulness, Understanding with the Heart and the Six Paramitas.

Publish quarterly magazine *Der Mittlereweg*.

Associated centre in countryside at Uetze where retreats are often held.

Founder/Guru	Klaus Kasten and Paul Debes are founders
Teachers	Resident: Dagmar Doko Waskönig – Soto Zen nun. Visiting teachers include pupils of Ayya Khema and Thich Nhat Hanh
Opening times	As programme times
Residents	Resident teacher and one lay person
Festivals	No
Facilities	Meditation room, library, meeting room and kitchen
Accommodation	Overnight stay during seminars
Food	Vegetarian food during seminars
Booking	8–14 days in advance by phone and post
Fees	Contact centre
Languages	German and English
Expected behaviour	Mindfulness in all acts, removing shoes; no smoking
How to get there	Fifteen minutes walk from main station, tram line 3 towards Lahe or Line 7 towards Fasanenkrug

Vien Giac (Zen – Vietnamese)
Karlsruher Strasse 6
30519 Hannover
Tel: +49 (0)(0)511 879 630
Fax: +49 (0)(0)511 879 0963

The largest Buddhist monastery in Germany, the largest Vietnamese Buddhist monastery outside Vietnam. Builidng work began in 1989 and finished in 1994. Four buildings in a 3000m² courtyard including a 20m-high pagoda. Serves as both a cultural and religious centre for Vietnamese in Germany.

Regular activities include recitation of the Lotus Sutra, retreats for lay Buddhists (in Vietnamese), weekend and evening seminars in German and daily morning and evening ceremonies.

Founder/Guru	Venerable Thich Nhu Dien – Abbot and Founder
Teachers	Resident monks and visiting teachers
Opening times	Contact monastery

Residents	Monks
Festivals	Vietnamese New Year, Vesak and Ullambana
Facilities	Prayer hall, meditation and seminar rooms, printers and theatre
Accommodation	Yes
Food	Yes
Booking	Contact monastery
Fees	Contact monastery
Languages	German and Vietnamese
Expected behaviour	Five Precepts
How to get there	Contact monastery

Dharmakirti (Tibetan – Drikung Kagyu)
Am Kahnplätzchen 31
35452 Heuchelheim
Tel & Fax: +49 (0)49 641 65196

Private house in a very quiet and peaceful village near Gießen. Family atmosphere. One of the residents is a Ladakhi who translates for lamas. Rent houses in the countryside for larger events.

Meditation once a week, study once a week, Tsok Pujas on important days in the Tibetan calendar and occasional weekend retreats. Regular courses in Tibetan medicine.

Founder/Guru	Spiritual guidance: H.H. Drikung Kyabgon Chetsang and Chungtsang Rinpoche
Teachers	Mainly Drikung Kagyu teachers but lamas from other schools also
Opening times	Phone as times change
Residents	Family of four
Festivals	According to Tibetan calendar
Facilities	Shrine room and library
Accommodation	Contact centre
Food	Vegetarian during courses
Booking	Please phone or fax for information on ongoing programme
Fees	Contact centre
Languages	German and English

Expected behaviour   Contact centre
How to get there   60km north of Frankfurt/Main

Dzogchen Gemeinschaft Deutschland (Tibetan – Dzogchen – Dzogchen International Community)
Head Office: Lindemannstrasse 12
40237 Düsseldorf
Tel & Fax +49 (0)211 68 26 57

Gompa: Hans Vogel
Höfen 12
91460 Baudenbach
Tel: +49 (0)9166 564

Part of the Dzogchen International Community whose main centre in Europe is **Merigar** in Italy (see separate entry on p283 for more details of activities).

   Local practice groups in Berlin, Hamburg, Düsseldorf, Höfen, Schwarzwald, München, Frankfurt and Pfauenhof meet frequently. Contact head office for details. Regular meetings for practice and socialising once a month. Teaching retreats with the master, individual or group retreats at different centres of the International Dzogchen community in Europe, America and Australia. Vajra Dance. Gompa is in rural area of South Germany on private property with a large wood and farm.

Founder/Guru   Chogyal Namkhai Norbu Rinpoche
Teachers   Visiting teachers from all Buddhist schools
Opening times   As per events programme
Residents   No
Festivals   According to Tibetan calendar
Facilities   At Gompa: Shrine room, library and study room
Accommodation   Only at Gompa: Full-board for around 40 DM
Food   Only at Gompa: Normal and vegetarian food according to requirements
Booking   Contact head office for programme details
Fees   Contact head office

Languages	German and English
Expected behaviour	Presence and awareness in all behaviour
How to get there	Not applicable

Kanzeon Sangha Deutschland (Zen – Kanzeon Sangha)
c/o Sekretariat – Marcela Tureckova-Strnad
Boltensternstrasse 7
40239 Düsseldorf
Tel: +49 (0)211 62 77 77
Fax: +49 (0)211 37 27 54
e-mail: kanzeon.@uni-duisburg.de.

Kanzeon Sangha Germany was founded in 1988 as part of Kanzeon Sangha, under the leadership of Genpo Merzel Sensei, a Zen Master who lives at their headquarters in Salt Lake City, Utah, USA. Affiliated sanghas in England, Poland, Holland, France and Germany.

Currently have no fixed centre and sessions and sesshins are held in members' homes, but are looking for a centre in the city. Zazen groups in Düsseldorf, Kaarst, Dresden, Mainz and Neukirchen. Zazen sittings are held two or three evenings and twice in the early morning every week. Schedules vary with different groups. Beginners are welcome to these and also to sesshins. Introductory weekends and weekly courses for beginners. Main sesshins in Germany are held at **Torweg** (see separate entry on p234). Regular weekend sesshins and twice yearly longer sesshins with Genpo Sensei in spring and late summer. Occasional one-month trainings in Europe.

Kanzeon Sangha International offers a three-month angos (training period) at their headquarters in Salt Lake City.

Founder/Guru	Genpo Merzel Sensei
Teachers	Visting teachers: Genpo Merzel Sensei, Tenkei Coppens Sensei, Nico Tydeman Roshi and others
Opening times	Not applicable
Residents	No
Festivals	Contact centre
Facilities	See above

Accommodation	During sesshins
Food	During sesshins
Booking	Write to Sekretariat for information, newsletter and registration forms
Fees	See programme
Languages	German and English
Expected behaviour	Usual sesshin rules
How to get there	Details given after registration

> Soundlessly and without scent, heaven and earth are incessantly repeating unwritten sutras.
>
> *– Zen saying*

EKO – Haus der Japanischen Kultur (Pure Land – Jodo Shinshu)
Brüggener Weg 6
40547 Düsseldorf
Tel: +49 (0)211 574071
Fax: +49 (0)211 573546

Japanese cultural centre in the Niederkassel suburb of Düsseldorf where there is the highest population of Japanese in Europe. Buddhist temple, Japanese garden, traditional-style house with tea room with exhibition gallery and three seminar rooms in the basement.

To promote understanding of Buddhism in general, especially Japanese Buddhism and Shin Buddhism and to give a chance for visitors to experience Japanese culture in surroundings of typical Japanese-style architecture. Cultural exchanges between East and West.

Zazen three or four times a year. On sixteenth of every month at 8am recitation of Shinran's Shoshinge. Also various ceremonies at festivals, Paramita or O-Bon ceremonies. Tea ceremonies. Garden parties with music or theatre performances and musical performances. Lectures on Buddhism, reading and discussion of Buddhist texts, symposiums on Buddhism, Jodo Shin and Japanese culture. Introductory courses in calligraphy, Ikebana (Japanese flower arranging) and Japanese cookery.

Publishes academic magazine and biannual newletter with

programme of events.

Founder/Guru	Founder: Yehan Numata
Teachers	Contact centre
Opening times	Tuesday to Sunday 1–5pm. Closed holidays and two weeks at end of March and September
Residents	Two priests
Festivals	Hana-matsuri (flower festival) in April/May. Joya no kane (ring out the old year) on 31 December each year
Facilities	Temple, three seminar rooms, altar room, tea room, gallery. Library and kindergarten planned – also see above
Accommodation	Three guest rooms planned
Food	No
Booking	By phone
Fees	Contact centre
Languages	Japanese, German and English
Expected behaviour	No special rules
How to get there	From Düsseldorf main station, U70, U74, U75, U76 or U77 to Belsenplatz. Change to bus 834, 836 or 828 to Niederkasseler Kirchweg

Zen Dojo (Zen – Soto – Association Zen Internationale)
Florastrasse 41a
42651 Solingen
Tel: +49 (0)(0)212 200 339

Founded in 1985 for zazen as taught by Taisen Deshimaru Roshi and current Dojo rented in 1991. Zazen sessions Tuesday 7.30am, Wednesday 7.30pm, Thursday 7.30pm, Saturday 6pm and first Sunday of the month 9am. Sesshins possible some weekends at the Dojo.

Founder/Guru	Taisen Deshimaru
Teachers	Visiting: Roland Rech Sensei
Opening times	See session times above

Residents	No
Festivals	Contact Dojo
Facilities	45m^2 meditation hall
Accommodation	No
Food	No
Booking	By phone
Fees	10 DM per session
Languages	German, English and French
Expected behaviour	According to the rules of a Zen Dojo
How to get there	Ten minutes from central bus station

Buddhistisches Zentrum Essen (Friends of the Western Buddhist Order)
Herkulesstrasse 13a
45127 Essen
Tel: +49 (0)201 230155
Fax: +49 (0)201 230050

City centre. FWBO in Germany since 1983. Essen centre opened in 1988 and renovated in 1995 when shrine room was extended and an over-lifesize rupa of Amitabha made by a member of the Order was installed.

Friends of the Western Buddhist Order (FWBO) was established in 1976 in Britain by a London-born Buddhist monk, Sangharakshita. It draws from all the main traditions of Buddhism, not with an attitude of eclecticism, but to take what is useful according to the spiritual needs of Westerners today. Each centre is autonomous, but linked by common practice and friendship between Order members.

Events include Introductory Evenings on Thursday at 7pm and Introductory days and weekends. Iyengar Yoga classes, study days, family days. Retreats are held regularly at rural centres in the Sauerland and other places for single or mixed sexes.

Founder/Guru	Sangharakshita
Teachers	Members of the FWBO and Sangharakshita
Opening times	All day – best to arrange beforehand
Residents	Seven FWBO members on site and five associated residential communites

Festivals	Wesak, Dharachakrapravartana, Sangha Day, Parinirvana Day, Padmasambhava Day, FWBO Day
Facilities	Shrine room, library, study room, bookshop and tape library
Accommodation	At rural retreat centres only
Food	Tea at courses in Essen, full-board and lodging for retreats – vegetarian or vegan
Booking	Not for Introductory Evening on Thursday, deposit needed for others
Fees	Approximately: evening events 12 DM; six-week evening courses 100 DM. Retreats according to net income
Languages	German, English and Dutch
Expected behaviour	Nothing special
How to get there	From Essen central railway station, walk down Hollestr and Herkulestrasse is ten minutes walk on the left hand side

Torweg (Zen – Kanzeon Sangha)
Hauptstrasse 6
50181 Bedburg-Altkaster
Tel: +49 (0)2272 83434
Fax: +49 (0)2272 82501

Retreat centre for **Kanzeon Sangha** which is based in Düsseldorf (see separate entry on p230) – contact should be through Düsseldorf centre. Old farmhouse in the centre of an ancient small city. Close to Köln and Düsseldorf.

Founder/Guru	Genpo Merzel Sensei
Teachers	Visiting teachers: Genpo Merzel Sensei, Tenkei Coppens Sensei, Nico Tydeman Roshi and others
Opening times	Only for sesshins
Residents	One monk and ten lay people
Festivals	Contact Kanzeon Sangha
Facilities	Large Zendo
Accommodation	Sleeping in Zendo during sesshins

Food	Three vegetarian meals a day during sesshins
Booking	In advance through **Kanzeon Sangha** in Düsseldorf (see separate entry)
Fees	Course fees include full-board – see programme for details
Languages	German and English
Expected behaviour	Usual sesshin rules
How to get there	Details given after registration

Buddhayana Zentrum (Theravada – Myanmar)
Meisenweg 11
51503 Rösrath
Tel: +49 (0)2205 81941

Monastic meditation and study centre. Based on approach outlined by the Myanmar Meditation Master H.H. Mahasi Sayadaw, but draws inspiration from other Buddhist traditions also. Main Buddhayana Centres are **Buddhayana Vihara** and **Ehipassiko Buddhist Monastery** in The Netherlands (see separate entries on pp293 and 295).

Offers a monthly programme of meditation and study.

The Buddhayana centres publish *Buddhayana Quarterly* in English and *Buddhayana Zeitung* in German.

Founder/Guru	Venerable Dhammawiranatha Thera
Teachers	Venerable Dhammawiranatha Thera visits
Opening times	Contact centre for programme
Residents	Four lay people
Festivals	Wesak
Facilities	Shrine room, library and study room
Accommodation	Contact centre
Food	Contact centre
Booking	Contact centre
Fees	Contact centre
Languages	German and English
Expected behaviour	Contact centre
How to get there	Contact centre

Mahamudra Retreat Zentrum (Tibetan – Karma Kagyu)
Auf dem Kuppen 7
51570 Windeck-Halscheid
Tel: +49 (0)2292 7438 and +49 (0)2292 6689
Fax: +49 (0)2292 6327

Building is a former school in the countryside, 300m from the village in a hilly area with forests and meadows at 300m altitude. Founded in 1986 when eighteen people did a three-year retreat under the guidance of Lama Gendun Rinpoche. Since 1990 a centre for short group and individual retreats and study courses. Open to all schools of Buddhism.

Retreats last between two and ten days and topics include Ngondro, Shambhala, Chenrezig, Longchen, Lodjong practice, children's weekends, Gonkar and Nyung-Neh.

Suitable for groups who want to do slightly longer retreats. People usually find it easy to settle into the centre.

Three programmes are published per year.

Founder/Guru	Lama Gedun Rinpoche, but the centre is not now associated with him
Teachers	Visting Tibetan and Western teachers
Opening times	Always open but make an appointment
Residents	Two lay people
Festivals	Sometimes in the context of a retreat
Facilities	48m^2 shrine room, small library with study room
Accommodation	14–6 rooms with 20–30 beds, in single, double and treble rooms. 40 DM per day including food
Food	Three vegetarian meals per day
Booking	In writing with 100 DM deposit
Fees	Variable, but weekend retreat around 80-90 DM; one week retreat 280 DM full board plus 100–200 DM course fee
Languages	German and English
Expected behaviour	To follow house rules – be cooperative, share in the work and not disturb others
How to get there	Phone for details

Drikung Sherab Migched Ling (Tibetan – Drikung Kagyu)
Zentrum für Tibetischen Buddhismus e.V.
Rütscherstrasse 205
52070 Aachen
Tel: +49 (0)241 154422

Old house on a little hill on the edge of the city with a big garden.
Founded in 1982 and moved to current location in 1991.

Two regular meditations a week, one for beginners and one for
more advanced practitioners. Weekend courses twice a year.
Tibetan teachers visit 4–6 times a year. 3–4 times a year there are
weeks or weekends for individual practice.

Once or twice a year, courses and consultations on Tibetan
medicine with Tibetan doctors are offered.

Home of the Drikung Kagyu Dharma Text Publication which
coordinates translation and publishing of Dharma texts (mainly
Drikung Kagyu) for German speaking countries.

Founder/Guru	Venerable Ayang Rinpoche
Teachers	Various Tibetan teachers visit
Opening times	No regular opening times
Residents	A nun who is president of the centre
Festivals	Tsog Pujas on full moons
Facilities	Shrine room and library
Accommodation	Only during courses, dormitory style at 10 DM per night
Food	Only during courses, three vegetarian meals a day at 25 DM per day
Booking	At least two weeks in advance
Fees	Contact centre
Languages	German and English
Expected behaviour	No alcohol or smoking in the house and help with house work
How to get there	Bus or car to the Pouttor (old town gate), take Roermonder Strasse and the first street on the right is Rütscherstrasse

Mokusho Zendo (Zen – Soto)
Schloß Wachendorf
53894 Mechernich-Wachendorf
Tel: +49 (0)2256 850

Founded in 1986 under the same roof as a Tibetan centre –
Kamalashila.

Zen practice every Thursday at 7pm and Sunday at 9am, comprising Zazen (sitting meditation), Kinhin (walking meditation)
and Kusen (learning) and ends with a short ceremony (tea drink-
ing on Sunday). Sitting meditation on Tuesday at 6pm. Beginners
should arrive fifteen minutes before the session starts. Regular
sesshins of one, three or four days.

Practitioners from any religious background who are willing to
accept the rules of the Zendo are welcome to join in the practices.

Founder/Guru	Taiku – a Zen monk
Teachers	Resident: Taiku and visiting Sekkei Harada Roshi
Opening times	See session times above
Residents	No
Festivals	Yes
Facilities	Dojo
Accommodation	Check with Zendo
Food	Vegetarian during sesshins
Booking	Contact Zendo
Fees	Contact Zendo
Languages	German
Expected behaviour	Contact Zendo
How to get there	Near Bad Münstreifel

> Without our familiar props, we are faced with just ourselves, a
> person we do not know, an unnerving stranger with whom we
> have been living all the time but we never really wanted to
> meet. Isn't that why we have tried to fill every moment of time
> with noise and activity, however boring or trivial, to ensure that
> we are never left in silence with this stranger on our own?
> – Sogyal Rinpoche, *The Tibetan Book of Living and Dying*

Waldhaus am Laacher See (Various)
Heimschule 1
Postfach 25
56643 Nickenich
Tel: +49 (0)2636 33 44
Fax: +49 (0)2636 22 59

Set in beautiful countryside near the Laacher lake, with garden and well. The nearest town is 1km away. Part of 'Buddhismus in Westen'.
Morning and evening meditation daily. Between thirty and forty courses of various length run throughout the year. Subjects include Buddhist meditations including Vipassana, Satipatthana, Zen and Vajrayana, bodywork including Yoga, Tai Chi and Kum Nye, healing and therapy including Qi Gong, Reiki and Naikan, art and creativity. Among the visiting teachers are Thich Nhat Hanh.

Founder/Guru	Dr Paul Köppler
Teachers	Resident: Dr Paul Köppler and many visiting teachers from appropriate disciplines
Opening times	Contact centre
Residents	About four lay people
Festivals	Contact centre
Facilities	Contact centre
Accommodation	Single, double, three- and four-bed rooms. Approx 40 DM per night
Food	Vegetarian wholefood included in accommodation costs
Booking ·	Contact centre
Fees	Various
Languages	German and English
Expected behaviour	Be aware, mindful. No smoking or drinking in house or grounds
How to get there	By train via Bonn-Andernoch

Shambhala Studiengruppe Frankfurt (Tibetan – Kagyu & Nyingma)
Schulstrasse 28
60594 Frankfurt
Tel: +49 (0)69 611 758 or +49 (0)69 635840

Founded in 1983. Part of Shambhala International (see *Schools of Buddhism*).

Shambhala offer three paths: The Shambhala Training (or Sacred Path of the Warrior) which is a non-denominational systematic training in meditation as a way to secular enlightenment; The Vajradhatu Gate which is a programme of Buddhist teaching and practice; and The Nalanda Gate which embraces all other cultural activities such as the Japanese art of archery, ikebana (Japanese flower arranging) and calligraphy.

Introductory evening of the first Wednesday of every month. Weekly meditation and study times as opening times below. Study courses for beginners and more advanced students. Nyinthun day courses once a month on Sundays. Intensive training seminars and weekend events.

Founder/Guru	Chogyam Trungpa Rinpoche
Teachers	Contact centre
Opening times	Wednesday 8–9.30pm and Sunday 6–9pm, plus event times
Residents	Not known
Festivals	Contact centre
Facilities	Shrine room
Accommodation	During events, private accommodation is possible at no cost
Food	No
Booking	Contact centre
Fees	Contact centre
Languages	German
Expected behaviour	Contact centre
How to get there	Contact centre

Zen Dojo Darmstadt (Zen – Soto – Association Zen Internationale)
Kirchstrasse 4
64283 Darmstadt
Tel: +49 (0) 6151 719355

Set in an apartment in the city. Founded in 1977 by disciples of Taisan Deshimaru.

Zazen practised on a traditional Zafu (cushion). For zazen with ceremony Tuesdays and Thursdays 8pm; Sunday 10am. Sutra chanting. Newcomers should arrive half an hour before start for instruction. One day sesshins held twice a year. Longer sesshins held in the temple, **Mokushozan Jakkoji** in Schönböken (see separate entry on p220). Two study weeks in spring.

Founder/Guru	Taisan Deshimaru
Teachers	Visiting: Narita Roshi from Japan
Opening times	See Zazen times above
Residents	No
Festivals	Check with Dojo
Facilities	Dojo
Accommodation	Possible only on a private basis
Food	Not regularly, sometimes breakfast in a private home after Zazen on Sunday
Booking	Check with Dojo
Fees	Check with Dojo
Expected behaviour	Check with Dojo
How to get there	Contact centre

Oekumenisches Zentrum (Zen – Ecumenical)
für Meditation and Begegnung
Neumühle
66693 Mettlach-Tünsdorf
Tel: +49 (0)(0)6868 1215
Fax: +49 (0)(0)6868 1270

Founded in 1975 by a Christian priest and his family as a centre that crosses the boundaries of different religions and includes Christian and Buddhist practices. Follows the inspiration of Pater Enomiya Lassalle and Graf Dürkheim.

Several buildings in own grounds in a beautiful setting which is quiet and peaceful. A very wide range of events of varying lengths including Zen, Vipassana, meditation and Bible study, meditation and Gestalt Work, Yoga, Shiatsu, Feldenkrais, special groups for parents and children and for teenagers. Also a publishing house.

Founder/Guru	Dr. theol. Willi Massa and Eleonore

	Gottfried Massa
Teachers	German and Japanese teachers of different disciplines
Opening times	All year. Office hours: Monday to Friday 8.30am–3pm
Residents	Christian priest and a Christian family
Festivals	Contact centre
Facilities	Meditation rooms, library, sauna
Accommodation	Single, double and treble rooms, dormitory – costs from 45–93 DM
Food	Vegetarian wholefood
Booking	Contact centre
Fees	Depends on event
Languages	German, some English
Expected behaviour	No smoking or drugs, open to help in the kitchen or garden
How to get there	By train to Saarbrücken, then bus

Karma Chang Chub Cho Phel Ling (Tibetan – Karma Kagyu)
(KCL-Heidelberg)
Friedensstrasse 20
69121 Heidelberg (Handschuhsheim)
Tel: +49 (0)6221 41 04 95
Fax: +49 (0)6221 47 32 85

Brick building with large red gate in a small, old, beautiful village with a castle, park and churches. Over ten years ago, the Karma Kagyu Trust, to which the centre is connected, received a large donation to buy the house which they renovated.

Regular weekly programme and one-day and weekend courses. Introductory events include talks on Buddhism, Shine weekends, Sangha evenings on Fridays, meetings once a month with videos on Buddhism and Tibetan language courses. Other activities include Chenrezig, Tara and Sangye Menla Pujas, Tibetan prayers and Guru Yoga.

The centre is led by three-year retreatants and is dedicated to H.H. the 17th Karmapa Urgyen Thrinley Dorje.

Founder/Guru	H.H. the 17th Karmapa Urgyen Thrinley

	Dorje
Teachers	Resident: L. Chonyi Dorothea and two other three-year retreatants plus visiting teachers
Opening times	Phone centre beforehand outside programme times
Residents	Four lay people
Festivals	Milarepa Tsog Puja on full moons
Facilities	Shrine room, library and study room / lounge for guests
Accommodation	Large guestroom with sleeping mats – 10 DM per night
Food	No
Booking	Not usually necessary
Fees	Ask for their programme
Languages	German, English and some French
Expected behaviour	To offer help with daily chores
How to get there	By train: from Heidelberg station, take tram no. 1 and OEG. By car: motorway no. 5, exit Dossenheim, take the direction of Heidelberg until you come to Handschuhsheim. Friedensstrasse is 700m on the left

Arya Maitreya Mandala Vajrayana Order (Tibetan)
Rose Kasper – Order Secretary
Weißdornweg 4
72076 Tübingen
Tel: +49 (0)7071 63280

Order is based on the guru-chela relationship. Founded 1933 in Darjeeling, India, by Lama Anagarika Govinda after the death of his guru, Tomo Geshe Rinpoche, and in his memory. It draws on this guru's teachings of the possibility of a Buddhism which transcends the differences of the different schools and concentrates on the essence of the Buddhist teachings, without unnecessary baggage of outdated thinking or of cultural influences which interfere with his vision of East and West joining in the Dharma for the good of all mankind. Set up to serve Bodhisattva ideal for the service of all sentient beings. Tibetan Buddhism is used as a starting point.

Students of the school need to have a good grounding in Buddhist teachings before they move into practice. Open for all over fourteen years old who have a basic understanding of Buddhism, feel inspired by the aims of this school and are willing to live by the Five Precepts of a practising Buddhist as an upasaka or upasika. Upasakas may attend all events such as meditations and teachings seminars, exercises of the Order and Puja celebrations. After one year membership, it is then possible to become a candidate to be an Order member.

Dharma studies in seminars, week of exercises. Open and individual guidance.

Contact addresses in Germany, England, Sweden and Singapore.

Various publications available.

Founder/Guru	Lama Anagarika Govinda
Teachers	Various
Opening times	Not applicable
Residents	Not applicable
Festivals	Maitreya ceremony and Vesakh
Facilities	Every member has a shrine room; library in main centre
Accommodation	In private or rented rooms
Food	Contact centre
Booking	By telephone
Fees	Contact centre
Languages	German and English possible
Expected behaviour	Five Precepts
How to get there	Contact Secretary

> Our ideas about what holiness is, that it is pious, bland, and meek, may make us blind to the dynamic and sometimes exuberantly playful manifestation of the enlightened mind.
>
> – Sogyal Rinpoche, *The Tibetan Book of Living and Dying*

Zen Institut Deutschland (Zen – Rinzai – International Zen Institute of America)

Striehweg 32
72820 Sonnenbühl
Tel: +49 (0)49 7128 784

Organises events at different locations in Germany, The Netherlands, Spain and the USA. A European centre is planned.
Offers Zen training, sutra classes, public lectures and Buddhist ceremonies. Also a training programme for meditation leaders or Zen teachers. Regional meditation groups – contact this address for more details.

Founder/Guru	Venerable Gesshin Myoko Prabhasad-harma Roshi
Teachers	Various
Opening times	Contact centre for programme
Residents	No
Festivals	Contact Centre
Facilities	Not applicable
Accommodation	No
Food	No
Booking	See programme
Fees	From 100–550 DM depending on length of course
Languages	German and English
Expected behaviour	Contact centre
How to get there	Various locations

Yogacara (Theravada, Zen and Tibetan)
Buddhistische Zentrum für geistige Entfaltung und Meditation
Hindenburgstrasse 54
74924 Neckarbischofsheim
Tel & Fax: +49 (0)(0)07263 6704

Founded in 1979 by Master Pema Dorje near the small town of Neckarbischofsheim halfway between Heidelberg and Heilbronn with a retreat centre in Austria. The retreat centre is in the Tirol 20km east of Innsbruck, 1200m above sea level in a mountain cabin.
Tea hour every Sunday 4–6pm for information and talk with

Master Pema Dorje. Weekend groups on different topics about once a month. A one-year course on Wednesday evenings and a four-year teacher training course. Regular retreats in the Tirol, individual retreats and individual guidance and tuition with Master Pema Dorje.

Master Pema Dorje is a German Buddhist. Studied philosophy, psychology and education. Studied Buddhism under various masters. Author of two books on Buddhism.

Founder/Guru	Master Pema Dorje
Teachers	Resident: Master Pema Dorje, visiting Lama Yeshe Tharchin and Zen priest H.R. Genpo Döring
Opening times	All year round apart from retreat times in May / June, August and October
Residents	None
Festivals	Tara Festival after Tara Retreat between New Year and Christmas
Facilities	Meditation room, large reception and tea room, retreat room, beautiful garden with shrine
Accommodation	Double rooms
Food	Wholefood vegetarian
Booking	In writing with deposit
Fees	Check with centre
Languages	German
Expected behaviour	Ask centre
How to get there	Ask centre

Buddhistisches Zentrum Freiburg der Karma Kagyu Linie
(Tibetan – Karma Kagyu)
Stadtstrasse 7
79104 Freiburg
Tel: +49 (0)761 22880
Fax: +49 (0)761 36553

One hundred-year-old house near an old cemetery in a quiet part of town. Founded in late 1970s. Group of sixteen people have lived together as a Buddhist community since 1990.

Activities include Three Light Meditation, Loving Eyes Meditation and Phowa practice. Lecture for beginners on the first Wednesday of each month. Visitors are welcome to help with work in the centre – cooking, building, etc.

Founder/Guru	Lama Ole Nyadahl
Teachers	Visiting teachers
Opening times	No fixed times
Residents	Twelve lay people
Festivals	Tibetan New Year and other festivals like birthdays
Facilities	20m^2 shrine room, library, study room and community room
Accommodation	Ask centre
Food	Southern German cuisine
Booking	Phone the day before arrival
Fees	Check with centre
Expected behaviour	Nothing special
How to get there	In the Herdern part of town

Kannon-Do (Zen – Rinzai)
Rinzai-Zen Vereinigung
Gilgenmatten 9
79114 Freiburg
Tel: +49 (0)761 41607

Bungalow with garden. Rather traditional practice of Rinzai Zen. Founded 1989 and Freiburg centre opened in 1990.

Practices include zazen, Buddhist ceremonies, study of Buddhist texts and Qi Gong. Weekly zazen sessions Tuesdays 8–9.30pm and Thursdays 7–9.30pm and for members Monday to Friday 6.30–7.30pm. Monthly sessions with Agetsu Osho on Sundays 10am–1pm. Newcomers receive individual tuition.

Longer practices are led by Agetsu Osho. 3–5-day Rohatsu sesshins are held regularly and use a traditional timetable similar to that in Japanese monasteries starting at 4.30am each day and finishing at 9.30pm.

Programme produced annually.

Founder/Guru	Agetsu Kudo Osho (Mrs Agetsu Agatha Wydler Haduch)
Teachers	Agetsu Osho visits from Zurich, Switzerland
Opening times	See session times above
Residents	One lay person
Festivals	Kannon-Day in September
Facilities	Zendo, small library and meeting room
Accommodation	During sesshins only in Zendo at 15 DM per night
Food	Vegetarian food during sesshins
Booking	By phone
Fees	For example: three-day sesshin 150 DM members, 190 DM non-members
Languages	German
Expected behaviour	Traditional Rinzai Zen rules
How to get there	Phone for details

Mamaki Zentrum (Tibetan – Gelug – New Kadampa Tradition)
Kandelstrasse 1
79224 Umkirch
Tel & Fax: +49 (0)7665 8648

Founded in 1995.

The New Kadampa Tradition (NKT) is a Mahayana Buddhist tradition founded by Geshe Kelsang Gyatso, a Tibetan Buddhist Master resident in the UK since 1977. Its main purpose is to preserve and promote the essence of Buddha's teachings in a form that is suited to the modern world and way of life.

Offers weekly public talks and guided meditations. Also holds meditations and talks at Im Dialog, Belfortstrasse 31, Freiburg at 7pm on Mondays. Subjects include Buddhist Life, Being a Bodhisattva and A Realistic Attitude to Death.

All NKT centres form a family spiritually following the same direction and its core is the Three Study Programmes. Of these, this centre offers the Foundation Programme to deepen understanding and experience of Buddhism through systematic study of five of Geshe Kelsang's books. It takes about four years to complete.

Founder/Guru	Geshe Kelsang Gyatso Rinpoche
Teachers	Resident: Gen Kelsang Nyima and visiting teachers
Opening times	Contact centre for details
Residents	Two monks and one lay person
Festivals	Ask for details
Facilities	Shrine room
Accommodation	No
Food	No
Booking	Contact centre
Fees	Contact centre
Languages	German and English
Expected behaviour	No special rules
How to get there	From Paduallee, bus 31/32 to Im Brünneleacker and then five minutes walk

Kagyu Benchen Ling (Tibetan – Kagyu)
Mühlematt 5
79682 Todtmoos-Au
Tel: +49 (0)7674 1011
Fax: +49 (0)7674 1082

Old renovated Black Forest house deep in the Black Forest with forest, streams, hills and valleys. Development of loving kindness and compassion. Founded in 1989 and inaurgurated by Sangye Nyenga Rinpoche in 1993. Centre founded from voluntary contributions of time and money and has been operating since 1994. Still expanding rapidly.

Daily activities are Tara Puja at 7am, Shine meditation and Chenrezig Puja at 8pm. Retreats and courses are generally open to people at all levels of experience. Classes in Tibetan language and study groups. The Trust organises an Annual Kagyu Summer School which is held elsewhere in Europe.

Founder/Guru	Lama Chime Rinpoche
Teachers	Visiting Tibetan teachers mainly from the Kagyu and Nyingma traditions
Opening times	7am to 10pm
Residents	Two lay people

Festivals	Contact centre
Facilities	Shrine room, library, study room, meeting room and dining hall
Accommodation	In house 200m from temple. Two- and three-bed rooms 20 DM per night, single 30 DM per night
Food	Breakfast, lunch and supper – ordinary food at 15 DM per day
Booking	Contact Secretary for details
Fees	Contact centre
Languages	German, English and some French
Expected behaviour	To attend morning and evening puja, show respect for the centre, for other visitors and for the local environment and its inhabitants and to help in kitchen
How to get there	Bus to Todtmoos from Freiburg railway station or train to Bad Säckingen from Basel, then bus to Todtmoos-Au

Rütte – Existential-psychologische Bildungs- und Begegnungsstätte Schule für Initiatische Therapie Todtmoos-Rütte (Zen)
Graf-Dürckheim-Weg 12
79862 Todtmoos-Rütte
Tel: +49 (0)7674 350

In the southern Black Forest at an altitude of 1000m. The founders started their work in the late Forties and founded their school in 1950. He is one of the main exponents in Germany and Western Europe for Zen meditation which they integrated into their Initiatory Therapy, which draws on Analytical psychology of C.G. Jung and Erich Neumann, and incorporates the insights and practice of Zen Buddhism, occidental Mysticism, Gestalt psychology and its precursors. Not a Buddhist centre, so not listed under *Schools* – please contact them direct for more information.

Visitors are those interested in transpersonal psychology and psychotherapy. Introductory sessions about three times a year costing 980 DM. Individual and group work using an wide range of esoteric, psychological and artistic methods. Courses, seminars and lectures. Programme of events published twice a year.

Associated centres: **Metafor** (see separate entry on p256) and **Benediktshof Münster**, Mauritz-Lindenweg 63, 48145 Münster, *Tel:* +49 (0)251 341 52, *Fax:* +49 (0)251 341 53.

Founder/Guru	Graf Dürckheim and Maria Hippius Gräfin Dürckheim
Teachers	Contact centre
Opening times	Secretariat Monday to Friday 10am–12 noon, 2pm–4pm
Residents	Contact centre
Festivals	No
Facilities	Zendo
Accommodation	Either in their guest house or in local farmhouses
Food	Yes
Booking	Initially send handwritten letter giving motivation and essential biographical information.
Fees	Weekly cost of 900–1300 DM for full board and lodging, private and group tuition
Languages	German, English and French
Expected behaviour	Contact centre
How to get there	Bus or taxi from Freiburg (50km), Basel (50km) and Bad Säckingen (30km)

The Way is perfect like a vast space
Where nothing is lacking and nothing is in excess.
Indeed, it is due to our choosing to accept or reject
that we do not see the true nature of things.

– Sengstan, *Hsin Hsin Ming*

Üma Zentrum für Buddhismus (Tibetan – Gelug – New Kadampa Tradition)
Reitmorstrasse 9
80538 München
Tel & Fax: +49 (0)89 221915
e-mail: 101373.270@compuserve.com

Town house near park. At time of writing looking for larger premises to house resident community. Large percentage of visitors are women.

Pujas held daily, meditations on Thursday evenings, teachings Tuesday evenings, weekly study programmes.

The New Kadampa Tradition (NKT) is a Mahayana Buddhist tradition founded by Geshe Kelsang Gyatso, a Tibetan Buddhist Master resident in the UK since 1977. Its main purpose is to preserve and promote the essence of Buddha's teachings in a form that is suited to the modern world and way of life.

All NKT centres form a family spiritually following the same direction. Its core is the Three Study Programmes, of which, this centre offers:

• The General Programme provides a basic introduction to Buddhist view, meditation and action in a form that is suitable for beginners. It also includes advanced teachings and practices of both Sutra and Tantra.

• The Foundation Programme to deepen understanding and experience of Buddhism through systematic study of five of Geshe Kelsang's books. This programme takes about four years to complete.

• The Teacher Training Programme is designed for people who wish to train as authentic Dharma Teachers. This seven-year programme involves studying twelve of Geshe Kelsang's books, observing certain commitments with regard to behaviour and way of life, and completing a number of retreats.

Retreats throughout the year including winter retreat for whole of January.

Spring and Summer Festivals with Geshe Kelsang Gyatso at **Manjushri** centre in Cumbria, England (see p74).

Founder/Guru	Venerable Geshe Kelsang Gyatso Rinpoche
Teachers	Resident: Gen Kelsang Legden and others visit
Opening times	At all times
Residents	One monk, and plans for 4–6 lay people
Festivals	Losar, Buddha's Enlightenment Day, Dharmachakra Day, Je Tsongkhapa Day, Tsog Days, Buddha's Return from Heaven Day

Facilities	Shrine room, library, study room
Accommodation	Contact centre
Food	Contact centre
Booking	1–2 weeks in advance with 10% deposit
Fees	Contact centre
Languages	German and English
Expected behaviour	Five Precepts, no meat, no TV
How to get there	München Lehel, near Friedensengel

Zen Zentrum (Zen – Soto – Association Zen Internationale)
c/o Karin Furtwängler
Emil-Riedel-Strasse 6
80538 München
Tel: +49 (0)89 22 16 26

In the city. Founded in 1977 for the practice of zazen.
Zazen meditation Wednesday and Sunday 6.30–8pm.
Newcomers should arrive twenty minutes before the session
starts.

Founder/Guru	Taisen Deshimaru Roshi
Teachers	Karin Furtwängler and Julius Ecke and visiting teachers from the AZI
Opening times	See session times
Residents	No
Festivals	Will be announced
Facilities	Dojo
Accommodation	Contact centre
Food	Contact centre
Booking	Contact centre
Fees	Contact centre
Languages	German, English and French
Expected behaviour	Contact centre
How to get there	Tram 20 from central station to Paradies-strasse

Buddha-Haus Stadtzentrum (Theravada)
Klarastrasse 4
80636 München
Tel: +49 (0)89 1238868
Fax: +49 (0)8376 592

Run by **Buddha-Haus** in Oy-Mittelberg (see separate entry p264).
Events every day. Topics such as meditation course with Ayya
Khema on video, study and practice, meditation for beginners,
Yoga and meditation, weekend seminars, meditation days.

Founder/Guru	Ayya Khema
Teachers	Venerable Ayya Khema and visiting teachers of all Buddhist traditions
Opening times	According to programme of events
Residents	Contact centre
Festivals	Vesakh
Facilities	Meditation room and shop
Accommodation	Contact centre
Food	Contact centre
Booking	Contact centre
Fees	Contact centre
Languages	Teaching mostly in German, English is spoken
Expected behaviour	Five Precepts
How to get there	Take underground line U1 to Maillinger Strasse

Buddhistische Gesellschaft München (All, but mainly
Theravada and Zen)
c/o Deutsche Buddistische Unione
Amalienstrasse 71
80799 München
Tel: +49 (0)(0)89 280104 or 3591525
Fax: +49 (0)(0)89 281053

City centre premises shared with the DBU (German Buddhist
Union) and other Buddhist groups. Loose group has existed since
1910 and registered in 1963. Open to all Buddhist opinions and

traditions.

Meetings Mondays and Wednesdays 7–9pm for meditation, Dhamma talks, teachings and discussions. Other practices when monks are visiting. Meetings with invited Buddhist teachers once a month at a public hall. Regular introductions to meditation and basic Dhamma instruction. Occasional one-day and weekend retreats.

Founder/Guru	Not known
Teachers	Visiting teachers
Opening times	During meetings Monday and Wednesday. DBU Secretary: Monday-Friday 10am–1pm
Residents	No
Festivals	Vesakh and occasional full moon festivals at a Nepalese pagoda in West Park
Facilities	Shrine room, library and DBU office
Accommodation	No
Food	No
Booking	Contact centre
Fees	Contact centre
Languages	German and English
Expected behaviour	Contact centre
How to get there	U-Bahn to 'Universität'

Hakuin-Zen-Gemeinschaft (Zen – Rinzai)
Werneckstrasse 29
80802 München
Tel: +49 (0)89 348 178
e-mail: 100303.1027@compuserve.com

In a quiet courtyard in the Schwabing district of München. Founded in 1988. Offers regular Zazen and lectures and seminars on Zen Buddhism. Japanese Rinzai Zen in a form suitable for Westerners and follows the Four Boddhisattvic Vows.

Mondays 7pm for beginners, Wednesdays and Fridays 7pm for beginners and more experienced students. Sessions may involve zazen and chanting of sutras or breathing exercises. If the teacher is present he can be asked questions.

Associated with **Bodaisan Shoboji Zen Institut** in

Dinkelscherben (see separate entry on p262).

Dorin Genpo Osho is a married Zen priest who trained as a monk in a Zen monastery in the Empukuji temple in Kyoto in Japan.

Founder/Guru	Dorin Genpo Osho (H.R. Döring) and Hozumi Gensho Roshi (from Japan)
Teachers	Resident: Dorin Genpo Osho and Hozumi Gensho Roshi visits
Opening times	See session times above
Residents	Dorin Genpo Osho
Festivals	Contact centre
Facilities	Dojo, shrine room, library, study room and shop
Accommodation	No
Food	No
Booking	Phone in advance
Fees	Contact centre
Languages	German and English
Expected behaviour	To follow the Dojo's guidelines and teacher's instructions and not to disturb the practice
How to get there	Five minutes from Münchener Freiheit underground station

Metafor (Zen and Tibetan)
The Integral Life School
Nikolaiplatz 1
80802 München
Tel: +49 (0)89 347533
Fax: +49 (0)89 349081

In the city centre. Founded in 1975. Affiliated to **Rütte** (see separate entry on p250).

Offer meditations, Tai Chi Chuan, Aikido, body work, therapy, weekend seminars, workshops, astrology and tarot. Chanting Tuesday evenings 8.15–10pm. Introductory sessions 5–10 times a year in the evenings. Introduction to meditation first Wednesday in the month at 7am.

Founder/Guru	Graf Dürkheim and Dr. Maria Hippius-Gräfin Dürkheim
Teachers	Resident: Dr. Norbert J. Mayer. Visiting Zen monks from Korea and Japan
Opening times	Office: Monday, Tuesday and Friday 10am–12 noon, Wednesday 3–5pm. Closed during school holidays
Residents	No
Festivals	Occasionally
Facilities	Seminar room with shrine, small library and study room
Accommodation	In hotels and pensions near the centre
Food	Snacks and drinks only
Booking	See programme
Fees	See programme
Languages	German
Expected behaviour	Quiet, helpful and to participate
How to get there	Take U-3 or U-6 from Marienplatz to Geselastrasse (one stop before Münchener Ereiheit)

Thubten Dargyie Ling (Tibetan – Rime)
Sallerweg 15
81476 Münich
Tel: +49 (0)891 755 4668
Fax: +49 (0)891 54757 / 145

A purpose-built modern building using only natural materials such as wood and stone and whose water is purified by an ioniser. Earth peace ceremony was performed by their teacher before building started. Stupa will be built in the garden. Returned from Dharamsala in India in 1990 to found centre with the blessing of their teacher and it opened in 1994. Seventeen flats occupied mostly by Buddhist practitioners so has something of the feel of a small monastery. Open to all schools of Buddhism – a Zen group also use the centre.

Daily sessions of Sadhana, prayer and ritutal. Thursday evenings Tantric self-healing practice by Lama Gangchen (incarnation of the medicine Buddha) for inner peace and freedom.

Workshops include healing and Thangka painting. Resident teacher on Lam Rim. Teachings by visiting masters. Activities for newcomers are planned.

Monthly programmes are sent out to people on their mailing list.

Founder/Guru	Geshe Gedun Sanypola
Teachers	Resident teacher and various visiting teachers
Opening times	7–10pm every evening
Residents	Eight lay people
Festivals	Contact centre
Facilities	Shrine room for 120 seats, library being built, room for massage, Reiki and Feldenkrais
Accommodation	Contact centre
Food	Tea with sometimes cake and snacks
Booking	Contact centre
Fees	According to costs of event
Languages	English, German and French
Expected behaviour	Take shoes off, be quiet and respectful, no dancing, playing games, dancing and fighting, no alcohol and don't touch the statues
How to get there	From main railway station, U5 or U4 to Odeonsplatz, then U3 to Forsteurieder-Allee. Walk down this street to Aral car station, turn left into Kriegelsteurerstrasse and Sallerweg is on the right

---

Kinzan, Ganto and Seppo were doing Zazen when Tozan came in with the tea. Kinzan shut his eyes. Tozan asked, 'Where are you going?' Kinzan replied, 'I am entering dhyana.' Tozan said, 'Dhyana has no gate; how can you enter into it?'

– Zen Sutra from *The Solitary Bird, Cuckoo of the Forest*

Jodo Shinshu Deutschland (Pure Land – Jodo Shinshu)
c/o Rev. Jotoku Thomas Moser
Edelweißstrasse 5
83435 Bad Reichenhall

Fax: +49 (0)8651 66180

In a small city about 20km from Salzburg in Austria in the south of Germany. Every two years there is a European Shin conference attended by Japanese, American, Brazilian and European Shinshu followers. The biggest Jodo Shinshu temple in Europe is in Düsseldorf (see separate entry for **EKO** on p231) and is mainly used by the 20,000 Japanese resident in that city. The German Sangha relies on the main temple in Kyoto. There are small Jodo Shinshu groups in six European cities including Berlin and Nanheim in Germany.

Hold regular services and lectures at various addresses (no fixed centre). Meditation is not as important for this Buddhist tradition as it is for others, but they do sitting meditation (Seiza) and Japanese Wasan (forms of poetry). There are introductions for newcomers and regular services held by the groups.

Founder/Guru	Shinran Shonin
Teachers	Various
Opening times	Phone for details
Residents	No
Festivals	Main Buddhist festivals and Yo-shoki (the founder's memorial day), Yotan-e (founder's birthday) and Zenman Kosho Ohtani's birthday
Facilities	No
Accommodation	No
Food	No
Booking	Phone for details
Fees	Phone for details
Languages	Phone for details
Expected behaviour	Phone for details
How to get there	Phone for details

Buddhist Centre Passau of the Karma Kagyu lineage (Tibetan – Karma Kagyu)
Löwengrube 16
84032 Passau
Tel: +49 (0)851 36750

Fax: +49 (0)851 931100
e-mail: compuserve 100605,3001

Renovated building in the old part of town. House bought ten years ago and is now one of the biggest centres in Bavaria.

Weekly meditations are Chenrezig on Tuesdays at 8.15pm, Three Lights on Thursdays at 8.15pm and Ngondro on Sundays at 6pm. Events include teachings by visiting lamas, Medicine Buddha weekend, Phowa courses, Karma Paksh weekends, Ngondro days and Karmapa days.

Retreats a few times during the year which are open to both newcomers and more experienced practioners.

Founder/Guru	Lama Ole Nydahl
Teachers	Many visiting lay teachers and Tibetan Lamas and three of residents teach
Opening times	Evenings and weekends when events are happening
Residents	Five lay people
Festivals	Contact centre
Facilities	Shrine room, library and shop for books, cassettes, pictures, videos, etc.
Accommodation	Facilities for approximately fifty people, 7 DM per night, 12 DM for breakfast
Food	Three vegetarian meals a day
Booking	A few days before the event
Fees	Contact centre
Languages	German
Expected behaviour	No dogs, no drugs
How to get there	In the Innstadt

Seminarhaus Engl (Open for all traditions)
Engl 1
84339 Unterdietfurt
Tel: +49 (0)8728 616

Converted farmhouse in Bavarian countryside. Established in 1991 to create a quiet retreat environment for all traditions. Has developed quite quickly with the help of some great teachers.

Retreats last between 3–10 days on a wide range of topics including Zen sesshins, Art of Calligraphy, Vipassana, Introduction to Zen Meditation, Tara retreats for Women, Vipassana and Movement, Who Am I (Advaita Vedanta), Hakomi and Balancing Faith with Wisdom.

Founder/Guru	Mostly inspired by Fred von Allmen
Teachers	Visiting teachers are invited from all traditions
Opening times	During retreats only
Residents	Three people
Festivals	No
Facilities	Meditation hall, yoga room, shrine room, library, study room
Accommodation	For course participants only: thirty-five beds mostly in double rooms. 50 DM per night including meals
Food	Three vegetarian meals a day
Booking	In writing at least two weeks in advance with 100 DM deposit
Fees	Varies with course and teacher
Languages	German and English
Expected behaviour	Five Precepts
How to get there	By train to Eggenfelden. Visitors can be picked up between 4 and 7pm if booked beforehand. By car – contact centre for details

Buddhayana (Open to all traditions)
Sonnehang 14
85304 Ilmmünster
Tel: +49 (0)8441 71774
Fax: +49 (0)8441 8895

Farmhouse which is currently being renovated and will be completed in 1997 or 1998. It will be a retreat centre, monastery and home for old Buddhists.

Founder/Guru	Members of centre

Teachers	No
Opening times	Monday 8–10pm
Residents	No
Festivals	Contact centre
Facilities	Contact centre
Accommodation	Contact centre
Food	Contact centre
Booking	Contact centre
Fees	Contact centre
Languages	German and some English
Expected behaviour	Contact centre
How to get there	40km north of Münich on Autobahn A8

Bodaisan Shoboji Zen Institut (Zen – Rinzai)
Burggasse 15
86424 Dinkelscherben
Tel: +49 (0)82 92 31 16
Fax: +49 (0)82 92 33 25

In the Bavarian countryside in a house on the edge of town. Large garden, many local walks, public swimming pool a few metres away. Founded in 1992 and of the Myoshinji line of Japanese Rinzai Zen. Offers an authentic Rinzai Zen in a form suitable for Europeans.

Tuesdays 7.30pm zazen for beginners, Fridays 7.30pm zazen for more experienced students. Two or three times a month there are sesshins and seminars lasting between two and seven days. Possible to live in the temple for a while. Daily zazen meditation, koan study and morning and evening chanting. Sesshins involve zazen, manual work and exercises. Topics such as sesshins for beginners, koan school and Zen and Qi Gong.

Zen seminars on zazen, Chado (tea ceremony) and ikebana (flower arranging); public lectures; open house twice a year with an introduction to zazen.

Toshiko Miyazaki teaches Chado and ikebana.

Founder/Guru	Dorin Genpo Osho (H.R. Döring) and Hozumi Gensho Roshi (from Japan)
Teachers	Resident: Dorin Genpo Osho and Toshiko

	Miyazaki. Hozumi Gensho Roshi visits
Opening times	See session times above
Residents	Dorin Genpo Osho and Toshiko Miyazaki
Festivals	Tanabata, New Year and Memorial Day
Facilities	Dojo, shrine room, rest room, garden and shop
Accommodation	For up to sixteen people
Food	Vegetarian German and Japanese cuisine
Booking	By post with payment in advance. For evening Zazen, phone in advance
Fees	Contact centre
Languages	German, English, Japanese
Expected behaviour	Follow teacher's instructions and daily schedule
How to get there	Train to Dinkelscherben, then walk straight ahead to the church which is the start of Burggasse

Altbuddhistische Gemeinde (Early Buddhism)
Buddhistisches Haus Georg Grimm
Zur Ludwigshöhe 30
86917 Utting / Ammersee
Tel: +49 (0)8806 7507

House with large grounds on the edge of the Ammer lake in the lower Alps. Oldest Buddhist centre in Europe and only one dedicated to early Buddhism. Founded 1920. Main stress on Anatta teaching of early Buddhism and on the four Brahmavihara. For serious students. Guided retreats according to individual's capacities. Regular meetings, training courses, retreats and seminars. Study undertaken individually. No fixed programme for newcomers – those sincerely interested should contact the centre for more information. Publish bimonthly magazine, *Yana*.

Founder/Guru	Founded by Dr George Grimm and Dr K Seidenstücker
Teachers	Resident: Ch. Schoenwerth and J. Hupfer-Neu
Opening times	As for events and courses

Residents	Varies – all lay people
Festivals	Vesakh, Commemoration Day and Uposatha Festival
Facilities	Shrine room, study room, library for use of vetted individuals and meditation tower
Accommodation	Only for personally known members during courses and retreats
Food	Self-catering during retreats
Booking	Written application
Fees	More information from centre
Languages	German
Expected behaviour	Strict rules including vegetarianism, abiding by the schedule during retreats and no smoking, TV or radio
How to get there	Train to Utting from Munich or Augsburg

Buddha-Haus (Theravada)
Uttenbühl 5
87466 Oy-Mittelberg 3
Tel: +49 (0)83 76 502
Fax: +49 (0)83 76 592

In a rural environment in the foothills of the Alps at 850m altitude. Founded in 1989.

Meditation courses for beginners. Meditation courses between one and seven days long on such topics as Sense and Meaning in Buddhist Teaching, Deepening Meditation Practice, Eight-fold Meditation and Yoga, Happiness and Sorrow in Buddhism (for Women). Offers individual retreats with the possibility of interviews with Ayya Khema.

Run **Buddha-Haus Stadtzentrum** in Münich (see separate entry on p254) and a forest monastery is being established at the time of writing. Meditation groups throughout Germany and in Austria, Switzerland, The Netherlands and England – contact centre for details.

Publish newsletter *Buddha-Haus Mitteilungsblatt*. Small publishing house, Dhana Verlag, for books in German and English – catalogue available on request. Cassettes and videos available.

Founder/Guru	Venerable Ayya Khema
Teachers	Venerable Ayya Khema and visiting teachers of all Buddhist traditions
Opening times	According to programme of events
Residents	One monk and four lay people
Festivals	Vesakh
Facilities	Shrine room, library and study room, garden with stupa
Accommodation	During meditation courses only: single and double rooms or dormitory
Food	Vegetarian meals during meditation courses
Booking	Details and booking form in programme. Book early to ensure a place
Fees	About 380 DM for a four-day course fullboard
Languages	Teaching mostly in German, English is spoken
Expected behaviour	Five Precepts
How to get there	Details in programme

Mahakala Ashram (Tibetan)
Zum Rebösch 26
88662 Überlingen
Tel: +49 (0)7551 3919
Fax: +49 (0)7551 3822
e-mail: 075513822-1@T-ONLINE.DE

In a small village outside Überlingen high above the Bodensee. A big wooden house with wonderful views across the lake. Study and meditation centre for Sutra, Yoga and Tantra founded in 1993 to support the development of Buddhism in the West. Meditation and religious training are based on a thorough philosophical study and understanding. External forms of practice are kept simple and made accessible to Westerners.

Weekly Yoga and meditation evening, Introduction to Buddhism philosophy classes for newcomers and more advanced students. Go Club for players of the Japanese game of Go. Group retreats three or four times a year for advanced meditators.

Individual retreatants can either make their own schedule or have one individually tailored on request. Pujas held daily during retreat times.

Lilavajra worked as a psychologist in Hungary and studied Buddhism since 1979. Vajramala was born into a Buddhist family and studied with, among others, Lama Anagarika Govinda.

Founder/Guru	Lilavajra and Vajramala
Teachers	Resident: founders and other visiting
Opening times	Visit only after registration. Office hours: Monday to Thursday 9am–12 noon and Monday-Wednesday 5.30–6.30pm. Closed during retreats
Residents	No
Festivals	Vesakh and Maitreya (December)
Facilities	Shrine room, study room and Dharma shop
Accommodation	Single room 50 DM, double 30 DM, plus tax
Food	Self-catering
Booking	Accommodation at least thirty days ahead. Courses book ahead and prepay. Retreats, thirty days in advance. Single sessions by ticket
Fees	Courses are 200 DM per semester or 20 DM per session. Retreats approximately 50 DM per day plus accommodation
Languages	German, English, Hungarian
Expected behaviour	No smoking, drugs or alcohol. Avoid sexual contact or eating meat while staying. Respect other meditators
How to get there	Train via Ulm or Lindau; car via Bodensee

Words!
The way is beyond language,
for in it there is
no yesterday
no tomorrow
no today.

– Sengstan, *Hsin Hsin Ming*

Chodzong Buddhistisches Zentrum (Tibetan – Gelug)
Hauptstrasse 19
91474 Langenfeld
Tel: +49 (0)9164 320
Fax: +49 (0)9164 1494

House bought in 1986.
Meditations daily at 7am and 7.15pm. Ask about puja times.
Run courses and seminars on such topics as Avalokitesvara, Lam
Rim, Aspects of Healing and Lojong. Individual retreats possible.
Headquarters for associated centres and groups in Germany.
Publish a magazine *Chökor – Tibetischer Buddhismus im Westen*
giving programme details for all their centres.

Founder/Guru	Spiritual Director: Dagyab Kyabgon Rinpoche
Teachers	Visiting teachers
Opening times	Contact centre
Residents	Eight people
Festivals	Contact centre
Facilities	Contact centre
Accommodation	Single rooms and dormitory or information given for accommodation in the area
Food	Yes
Booking	At least one week before with deposit
Fees	About 186 DM full-board for two-day course
Languages	German
Expected behaviour	Contact centre and help in the kitchen
How to get there	Train to Neustadt / Aisch. With two days' notice, they will pick you up from the station

This is the quintessence of wisdom: not to kill anything.

– Sutra Kritanga

HUNGARY

Ri-me Tenzin Sedrup Ling, Rime Buddhista Centrum (Tibetan – non-sectarian)
1221 Budapest
Gerinc u. 109, 1/4
Tel: +36 (0)1 226 4077
Fax: +36 (0)1 142 2849

In a block of flats. Contact centre for programme and further information.

Founder/Guru	Contact centre
Teachers	Contact centre
Opening times	Contact centre
Residents	Contact centre
Festivals	Contact centre
Facilities	Contact centre
Accommodation	No
Food	No
Booking	Contact centre
Fees	Contact centre
Languages	Hungarian, English, Tibetan
Expected behaviour	Contact centre
How to get there	Contact centre

Tan Kapuja – The Gate of Dharma Buddhist College (Non-sectarian)
1098 Budapest
Börzsöny u. 11
Tel: +36 (0) 1 280 6712
Fax: +36 (0) 1 280 6714

Grey building surrounded by blocks of flats on a housing estate. Founded 1991. College for·people interested in Eastern philosophies. 120 full-time students in 1996, not all Buddhists, but often open-minded young people looking for different ways of living and thinking. Non-missionary. Aim to establish a free spiritual community where those with different beliefs and preferences inspire each other. Experimental in nature and very badly financed (mostly through government support), but spiritually very rich and exciting.

Offers four-year full-time higher education courses in Buddhist and Buddhism-related studies for Hungarian students of all ages. Aims to encompass all Buddhist traditons in order to grasp that 'single taste' behind the manifold manifestations of doctrine which was repeatedly emphasised by the Buddha as the only ultimately valid instruction. Students encouraged to be open-minded to different approaches and to combine assiduous study of traditional doctrines with free intellectual probing into their truth. Students can specialise in: comparative religion and philosophy; translation from Eastern languages; Yoga; Dharma teaching of a particular tradition (Tibetan or Zen) or martial arts. Graduates qualify as Buddhist teachers and are encouraged to take an active part in society with such work as teaching, social assistance, etc.

Morning meditation, classes during the day and evening classes open to those not wishing to embark on full-time study. Varied and extensive programme – phone for full details.

Founder/Guru	The Gate of Dharma Buddhist Church – a non-sectarian joint association of several Buddhist groups
Teachers	Resident teachers include the Venerable Losang Sonam, delegated to the school by H.H. the Dalai Lama. Many visiting teachers
Opening times	20 August–20 December and 2 January–30 June, 7.30am–10pm
Residents	Two monks
Festivals	Contact centre
Facilities	Shrine room, library, study room, classrooms
Accommodation	Can be arranged as the case requires
Food	Contact centre
Booking	Phone, no deposit or advance booking required
Fees	Usually very low
Languages	Hungarian, English, German, Chinese, Japanese, Tibetan

Expected behaviour	Normal decent behaviour
How to get there	Underground (blue line) from city centre. Ten minutes walk from the Pöttyös utca stop

Magyországi Nyingmapa Kòzòsség (Tibetan – Nyingma)
Budapest 1098
Börzsöny u. 11
Tel: +36 (0) 1 280 6712
Fax: +36 (0) 1 280 6714

Situated in **Tan Kapuja Buddhist College** (see separate entry on p268). Community founded in 1991 in conjunction with the College.
Tarob Rinpoche from Copenhagen visits regularly each year to give teachings. Students and people from town visit. Meditation practices and basic teachings of Buddhism.

Founder/Guru	Tarob Rinpoche
Teachers	Visiting Lamas: Tarob Rinpoche, Sogyal Rinpoche
Opening times	During the academic year, closed July–August and most of September
Residents	Contact centre
Festivals	Contact centre
Facilities	Contact centre
Accommodation	Contact centre
Food	Contact centre
Booking	Contact centre
Fees	Contact centre
Languages	Hungarian and English
Expected behaviour	No drugs including alcohol
How to get there	See **Tan Kapuja Buddhist College**

Sangye Menlai Gedün, Community of the Medicine Buddha
(non-sectarian with strong influence of the cult of the Medicine Buddha)
Budapest 1135
Reitter Ferenc utca 12/b

Tel & Fax: +36 (0) 1 1401 094

In a private apartment in an old house in the 13th district of Budapest. Currently in a private apartment. Founded in 1992 as a group of Buddhist friends of different nationalities, though mostly Hungarian. Later by slow growth, the number went up to approximately 200 followed by a decline, mostly because the younger members sought other directions. Follow the general ethos of Buddhism with special emphasis on the way of life described in Tibetan Medical literature, the Gyüshi and its commentaries, which they consider as moral prescriptions having direct reflections on the health of the human organism.

Religious practice – only meditations and celebration of Parinirvana Day.

Founder/Guru	By a group, nominally by Zoltán Nagy
Teachers	In negotiation with Mongolia
Opening times	Not really, as private apartment
Residents	Contact centre
Festivals	Parinirvana Day
Facilities	Possible to use library of Tibetan, Mongolian, Russian, Hungarian and some English texts
Accommodation	No
Food	Tea
Booking	Contact centre
Fees	Contact centre
Expected behaviour	Contact centre
Languages	Usually Hungarian, English, Russian, Mongolian and can read classical Tibetan
How to get here	Contact centre

Karma Dechen Ösel Ling (Tibetan – Karma Kagyu)
Office: 1024 Budapest
Buday Làszlò u.7.
Tel: +36 (0)1 274 1006 or +36 (0)1 302 1070
Fax: +36 (0)1 274 1006
e-mail: cis100324,435

Founded 1990. Looking for larger premises at the time of writing.
Meditations Monday to Saturday 7–8pm. Some courses at other
locations.

Founder/Guru	Lama Ole Nydahl
Teachers	Lama Ole Nydahl, LopenTchechu Rinpoche and young teachers from Germany
Opening times	Open house policy
Residents	Two Sangha members in new flat
Festivals	Contact centre
Facilities	Contact centre
Accommodation	Possible in Gompa in new premises
Food	No
Booking	One month in advance
Fees	Contact centre
Languages	Hungarian and English
Expected behaviour	Contact centre
How to get there	Phone for details

Karma Ratna Dargye Ling Buddhist Community (Tibetan –
Karma Kagyu)
3073 Tar
Address for correspondence: 1039 Budapest. Hunyadi u. 45
Budapest Info Office Tel: +36 (0) 1 160 8847

Stupa and cottages in countryside, although close to a village and
one hour's drive from Budapest. Founded in 1989. Stupa built in
1992 and consecrated by H.H. the Dalai Lama. Spiritual leader of
the centre is Venerable Lama Ngawang who lives in Stockholm.

Daily routine for visitors is Tara ritual at 6am, two hour's work
during the day and Chenrezig ritual at 7pm. Meditations open to
everyone. Teachings with meditation. Lodjong classes are run
(Lodjong is teaching and meditation for the development of bodhicitta – the mind of enlightenment), a Lodjong course in July and
Lodjong weekends every month.

Run regular classes and meditations in Budapest at **Tan Kapuja
Buddhist College** (see separate entry on p268).

Contact Budapest information office for programme.

Founder/Guru	H.H. the Seventeenth Gyalwa Karmapa
Teachers	Resident – Lama Chöpel, Hungarian disciple of Venerable Lama Ngawang. Lama Ngawang spends one month in the centre every year
Opening times	All year round, except for August
Residents	Contact centre
Festivals	Tibetan New Year, Saka dawa, Wesak, Parinirvana, H.H. Dalai Lama's Birthday, Chökor düchen (first teaching of Buddha) and Lhabab düchen (Buddha's return from Tushita)
Facilities	Shrine room, small library and 12m high stupa
Accommodation	Single or double rooms, dormitory or camping possible
Food	Provided during programmes or can be bought in the village nearby
Booking	Write to centre ten days in advance
Fees	Contact centre
Languages	Hungarian, English, Swedish
Expected behaviour	No drugs or cigarettes. See also daily routine for visitors above
How to get there	Budapest-itépsladion coach station – regular bus service in direction Òzd, or Salgótarján – bus stops at stupa – ask for ticket to Sámsonházi elágazás

All I am is 'see*ing*' when I see,
All I am is 'hear*ing*' when I hear,
All I am is 'sentience' when I feel,
All I am is understand*ing* when I know.

– Wei Wu Wei, *Open Secret*

ITALY

Dharma Ling di Roma (Tibetan – Changpa Kagyu)
Paolo Rexha
Via A. Friggeri 55
00136 Rome
Tel: +39 (0)6 353 46437

Courses are held at: Circolo Orfeo, Vicolo Orfeo 1, 00100 Rome.
Founded in 1995 by Lama Denys Teundroup, director of **Karma
Ling** in France (see separate entry on p207). Emphasises meditation practice with a strong emphasis on the lama-disciple
relationship.
   Meditations on Mondays 6.00–7.30 pm, teachings on Tuesdays
6–7 pm. Meditation days, retreats and intensive courses are also
held.

Founder/Guru	Lama Denys Teundroup
Teachers	Resident: Lama Neljorpa Lodro. Founder and others visit
Opening times	See session times above
Residents	No
Festivals	Ask for details
Facilities	Not applicable
Accommodation	No
Food	No
Booking	Write for details
Fees	Write for details
Languages	Italian and French
Expected behaviour	Normal decent behaviour
How to get there	Near the Vatican

Centro Studi Maitri Buddha (non-sectarian)
Corso Novara 35 1º P
Torino
Tel: +39 (0)11 455 3240

Two-storey house in city centre. Founded by Rabten Rinpoche in
1980 and closed after his death in 1987, then opened again in 1993

by the Italian monk Thubten Rinchen under the spiritual guidance of Jampa Tegchog Rinpoche, Abbot of the Seraje Monastery University in India.

Philosophy, logical sciences, commentaries and sutras. Fridays 7pm seminars/courses and Sundays 10.30am meditation. Individual and group retreats are possible in the Masero Retreat House in the countryside, 30km out of Torino. Tapes and brochures of teachings available. Programme of events available annually.

Founder/Guru	Jampa Tegchog Rinpoche with his student Thubten Rinchen
Teachers	Resident: Thubten Rinchen and visiting teachers from different disciplines
Opening times	See event times above
Residents	No
Festivals	Contact centre
Facilities	Library and study room
Accommodation	Guests accommodated by friends of the centre
Food	No
Booking	Contact centre
Fees	By donation
Languages	Italian
Expected behaviour	Kindness and generosity
How to get there	Easy access

Centro D'Informazione Buddhista (non-sectarian)
(Buddhist Information Centre)
Via Pio Rolla 71
10094 Giaveno (Torino)
Tel: +39 (0)11 93 78 331

Private home. Founded in 1974 to provide information about Buddhism in Italy and abroad as it was not easily available at this time. Mutual respect for all spiritual teachings.

Arrange seminars, conferences, seminars and courses by masters of different schools. Organise lectures by lamas in public halls which are open to the general public. Library of around 1,000 reviews and books about Buddhism in many languages. Also videotapes and an interesting photograph archive. All information given, public lectures and use of the library are free of charge.

Founder/Guru	Dr. Bruno Portigliatti
Teachers	Various from different traditions
Opening times	Make appointment in advance
Residents	Founder
Festivals	Contact centre
Facilities	Small place to meditate and library
Accommodation	Several small hotels in Giaveno
Food	No
Booking	Phone or write for information
Fees	Free of charge
Languages	Italian, French, English
Expected behaviour	Silence in the library
How to get there	From Torino, follow the motorway towards Frejus and leave it at Avigliana. From there follow the signs for Giaveno which is uphill

Kunpen Lama Gancen (Tibetan – Gelug)
Via Marco Polo 13
20124 Milan
Tel: +39 (0)2 290 10263
Fax: +39 (0)2 290 10271
e-mail: ganchen@micronet.it (internet connection)

In the town centre. Headquarters of Lama Gangchen's activities worldwide as well as a Dharma centre. Headquarters of the Lama Gangchen World Peace Foundation (LGWPF) which aims to support the development of World Peace. It seeks to do this by creating conditions for an educational system which promotes real inner peace at all levels, and by promoting a concrete cultural, spiritual and material exchange between East and West. This involves the promotion of a dialogue between science and religion, a necessary condition for real human growth. It particularly focuses on self-healing for body, mind and the environment, using methods taken from traditional Tantric Buddhist philosophy and adapted by Lama Gangchen for our busy modern society.

Works to spread the Tibetan healing and medical tradition and for mutual exchange between East and West medical systems.

Visiting monks stay for 3–6 months at a time and perform daily prayers in the meditation hall, perform Cham Dances throughout the country, build sand mandalas and perform pujas.

Events include massage, moxibustion, physiotherapy, counselling. Prayers and pujas 7.30am daily. Self-healing practice and meditation with tuition for beginners. Daily classes in NgalSo Yoga, guided meditations and basic teachings three times a week, group studies and discussions, teachings and initiations and weekly meditation for children. Children's puja 6pm Wednesdays. Retreats at various locations.

Five-year courses in Tibetan medicine with a Professor of Tibetan Medicine and Astrology.

Founder/Guru	Lama Ganchen Tulku Rinpoche. Spiritual director is Mr Giuseppe Tommasi (Pino)
Teachers	Founder is resident teacher and various Tibetan teachers visit
Opening times	Open daily, closed during August
Residents	Ten monks and fifteen lay people
Festivals	Contact centre
Facilities	Shrine room, reference library, shop, publication house, medical reference department
Accommodation	No
Food	No
Booking	Not usually necessary
Fees	Contact centre
Languages	Italian, English, German, French and Tibetan
Expected behaviour	Respect towards all and respectful behaviour in the meditation hall
How to get there	Near the Centrale train station, tram 2 or tram 9

Mandala Centro Studi Tibetani (Tibetan – Gelug)
Viale Aretusa 29
20147 Milano
Tel: +39 (0)2 487 01119

In ground-floor apartment. 100m² divided into two rooms. Established 1987 as a centre for spiritual research and later became a Buddhist centre. Separate retreat centre in the mountains. Open to dialogue, tolerance and selflessness. Offer teachings that are understandable for beginners and study of the esoteric values of the practices.

Meditations daily 7–8am. Meditation course fortnightly on Thursdays 8.30–9.30pm. Study class fortnightly on Wednesday evenings. Introductory session fortnightly on Friday evenings. Yoga Monday and Tuesdays 8–11pm. Four-day Easter retreat, 15–20-day summer retreat in August and three-day winter retreat in December.

Visit other centres in Europe and participate in the Italian Buddhist Union. Organise trips to India, Nepal and Tibet in January, July and August.

Founder/Guru	Lama Paljin Tulku Rinpoche. Spiritual director: Venerable Lama Tamthog Rinpoche
Teachers	Resident: Lama Paljin Tulku Rinpoche and spiritual director
Opening times	7am–11pm with classes 8.30–11pm. Closed July and August
Residents	No
Festivals	Tibetan New Year and Vesak
Facilities	Shrine room, library and meeting room
Accommodation	At retreat centre only – US$ 20 per night
Food	At retreat centre only – vegetarian food, costs shared
Booking	For lessons, not necessary. For retreats, book one month in advance. For courses and seminars book two weeks in advance
Fees	Contact centre
Languages	Italian, English, French and Spanish
Expected behaviour	To follow instructions with an open mind and to cooperate with others. Polite behaviour and respect for the environment. No smoking, alcohol or gambling
How to get there	Metro n.1 direction Bisceglie to Gambara or Bande Nere. Bus 95

Sakya Kun-ga Choeling (Tibetan – Sakya)
Via Marconi 34
34133 Trieste
Tel: +39 (0)40 571048

On first floor of old-style building in downtown Trieste near park.
Work towards love and compassion for the benefit of all sentient
beings. Established in 1989 and current spiritual director is the
nun Savio Malvina-Sherab Choden.

Offer a basic course on Dharma study for newcomers. Studies
of Tibetan culture and philosophy, meditation classes, videos
about Tibet, occasional meetings with the founding Lama and
individual tuition. Retreats once a year. Courses are for all age
groups including children. See local newspapers for programme
of events.

Works for the unity of the four Tibetan Buddhist traditions and
organised the first conference on this in 1995. Sponsor Tibetan
children in refugee camps in India and promote welfare through
medicine, nursery, doctors, etc. for Tibetans.

Founder/Guru	Venerable Lama Sherab Gyaltsen Amipa Rinpoche
Teachers	Resident: Sherab Choden and founder visits
Opening times	Tuesday, Wednesday and Thursday 7–9pm and Tibetan holidays
Residents	One nun
Festivals	No
Facilities	Shrine room and library
Accommodation	No
Food	No
Booking	See local newspapers
Fees	Contact centre
Languages	Italian, English and German
Expected behaviour	Respect for shrine
How to get there	30km west of Trieste by road

Soto Zen Monastery Shobozan Fudenji (Zen – Soto)
Bargone 113
43039 Salsomaggiore (PR)
Tel: +39 (0)524 565667

Country house converted for use as a monastery and for Zen activities. Founded in 1984. Dedicated to the practice of zazen, to living daily life moment by moment and in harmony with everything and to experimenting with the contemplative quality possible in daily life using a concrete and direct approach. Follows the Zen tradition strictly. Well-connected with local cultural and spiritual traditions.

Daily routine is generally an early call before dawn, zazen practice, morning service and meal ceremony, room cleaning, a possible meeting with the Master (for lesson, tea or to ask questions), Samu (work) or other activities, meal ceremony, Samu or other activities, evening meal, zazen, and then early to sleep.

Beginners' introductions some Sunday mornings at 10am–2pm. See programme for other activities for beginners. Zazen every morning at 4.20am for those who have attended the introductory class. Study meetings for beginners and more experienced practitioners. Lectures on various Buddhist subjects, e.g. politics, anthropology, philosophy. Practice and study meetings Tuesdays 7–9pm. Possibility of practising martial arts (kendo and judo), sewing of traditional Zen garments and Shodo (calligraphy). Weekend sesshins once a month for both beginners and more experienced practitioners. Retreats of ten to twenty days throughout the year. In May 1997 an International meeting was held here on creating a Buddhist and Christian dialogue towards a new science.

Publish a quarterly magazine *Zen Notiziario* giving the programme and also information on other Zen centres in Italy.

Founder/Guru	Shuyu Narita Roshi, Master of Rev. F. Taiten Guareschi
Teachers	Resident: Rev. F. Taiten Guareschi, many visiting teachers from all religious traditions and walks of life
Opening times	See programme in the magazine *Zen Notiziario*

Residents	Two monks and one lay person
Festivals	Buddha's Birthday, Buddha's Awakening, Buddha's Parinirvana, Opening and closing days of summer retreat (June and September), some traditional Italian festivals
Facilities	Meditation Hall, Dharma Hall, library, martial arts Dojo
Accommodation	Dormitories using own sleeping bags
Food	Three times a day, usually vegetarian
Booking	Contact Secretary Monday, Thursday and Saturday 9–11.30am (preferably in Italian)
Fees	Usually 50,000 Lira per day including food
Languages	Italian; German, French and English translation possible
Expected behaviour	To participate with an open heart and mind, to be respectful to others, to wear clothing that is dark, comfortable, loose and decent
How to get there	Nearest railway station is Fidenza, from there about 5km by taxi. By car: from Fidenza towards Tabiano. After 3–4km, Bargone is signposted to the right. The road turns to the left and the second building on the right is the monastery

Instituto Lama Tzong Khapa (Tibetan – Gelug – Foundation for the Preservation of the Mahayana Tradition)
Via Poggiberna 9
56040 Pomaia (PI)
Tel: +39 (0)50 685 654
Fax: +39 (0)50 685 768

A large castle-like villa set in the hills of Tuscany near the small village of Pomaia. About twenty minutes drive from the coast. Have three stupas and will soon have a beautiful large prayer wheel in the gardens. The monastery of Takden Shedrup Targye Ling is also located within the grounds. Originally founded in Milan in 1976 by disciples of Lama Thubten Yeshe and Lama Zopa Rinpoche. Moved to its present location in 1977.

Residential centre with a regular study programme. A wide variety of visitors and guests attend who are free to choose their daily activities as long as they do not disturb the other guests. Daily Lama Tzong Khapa puja in the morning and teachings in the evening Monday to Friday.

Offer a variety of courses ranging from Introductions to Tibetan Buddhism, Vipassana retreats, Tantra retreats, daily study programmes of Buddhist texts, and non-Buddhist courses on subjects such as Tai Chi, psychology, astrology, Yoga, etc.

Open house on Sunday afternoons with a brief introduction to the Institute and Buddhism.

Founder/Guru	Lama Thubten Yeshe
Teachers	Resident: Geshe Jampa Gyatso, and visiting Tibetan teachers
Opening times	Visitors should arrive before 5.30pm
Residents	Six monks, six nuns and 10–15 lay people
Festivals	Full moon of Saka Dawa and Lama Tzong Khapa Day
Facilities	Two large meditation rooms, combined study room and library of English, Italian and Tibetan texts and three large stupas
Accommodation	Dormitory 40,000 lira, double room 55,000 lira, single room 65,000 lira. Prices include meals
Food	Vegetarian, traditional Italian dishes
Booking	By phone or post – deposit required for some courses
Fees	See accommodation
Languages	Teachings in Italian and English
Expected behaviour	Five Precepts
How to get there	Train to Pisa Centrale, change to train to Rosignano, then taxi or call Institute for a lift to Pomaia

Merigar, Associazione Culturale Comunità Dzogchen (Tibetan – Dzogchen)
58031 Arcidosso
Grosseto
Tel: +39 (0)564 966837
Fax: +39 (0)564 968110

On the lower slope of Monte Amiata in Tuscany with chestnut and cherry trees. Hot springs within thirty minutes to one hour by car. Comprises main house, another large building, a gompa, a complex of buildings and around sixty hectares of land. Founded in mid-seventies as first base of the now worldwide Dzogchen community. Main seat of the Dzogchen Community Cultural Association and houses also a Tibetan medicine room, tape library of the teachings, library for many important Tibetan texts, a large hall with the Vajra Dance Mandala painted on the floor and the offices of the Association information bulletin.

Regularly organises teaching retreats and practices as well as various courses and seminars on topics such as Yantra Yoga, Tibetan for beginners, Tibetan medicine, Dance of the Vajra. For further information, contact the Secretary with your name and address or see the periodicals they publish.

Shang Shung Editions produces works about Tibetan and Oriental culture and humanistic studies in general, as well as being particularly committed to works on the Dzogchen teaching. Shang Shung Institute for Tibetan Studies was officially inaugurated by H.H. the Dalai Lama to encourage study and research to safeguard the cultural tradition of Tibet. Involved in arts and literature preservation and restoration and archaeological support. Collaborates with various international and national social and cultural bodies. Association for International Solidarity in Asia (ASIA) is a non-political organisation which aims to aid countries whose ethinic and cultural survival is seriously threatened and acts primarily in Asia, particular in the Himalayas and Tibetan plateau.

European office for *The Mirror – Newspaper of the International Dzogchen Community* published in English. *Il Bollettino* published every 4–6 weeks in Italian with news and information on events.

Founder/Guru   Chogyal Namkhai Norbu Rinpoche

Teachers	Resident: Chogyal Namkhai Norbu and visiting teachers from all schools of Tibetan Buddhism
Opening times	10am– 5.30pm daily
Residents	One lay person who changes every couple of years
Festivals	See programme
Facilities	Large teaching hall and library by appointment only
Accommodation	No – information given on local hotels
Food	No
Booking	Book hotel accommodation about two months in advance. For Merigar, register and pay contribution to expenses on arrival
Fees	Around 20,000 to 30,000 Lira per day, reductions for members
Languages	Italian, English, French, German, Dutch and others depending on who is present – teachings are translated into as many languages as necessary
Expected behaviour	See programme
How to get there	Train to Grosseto, Rama Bus to Acridosso, ask for Hotel Faggio Rosso and follow sign for Merigar

Scaramuccia – Luogo di Pratica Buddista (Zen – Rinzai)
Della Scuola Linci di Chan
05019 Orvieto Scalo (TR)
Tel: +39 (0)763 25054
Fax: +39 (0)763 93046

Located on an old farm of forty-four hectares. Consists of a zendo used for zazen, sleeping and eating, big kitchen and rest room.

Ceremony every morning and zazen in the evening from 7–9pm. Holds sesshins every month from 4pm Saturday evening to 7am Sunday morning. During July and August, the sesshins start Sunday evening and run till Saturday afternoon.

Daily routine during sesshins: 6am ceremony and meditation, 7am breakfast, 8am light work in the garden, 10.30am tea, 11am meditation, 12 noon lunch, 2pm work with tea break at 3.30pm, 6pm dinner, 7–9pm meditation.

Before going to Japan, Luigi Mario was an Alpine guide and ski instructor, so there is a strong emphasis on sport and Tai Chi.

Founder/Guru	Engaku Taino (Luigi Mario)
Teachers	Founder
Opening times	For sesshins only
Residents	Lay people occasionally
Festivals	Contact centre
Facilities	Zendo
Accommodation	Sleeping in zendo – 1,000 Lira
Food	7,000 Lira
Booking	Reservation not needed
Fees	See above
Languages	Italian
Expected behaviour	Contact centre
How to get there	Taxi or by foot from Orvieto railway station

Tibet House (Tibetan)
Votigno di Canossa
42026 (RE)
Tel: +39 (0)522 877177 323832
Fax: +39 (0)522 293665 322033

In a village of about ten houses on a hill with an old tower. Opened in 1990. Founder and resident teacher is a Tibetan painter. Mostly a Tibetan cultural centre, but open to all spiritual paths.

Activities include meditation and Tibetan thangka painting. Meetings every Sunday.

Founder/Guru	Tashi Tsering Iana
Teachers	Founder and Ribor Rinpoche visits from Dharamsala
Opening times	Every Sunday from March to October or by appointment
Residents	Five lay people
Festivals	Contact centre
Facilities	Big hall, library, study room

Accommodation	Maximum of twenty people, US$ 40 full-board and lodging
Food	Tibetan and Italian, lunch and dinner about US$ 20
Booking	Contact them in advance
Fees	See above
Languages	Italian, English, Tibetan and French
Expected behaviour	Respect the peace of the place and where possible help to develop centre (e.g. carpentry or gardening)
How to get there	About 2km from Canossa Castle

Centro Atisha Serlingpa (Tibetan – Gelug)
C.P. 187 C. Da Vallegrande
94015 Pizaaz Armerina (EN)
Sicilia
Tel & Fax: +39 (0)935 684 119

Country house in beautiful landscape of hills and woods. Run an organic farm. Cold winters and hot summers. Very peaceful with friendly atmosphere. Open to practitioners of other religions. Founded 1991.

Courses May to June. Weekend and weekly courses. Courses in Lam Rim, Guru Yoga and occasionally alternative medicine. During courses on Buddhism, teachings are usually in the afternoon and participants are free in the mornings.

Founder/Guru	Venerable Lama Lobsang Yeshi Rinpoche
Teachers	Founder visits
Opening times	3–6pm daily
Residents	Two lay people
Festivals	Contact centre
Facilities	Library
Accommodation	Houses for 4–6 people. 35,000 Lira per night per person
Food	Vegetarian at 30,000 Lira each, cheaper during courses
Booking	By phone. Book well in advance for accommodation and send 30% deposit

Fees	Contact centre
Languages	Italian and English
Expected behaviour	Respect environment and the centre
How to get there	Details from centre

What do you have to do?

Pack your bags,
Go to the station without them,
Catch the train,
And leave your self behind.

Quite so: the only practice – and once.

– Wei Wu Wei, *Open Secret*

THE NETHERLANDS

Nyingma Centrum Nederland (Tibetan – Nyingma)
Reguliersgracht 25
1017 LJ Amsterdam
Tel: +31 (0)20 620 5207
Fax: +31 (0)20 622 7143

In the most beautiful, old part of the city, on a quiet, tree-lined canal. Branch of the Nyingma Centers, California, USA which were founded by Tarthang Tulku Rinpoche. Nyingma Centrum Nederland founded 1984 and at this location since 1991. Aims to integrate meditation with daily life and work.

Mantra chanting on full moon evenings. Long term individual study programmes. Weekly classes, weekend programmes and retreats in Dutch. Retreats suitable for all levels in English twice a year.

Founder/Guru	Tarthang Tulku Rinpoche
Teachers	Visiting close students of the founder from California
Opening times	All year round
Residents	Four or five lay people
Festivals	Contact centre
Facilities	Library, study room and book shop specialising in Tibetan Buddhism
Accommodation	For programme participants only
Food	For programme participants only
Booking	By telephone or post. Deposit requested from people outside the Netherlands in the letter of confirmation
Fees	Mantra chanting no charge, donations welcome. See programme for other activities
Languages	Dutch, English, German
Expected behaviour	Train to Amsterdam Central, then tram No. 4 or 9 to Rembrandtplein. Three minutes walk from there

Buddhayana Centrum Amsterdam (Theravada – Myanmar)
Bellamyplein 36-3
1053 AT Amsterdam
Tel: +31 (0)20 6165452

House in a residential area of central Amsterdam. Meditation classes have been held in Amsterdam since 1978, this centre opened in 1988.
Meditation and Dhamma classes every two weeks on Tuesdays 7–10pm. Individual advice is also possible. Seminars, retreats and Dhamma weekends are held at **Buddhayana Vihara** in The Hague and **Ehipassiko Maha Vihara** in Makkinga (see separate entries on p293 and p295).

Founder/Guru	Most Venerable Dharmmawiranatha Nayaka Thera
Teachers	Founder and other visiting monks from Holland and abroad
Opening times	Meditation classes and outside of this time, phone for an appointment
Residents	One lay person
Festivals	Celebrated at **Buddhayana Vihara** in The Hague and **Ehipassiko Maha Vihara** in Makkinga
Facilities	Shrine room. Buddhist literature and other items such as meditation cushions for sale
Accommodation	No
Food	No
Booking	Contact centre
Fees	12.50 DFl per class
Languages	Dutch and English
Expected behaviour	Behave with respect and keep the Five Precepts
How to get there	Tram 12, 13 or 17 or by car exit 105 or 106 from the ring road

Buddhayana Centre Utrecht (Theravada – Myanmar)
Maria van Reedestraat 9
3515 XJ Utrecht
Tel: +31 (0)30 27 10 197

House in a peaceful part of town. Founded 1984. Open for everyone who seriously wants to practise Buddha's Teaching.

Meditation classes once every two weeks for nine months of the year on Thursdays at 7.30–9.30pm sometimes involve chanting and study. Daily activities are Buddha puja, recitation and discussions about Dhamma.

Plans to create accommodation for guests, but at the moment, people who wish to visit for a longer period of meditation and study can stay at the Buddhayana monasteries, **Buddhayana Vihara** and **Ehipassiko Maha Vihara** (see separate entries on p293 and p295), with whom they have a close connection.

Founder/Guru	Most Venerable Dharmmawiranatha Nayaka Thera
Teachers	Visiting Theravada teachers
Opening times	9am to 9pm for information and for the shop
Residents	Three lay people
Festivals	Vesak, Asalha and Kathina – everyone welcome
Facilities	Shrine room, small library, study room and small Buddha Hall
Accommodation	See above
Food	Contact centre
Booking	Contact centre
Fees	Meditation classes by donation, longer periods in monasteries, one month paid in advance
Languages	Dutch and English
Expected behaviour	Not to sit with feet towards the Buddharupa or Sangha members, not to interrupt during a Dhamma discourse and respect the rules the Sangha have taken, e.g. not shaking hands. Behave quietly and thoughtfully to make the visit of others restful and peaceful
How to get there	Bus 5 from Utrecht Central Station to Willem van Noortplein then short walk from Utrecht Overvecht Station

Buddhayana Centrum Santpoort (Theravada – Myanmar)
Burgemeester Enschedélaan 57
2071 AT Santpoort
Tel: +31 (0)23 5372887

Family home in a mainly residential village which serves for bringing people into contact with the Sangha of **Ehipassiko Maha Vihara** and **Buddhayana Vihara** (see separate entries on p295 and p293). Regional meeting point for people interested in this tradition.

Meditation and Dhamma evenings once every two weeks on Sundays at 7pm led by Most Venerable Dharmmawiranatha Nayaka Thera who explains the teachings of the Buddha and instructs in Vipassana meditation (Bhavana). Weekends on the teachings of the Buddha and a summer course at **Ehipassiko Maha Vihara** or **Buddhayana Vihara**. Newcomers are welcome on instruction evenings or can arrange an interview before coming. Vipassana meditation retreats are organised at Ehipassiko for people with some experience.

Books in the Boeddhayana Publikaties series available and cassette tapes of Dhamma instructions can be borrowed by frequent visitors. Subscription to *Boeddhayana*, the monthly Buddhist newspaper in Dutch or the bimonthly children's magazine, *Ayo Ayo*.

Founder/Guru	Most Venerable Dharmmawiranatha Nayaka Thera
Teachers	Most Venerable Dharmmawiranatha Nayaka Thera
Opening times	Meditation times (see above) and outside these hours by telephone to make an appointment
Residents	Family of four
Festivals	Vesak, Asalha and Kathina at **Ehipassiko Maha Vihara**
Facilities	Contact centre
Accommodation	Contact centre
Food	Contact centre
Booking	Contact centre
Fees	Contact centre
Languages	Dutch and a little English

Expected behaviour	To be respectful and willing to listen and learn, to take off shoes in the hall, not to point feet towards the Buddha rupa or the teacher
How to get there	Railway station Santpoort Noord, Bus 70 to Santpoort Slaperdijk or car to exit N208 – Santpoort-Haarlem Noord

Buddhayana Centrum Deventer (Theravada – Myanmar)
Grote Ratelaar 55
7422 NJ Deventer
Tel: +31 (0)570 656502

Family house with little front garden. Meeting place is a big living room with shrine room. Started in 1992 by Winita and Palita van Iersel. A group of Buddhists and non-Buddhists practise Vipassana meditation and listen to Dhamma teachings.

Classes every two weeks on Thursdays at 7.30pm when a monk or nun visits. No classes from June till September. Newcomers will receive instruction in meditation. Seminars and retreats held at **Ehipassiko Buddhist Monastery** (see separate entry on p295).

Sometimes give interviews to local papers and information to schools to help publicise Buddhism.

Founder/Guru	Most Venerable Dharmmawiranatha Nayaka Thera
Teachers	Visiting nuns and monks
Opening times	For meditation times above and for telephone enquiries outside these hours
Residents	Family of four
Festivals	Celebrated at Ehipassiko Monastery and Buddhayana Monastery
Facilities	Shrine room and they sell books about Buddhism
Accommodation	No
Food	No
Booking	Phone in advance
Fees	Donation of 12.50 DFl compensation for visiting teacher's travelling expenses

Languages	Dutch and English when necessary
Expected behaviour	To listen to teachings, respect for teacher, don't point feet towards teacher or Buddha rupa, no shoes in house
How to get there	Ask centre for details

Buddhayana Vihara (Theravada – Myanmar)
Stephensonstraat 13
2561 XP The Hague
Tel: +31 (0) 70 3600605
Fax: +31 (0)70 3600213

Three-storey building in a quiet street just outside the centre of one the largest cities in The Netherlands. Established in 1978 and moved to present location in 1986. Since 1991, the main office has moved to the quieter monastery at **Ehipassiko Maha Vihara** (see separate entry on p295). Respect all schools of Buddhism and emphasise the equality of all Buddhists. Although Theravadins, they do not adhere to the idea of the School Caste System as sometimes practised and taught in Europe. Everyone is welcome irrespective of caste, creed, race, etc.

Mostly they host members of their own Buddhist community in The Netherlands and Germany and all regional centres of Boeddhayana Centrum Nederland organise weekend meditation retreats in the Vihara.

Morning and evening meditation sessions preceded by recitation from the Buddha's discourses. Retreats on a bimonthly basis on the first full weekend of the month. Weekends are open to all, but attendees are advised to have attended meditation classes with Most Venerable Dharmmawiranatha Nayaka Thera beforehand at any one of the regional centres.

Boeddhayana Centrum Nederland is the mother organisation for The Netherlands. Members pay 120 DFl minimum annually. Publish a Dutch Buddhist monthly, *Boeddhayana*, for a 25 DFl contribution to mailing costs which contains international Buddhist news, articles and a full programme of activities. German and English versions are published quarterly. Also publish Dutch books on Buddhism, printed, bound and sold by their own community to ensure the lowest possible price.

Founder/Guru	Most Venerable Dharmmawiranatha Nayaka Thera
Teachers	Resident: Most Venerable Dharmmawiranatha Nayaka Thera and other visiting Theravada teachers
Opening times	Daily 8–10am and 2–9pm – visitors should contact the Vihara beforehand
Residents	Two monks/nuns
Festivals	Contact centre
Facilities	Special dana hall with small shrine and small library. 50m² sala for meditation with Bodhi Tree
Accommodation	For up to ten guests
Food	Only for weekend retreatants when vegetarian food is included in the costs
Booking	One month in advance and payment in advance
Fees	Residence for non-members 150 DFl per weekend
Languages	Contact centre
Expected behaviour	Respect the rules the Sangha (monks and nuns) adhere to and to address them politely. All lay people should observe the Eight Precepts. Ask for an information sheet
How to get there	Tram 3 from Central Station or Tram 11 from Holland Spoor station to Laan van Meerdervoort or Conradkade, then three minutes walk

Words!
The way is beyond language,
for in it there is
no yesterday
no tomorrow
no today.

– Sengstan, *Hsin Hsin Ming*

Ehipassiko Maha Vihara (Theravada – Myanmar)
Veneburen 23
8423 VH Makkinga
Tel: +31 (0)516 441848
Fax: +31 (0)516 441823

In the province of Friesland between the towns of Wolvega and Oosterwolde. In a modern farmhouse with five acres of land to ensure the silence necessary for the practice and study of the Dhamma. First established 1991, but moved to present location because of expansion. Apart from the main building, there is a large Buddha Hall, a barn with caravans, a shop, printing press, a small sala, a library and some extra rooms.

Retreats are organised bimonthly on first full weekend of the month. Weekend retreats are open to all, but attendees are advised to have attended meditation classes with the Most Venerable Dharmmawiranatha Nayaka Thera beforehand at any one of the regional centres.

Regional centres of Boeddhayana Centrum Nederland organise weekend, five-day, ten-day and individual meditation retreats here as well as seminars on the main Buddhist topics.

See **Buddhayana Vihara** in The Hague on p293 for further details of the Buddhayana Centrum Nederland organisation.

Founder/Guru	Most Venerable Dhammawiranatha Nayaka Thera
Teachers	Founder resident visiting Theravada teachers
Opening times	5am to 11pm daily. Weekend visitors should make contact beforehand
Residents	Two monks/nuns, three lay people
Festivals	Wesak, Asalha, Kathina
Facilities	See above
Accommodation	Four dormitories with space for 15–25 people
Food	Strictly vegetarian and cost included in course fees. Not served after 1pm unless for nursing and pregnant women, children and for people with health problems. In these cases, please inform them beforehand

Booking	One or two months in advance, prepayment in full
Fees	Non-members 50 DFl per day, 150 DFl per weekend, 250 DFl five-day retreat, 500 DFl ten-day retreat
Languages	Contact centre
Expected behaviour	Respect the rules the Sangha adhere to and address them politely. All lay people should observe the Eight Precepts. Ask for an information sheet
How to get there	Bus 27 from Steenwijk to Makkinga, Veneburen bus stop

Shambhala Centrum Regio Leiden (Tibetan – Karma and Nyingma – Shambhala)
Geversstraat 48
2342 AB Oegstgeest
Tel: +31 (0)71 5410928 or 5153610

First and second floor on main street near a park. Founded 1986. Open, hospitable and active centre.

Shambhala offer three paths: The Shambhala Tràining (or Sacred Path of the Warrior) which is a non-denominational systematic training in meditation as a way to secular enlightenment; The Vajradhatu Gate which is a programme of Buddhist teaching and practice; and The Nalanda Gate which embraces all other cultural activities such as the Japanese art of archery, ikebana (Japanese flower arranging) and calligraphy.

Members may attend daily for meditation practice. Visitors welcome at Wednesday and Thursday classes and for scheduled events. Classes for sitting meditation and instruction Wednesdays 9–11am and Thursdays 8–10pm. Meditation sessions start and finish with recitations. Regular courses to study Buddhism and Shambhala teachings at different levels. Introductory programmes to Buddhism twice a year and Introduction to Shambhala teachings once a year. Newcomers are offered free meditation instruction on Thursday evenings without appointment. Other events include Mudra, ikebana and Qi Gong.

New programme every spring and autumn.

Founder/Guru	Chogyam Trunpa Rinpoche
Teachers	Visiting Kagyu lineage teachers and Mr. Han de Wit
Opening times	See meditation times above
Residents	No
Festivals	Milarepa Day, Shambhala Day and Sadhana of Mahamudra (full moon days)
Facilities	Shrine room, library and study room
Accommodation	No
Food	Oryoni-style lunch and dinner during weekend programmes 15 DFl per day
Booking	By phone, post or in person
Fees	No fee for meditation classes
Languages	Dutch, English, German, French
Expected behaviour	No shoes in meditation hall
How to get there	Easily accessible by train, bus and car

Vipassana Meditation Foundation (Theravada)
Kamerlingh Onnesstraat 71
9727 HG Groningen
Tel: +31 (0)50 5276051

Formerly a school that has been converted to a meditation centre.
Grown from a meditation group inititated by Venerable
Mettavihari of Thailand.

  Practice of Vipassana and study of Buddhist psychology, based
on the teachings of the late Venerable Mahasi Sayadaw from
Myanmar. Session times are Tuesdays and Fridays 7.30–9.30pm.
Study first Monday evening of the month. Yoga Monday
evenings. 4–6 day retreats every three or four months. Regular
weekend and other activities including weekend retreats and
silence days.

Founder/Guru	Venerable Mettavihari
Teachers	Frits (Jhananando) Koster and visiting teachers
Opening times	See programme times above
Residents	No
Festivals	Visakha Puja

Facilities	Shrine room, library, study room and meditation hall
Accommodation	See programme
Food	Vegetarian
Booking	Call Karina Rol on +31 (0)50 5775562 or the centre
Fees	Contact centre
Languages	Dutch and English
Expected behaviour	Contact centre
How to get there	Close to the railway station

De Tiltenberg (Zen)
Zilkerduinweg 375
2114 AM Vogelenzang
Tel: +31 (0)2520 17044
Fax: +31 (0)2520 24896

Main house, outbuildings and other small houses situated in ten acres of dune land in the middle of bulb fields. Special places in the grounds include herb and vegetable gardens and a cemetery for Grail women in the ten acres of woods. Beach is close enough to be reached by bicycle, bus or car.

This centre is a project of The Grail Movement, a lay movement of women which began in the Netherlands in 1921. It is rooted in Christian faith, ecumenical and open to women committed to the spiritual dimension of life and the transformation of society. Now spread to twenty-two other countries. Built in 1932 and Neo-Romanesque chapel added in 1953 which was originally intended for Roman Catholic worship, but it easily lends itself to services of many different religions, especially Zen meditation. Centre is directed by women but programmes are designed for both women and men. Welcome all kinds of groups which fit with the spiritual ethos of the centre. Facilities include large library and sun room which can be divided into three small rooms and used as meeting/work spaces; a chapel which can be used for all kinds of religious and spiritual practice; and two self-contained staff suites.

Zen activites include four-, seven- and ten-day sesshins, Zen weekends, Introductory courses in Zen Meditation and study programmes about Zen Buddhism in a Western context.

Contact them for full details of their programme including other types of events and for details of using the facilities for other groups.

Founder/Guru	Mimi Maréchal
Teachers	Visiting Zen teachers
Opening times	Telephone weekdays 10am–12.30pm for information or to make an appointment
Residents	Three lay people
Festivals	Contact centre
Facilities	Shrine room, library and study room
Accommodation	For groups of ten to fifty people
Food	Vegetarian
Booking	Contact centre
Fees	For example, Zen weekend 215 DFl. Concessions available
Languages	Dutch, English and German
Expected behaviour	Contact centre
How to get there	Train to Heemstede and then bus 90 to De Tiltenberg which is right outside the house

Kanzeon Zen Centre Amsterdam (Zen – Soto / Rinzai synthesis – Kanzeon Sangha)
Krayenhoffstraat 151
1018 RG Amsterdam
Tel: +31 (0)20 6276493 and 6187922

On the top floor of a school building in the harbour area. Group started by Nico Tydeman, a student of Genpo Sensei and moved to current location in 1991.

Meditation times: 8–9am every morning, Tuesdays 8–10pm for more experienced practitioners and Thursdays 8–10pm for beginners. Lectures on Buddhist and non-Buddhist subjects Monday evenings at 8–10pm, suitable also for beginners. Day event last Sunday of every month for more experience practitioners. Closed during summer holidays in July and August. Zen weekend last weekend of every month. Activities may include zazen, kinhin (walking meditation), samu (manual work) and daisan (interview with the teacher). Nine-day sesshins with Genpo Sensei in May and September held at **De Tiltenberg** (see separate entry on p298). Four- day sesshins in summer and winter held at centre.

Founder/Guru	Genpo Merzei Sensei
Teachers	Resident: Nico Tydeman and visiting teachers from Zen Center Salt Lake City, USA and Zen Centre Paris
Opening times	See meditation times above
Residents	No
Festivals	Contact centre
Facilities	Zendo and daisan room, Buddhist and Zen library, coffee and tea room
Accommodation	Can be arranged in private homes by request
Food	Only during events: bread, soup and fruit/salad
Booking	Phone the centre for programme and other information
Fees	See programme
Languages	Dutch
Expected behaviour	Basic zendo rules which will be explained to those not familiar with them
How to get there	Bus 28 from Central station to Czaar Peter Straat

---

Have confidence in the truth, although you may not be able to comprehend it, although you may suppose its sweetness to be bitter, although you may shrink from it at first. Trust in the Truth . . . Have faith in the Truth and live it.

– The Buddha

Karma Deleg Cho Phel Ling (Tibetan – Karma Kagyu)
Stoepawei 4
9147 BG Hantum
Tel: +31 (0)5190 97714

Retreat centre with stupa located in a farmhouse.

Daily meditations including Green Tara Sadhana, Mahakala Bernachen Sadhana and Chenrezig Sadhana. Retreats, work retreats – contact centre for full programme.

Founder/Guru	H.H. the 16th Gyalwang Karmapa
Teachers	Resident: Chodje Lama Gawang and many visiting teachers
Opening times	Always open
Residents	Two lay people
Festivals	Contact centre
Facilities	Shrine room, small library, study room and retreat rooms
Accommodation	Yes
Food	Vegetarian and non-vegetarian
Booking	Contact centre
Fees	Contact centre
Languages	Dutch, English, German and French
Expected behaviour	Contact centre
How to get there	Train to Leeuwarden, then bus 54 to Hantum

Us Thús (Tibetan – Nyingma and Rime)
De Ryp 6
8658 LL Greonterp
Tel & Fax: +31 (0)515 579628

In the province of Friesland in the north of the Netherlands. 150-year-old farmhouse typical for the area. Very quiet location with only a few farmers for neighbours. Landscape is very flat with many meadows and lakes, cows and birds. Also a refuge for animals. Ethos is to develop a kind heart and respect for all sentient beings.

Affiliated to **Centre d'etudes de Chanteloube** in France (see separate entry on p181). Lineage of founding teachers connected with Nyingma school, but the spirit of current teachers and teachings follow the Rime tradition. This encourages respect for all schools. Founded 1991 by teachers who live in France but visit often to give talks, seminars and personal guidance.

Four retreat rooms, coffee/eating room, room for teachings,

gompa, and single rooms with view over lakes for guests and small bookshop. Tibetan doctor visits twice a year. Mainly a retreat centre for small groups and individuals. Newcomers may come for retreats with guidance. Groups retreats held throughout the year under the guidance of one of the teachers or their disciples.

Weekly meditation group suitable for beginners and those wishing to continue with their Shine practice. Also a group practising Vajrayana Preliminary Practices. Study group meeting once a month and teachers advise a different topic of study each year. Newcomers may have a personal talk and join the meditation group.

To stay informed of all activities, subscribe to newsletter for 25 DFl a year.

Founder/Guru	Tulku Pema Wangyal Rinpoche, Tulku Jigme Khyentse Rinpoche and Tulku Rangdrol Rinpoche
Teachers	Founders visit and other visiting teachers.
Opening times	Check before arriving
Residents	Two lay people
Festivals	Full moons and Tibetan 10th Tsog ceremony
Facilities	See above
Accommodation	During seminars and retreats only. Bed and breakfast 25 DFl
Food	For retreatants – cooked vegetarian lunch and rest self-catering
Booking	By phone, fax or letter, no deposit needed
Fees	For retreat 50 DFl per day including food and lodging
Languages	Dutch, English, German and some French
Expected behaviour	To behave with a kind heart and respect for all sentient beings
How to get there	Train to Sneek then bus to Greonterp

Buddhavihara Temple (Theravada – Thai)
Den Ilp 38
1127 PC Den Ilp

Tel: +31 (0)20 4826512 or +31 (0)20 4826883
Fax: +31 (0)20 4826883

Dutch farm in a suburb of Amsterdam has been converted into a semi-Thai-style temple.

Activities include celebration of pujas, Vipassana meditation (weekends and retreats from ten days up to a month), Abhidhamma study, cultural services such as Thai lessons and social advice. Marriage and funeral services also performed. Newcomers must first consult with a resident monk or one of the teachers at the centre. Individual retreats by special arrangement.

Branch at the Buddhavihara's previous address: St Pieterspoortsteeg 29, 1012 HM Amsterdam.

Young people involved with the Buddharama temple formed the **Stichting Jonge Boeddhisten Nederland** (SJBN) in 1978 to spread Buddhist teachings in West, give information to those involved in Theravada Buddhism – 400 people involved. Issues a newsletter three times a year *Vipassana Sara*. Post box address only: Stichting Jonge Boeddhisten Nederland, Postbus 1519, 3500 DM Utrecht.

Founder/Guru	Venerable T. Mettavihari
Teachers	Resident: Venerable T. Mettavihari and visiting teachers
Opening times	Year round preferably by appointment
Residents	Two monks and one lay person
Festivals	Vesak, Magha, Start and End of Rains retreat and Kathina Puja
Facilities	Upasatha with Sima, library, study room and social room
Accommodation	Contact centre
Food	Eastern, vegetarian and normal Western food
Booking	Make an appointment
Fees	Contact centre
Languages	Dutch, English, Thai
Expected behaviour	Five Precepts
How to get there	91 bus from CS Amsterdam, then ten minutes walk

Maitreya Institute (Tibetan – Gelug – Foundation for the Preservation of the Mahayana Tradition)
Heemhoeveweg 2
8166 HA Emst
Tel: +31 (0)578 661450
Fax: +31 (0)578 661 851
e-mail: maitre @pi.net

Former youth hostel with seven hectares of woodland with Tara statue. Buildings are a villa with shop, office and living rooms and a wooden building with meditation hall, dining room, large kitchen, four dormitories (ten-bed) and seven double rooms and some rooms for residents. Five caravans for students and retreats. Shop sells Tibetan Buddhist books, incense and ritual objects. Maniwheel, stupa and a place for cremation urns are planned. First Lam Rim courses held in the seventies. Moved from Brughem to Massabommel in 1984 and to present property in 1987. Strong ties to the NSTG (Nederlanse Stichting voor for Tibetaanse Geneeskunde) in Amsterdam.

Resident teacher offers a study programme covering the main philosophic topics of Tibetan Buddhism. Five pujas a month. Two weekend courses a month, one for beginners and more advanced students and the other for more advanced students only. Annual Lam Rim summer course in July – excellent introductory course. Two weekend thangka painting courses in March and November and a fourteen-day thangka painting course in June. One week Lam Rim meditation retreats for those who have done a course, usually at end of July and December. One-week Tara retreat for those who have received the initiation, generally in spring. Several Nyung Na fasting retreats at holy day for advanced practitioners. Topics for study include Lam Rim, Bodhicaryavatara and Abhisamaya Alankara. People may attend one teaching session at no cost to orient themselves. Personal advice on appointment. Tibetan language class Thursday evenings 6.30–7.30pm.

Regular visits by Tibetan doctor arranged in cooperation with the Tibetan Medical Institute in Dharamsala, India, and one will be resident 1996–1998.

Accommodation offered during courses and for volunteers on organised weekends to work in the woods (the latter stay for free). Only those connected with the centre or following Buddhist teachings elsewhere may do retreats. Not open for general visitors other than for courses.

Distribution centre for publishers of books on Tibetan Buddhism to Dutch bookshops. Publish Buddhist books in Dutch. Distributes healing incense. Quarterly magazine in Dutch.

Resident Geshe gives evening teachings once a month in Amsterdam. School groups visit.

Founder/Guru	Lama Thubten Yeshe and Lama Thubten Zopa Rinpoche
Teachers	Resident: Geshe Sonam Gyaltsen and visiting teachers
Opening times	Visitors by appointment only on Sunday to Friday 9am–4pm. Closed Mondays and months of January and August
Residents	Two monks, a nun who lives nearby and two lay women, but more expected
Festivals	Losar, Saka Dawa, First Teaching of the Buddha, Buddha's Descent from Heaven, Tsongkhapa Day
Facilities	See above with shrine room, small library
Accommodation	See above. Dormitory 15 Dfl, double rooom 25 DFl
Food	During courses and volunteer weekends. Retreatants cook their own food, but occasional meals may be prepared for them during the week. Three meals 25 DFl
Booking	By phone. Course fees to be paid fourteen days in advance
Fees	Weekend course 180–210 Dfl, two-week course 985 Dfl. Retreat 210 Dfl for one week including meals, 125 Dfl without meals
Languages	Most teachings in Dutch, occasionally in English. Residents speak Dutch, English, French, German and Tibetan
Expected behaviour	Five Precepts, and smoking only outside the building. Take responsibility for the environment
How to get there	Train to Apeldoorn or Zwolle, then bus 124 to Laarstraat and 15 minutes walk. If you

arrive an hour before courses start, a car will
pick you up from the bus stop

There is no enlightenment outside of daily life.

– Thich Nhat Hanh, *Zen Keys*

SPAIN

Zen Dojo Nalanda (Zen – Soto)
Montcada 31, Principal 2°
08003 Barcelona
Tel: +34 (9)3 215 66 53

Montcada is the historic street where the Picasso Museum is situated. Founded in 1981 and inaugurated the same year during Master Taisen Deshimaru's only visit to Spain.
Activities include Zazen, Kyudo and Chado.

Founder/Guru	Master Taisen Deshimaru
Teachers	Contact centre
Opening times	Monday–Friday 8am–8pm, Saturdays 9am to 8pm. Closed bank holidays
Residents	No
Festivals	Contact centre
Facilities	Dojo
Accommodation	No
Food	No
Booking	Contact centre
Fees	Contact centre
Languages	Spanish
Expected behaviour	Respectful behaviour
How to get there	Contact centre

Samye Dzong, Karma Lodro Gyamtso Ling (Tibetan – Karma Kagyu)
Pau Claris, 74, 2
0810 Barcelona
Tel & Fax: +34 (9)3 301 5472

Apartment in a block. Founded in 1978 as the first Tibetan Buddhist Centre in Spain on Akong Rinpoche's visit which was the first visit of a lama to Spain. Affiliated with **Samye Ling** in Scotland (see separate entry on p139) together with several in Europe and Africa. Give a gradual, step-by-step instruction on meditation and Buddhist principles from the very fundamental to the highest teachings. Aim is that people develop a solid, thorough and effective understanding.

Regular meditation practices with recitation, mantras and music are 8.30–9.15pm Tuesdays (Chenrezig Puja), 7.30–8.30am Fridays (Green Tara Puja) and 8–9pm Fridays (Guru Rinpoche puja). Advanced meditation courses on Tuesday evenings on such subjects as The Seven Points of Mental Training and The Bejewelled Ornament of Liberation. When lamas visit, they give teachings and initiations. Occasional weekend and day courses and retreats. Basic meditatation courses on Thursday evenings and Saturdays and Introduction to Buddhism courses on Tuesday evenings and Saturdays are for newcomers.

Also run Yoga, Tibetan language, Western and Chinese astrology and I Ching classes.

Founder/Guru	H.H. 16th Gyalwa Karmapa and Akong Tulku Rinpoche
Teachers	Resident monks and visiting Tibetan teachers
Opening times	October to July. Office hours: Tuesday, Thursday and Friday 6-8pm
Residents	Monks and one or two lay people
Festivals	Usually nothing public
Facilities	Shrine room, library and study room
Accommodation	No
Food	No
Booking	Not necessary to book in advance
Fees	2500 ptas per month for courses
Languages	Spanish and English
Expected behaviour	Normal polite and respectful behaviour
How to get there	Underground to Plaza Cataluna or Plaza Unquinaona

C.E.T. Nagarjuna (Tibetan – Gelug – Foundation for the Preservation of the Mahayana Tradition)
C/. Duque de Osuna, 8 Externior – 2° Izda.
28015 Madrid
Tel: +34 (9)1 541 3755

In the centre of Madrid by the Plaza Espana. Founded 1985 and at this address since 1993. More meditation courses, particularly Lam Rim, than studies.

Introductory courses in meditation and Buddhist philosophy. Regular activities include Tara Puja, Tsog Puja, Samatha and Vipassana meditations. One day retreats once a month. Hatha Yoga, Qi Gong, healing courses.

Founder/Guru	Lama Yeshe and Lama Zopa Rinpoche
Teachers	Resident teacher, Lama Thubten Tsering, five months of the year and many visiting teachers
Opening times	Closed mornings and during July to October
Residents	Spiritual director
Festivals	All Buddhist festivals celebrated
Facilities	Shrine room and library for use of members only
Accommodation	No
Food	Only during retreats
Booking	Contact centre
Fees	Free apart when expenses need to be covered
Languages	Spanish and some English
Expected behaviour	Five Precepts
How to get there	Metro or bus to Plaza Espana, up Princesa Street

Euskal Herriko Zen Instituto Nazioartekos
Instituto Internacional del Zen de Euskal-Herra
EHZIN (International Zen Institute of the Basque Country
(Zen – Rinzai – International Zen Institute)
C. Catalina de Erauso, 21, Sol D.
20.010 Donostia (Basque Country)
Tel: +34 (9)43 464476 or for English (9)43 212543 (Karmele)
Fax: +34 (9)43 470338 (Eragin)

In the Basque country on the Cantabrian coast. Created formally in 1995 although in existence since 1992. Part of International Zen

Institute under Venerable Roshi Guesshin Prabhasa Dharma which is based in the USA and has several centres in the USA, Spain, Holland and Germany.

Meditation times: Wednesday and Friday 8–9.30pm, new and full moon Saturdays 6–10pm, full moon Sundays 10am–2.30pm (lunar calendar published by the centre). Sessions involve Zazen, recitation of sutras and meditation walking. Also koan practice and Chado (tea ceremony). During retreats with Roshi there are personal interviews with the Master (Dokusan), Nitten Sotji (cleaning), Yoga, formal teachings of the Dharma (Theiso), informal talks on the teachings, informal and formal meals. Newcomers should make an appointment with a teacher before attending an introductory course.

To be able to attend a sesshin led by Roshi Guesshin Prabhasa Dharma, it is necessary to have previously done a three-day retreat at any IZI centre.

Founder/Guru	Venerable Roshi Guesshin Prabhasa Dharma; founders Edurne López and Antton Jauregizuria
Teachers	Founder visits
Opening times	See meditation times above
Residents	Contact centre
Festivals	Contact centre
Facilities	Contact centre
Accommodation	Not at centre. Advice given on inexpensive accommodation in the town
Food	No
Booking	Contact centre
Fees	Contact centre
Languages	Contact centre
Expected behaviour	Respect for others, kindness and willingness to perform the meditation in silence and stillness
How to get there	110km east of Bilbao, 40km west of Biarritz

Jiko An Zen Centre (Zen – Soto)
El Alamillo
18460 Yegen (Granada)

Tel & Fax: +34 (9)58 343185

Set in the Sierra Nevada in the mountains at 4,500ft above sea level. Rustic buildings in the picturesque Alpujarra area. Rugged, arid mountains in a Nature Park with view of the Mediterranean. 6km up a dirt track from the nearest village.

Visitors are welcome to join in the practices, practise on their own or just stay to enjoy the local environment by hiking, studying, resting, etc. All visitors are welcome to contribute to the centre in whatever way – work, donations of money or gifts, offering skills, etc.

Daily activities are zazen, Mantra running or walking meditation, Samu (manual work), yoga, chanting and zazen. Every three or four months there are weekend courses in Introduction to Zen Meditation, Relaxation Courses. Sesshins are open to both newcomers and more experienced people. Weekend sesshins once a month, and six- or nine-day sesshins a few times a year. Six-day sesshin with Hogen Daido Roshi once a year. Weekend and six-day courses in topics such as Tai Chi Chuan, Shiatsu, Qi Gong and NLP with visiting teachers. Reiki or vegetarian cooking weekends two or three times a year each.

Shingan Francis Chauvet is a disciple of Hogen Yamahata and also practised and studied with the Vietnamese Zen Master Thich Nhat Hanh.

Founder/Guru	Hogen Daido (Yamahata) Roshi
Teachers	Resident: Francis Shingan Chauvet and many visiting teachers of different disciplines
Opening times	All year round
Residents	One monk and up to five lay people
Festivals	Contact centre
Facilities	Large and small Zendo
Accommodation	Dormitory for 4–12 people, single and double rooms. 3,400 ptas a day for single room full-board
Food	Three ovo–lacto–vegetarian meals a day
Booking	Phone or letter. Deposit sometimes required
Fees	Teachings are free of charge. 2,200–3,400 ptas per day to cover expenses depending

	on course and participant's economic situation. Donations welcome
Languages	Spanish, English and French
Expected behaviour	Mindfulness. No drugs or alcohol. No tobacco in the buildings
How to get there	6km from the village of Yegen by dirt track. Bus service twice a day from Granada to Yegen where you can be picked up if you give warning in advance of your time of arrival

O Sel Ling Centro de Retiras (Tibetan – Gelug – Foundation for the Preservation of the Mahayana Tradition)
Apartado 99
18400 Orgiva (Granada)
Tel & Fax: +34 (9)58 343134

Set in Alpujarra mountains in the south of the Sierra Nevada at 1600m altitude with excellent view of the Costa del Sol and about 30km from the sea. Weather very good from May to September, but in winter it can be cold with snow possible, but generally dry. Founded around 1980 and built by the effort of the residents. Specially set up to offer the opportunity to engage in secluded meditation and retreats. Good library with Spanish and English books.

Retreatants are given a 'retreat cave' which is a small house in a quiet spot. Vegetarian lunch is delivered nearby and each house has a small kitchen, outside toilet and shower. Some have solar electricity. Facilities are fairly basic and visitors should be aware of the lack of physical comforts. Important to have received extensive advice on your personal practice from a qualified teacher before arrival, although there is a resident lama with translator living at the centre most of the year who gives daily teaching and advice.

Weekend courses Introduction to Meditation and Introduction to Buddhism twice a month. Larger courses in spring and summer on Buddhist philosophy, Shiatsu, floral medicine and Tai Chi.

Founder/Guru	Founder: Venerable Lama Thubten Yeshe.

	Spiritual Director: Lama Thubten Zopa Rinpoche
Teachers	Visiting Tibetan and Western teachers
Opening times	Always open
Residents	Monks on retreat occasionally and five lay people
Festivals	Major Buddhist holidays
Facilities	Gompa, shrine room, library, study room and twelve small individual houses for retreat in isolation
Accommodation	Three- and four-bed dormitories for visitors and small houses for retreatants
Food	Three vegetarian meals a day included in accommodation costs or 700 ptas each for lunch and dinner
Booking	Phone at least one week in advance and send 20% deposit
Fees	Up to three months 3/4,000 ptas per day, three months to a year 10% discount, more than one year 20% discount
Languages	Spanish, English
Expected behaviour	Five Precepts and quiet around the small houses
How to get there	Three buses daily from Granada to Padre Eterno (two hour trip). From there people are collected by jeep

Sangye Menkhan (Buda de la Medicina) (Tibetan – Gelug)
Avda. Velazquez, 9
Portal 1
6°E-2
29003 Malaga
Tel: +34 (9)5 2 32 07 54 or 235 66 25
Fax: +34 (9)5 2 35 66 25

In one of the most famous streets of the city. Founded in response to the petition of Spanish friends in 1990 in a house donated by members. Teaches on Tibetan Buddhism and Tibetan medicine and offers services to the community. Lama Gangchen wants all his centres to be schools for peace, so they have a special interest in teaching inner and outer peace and the use of Tantric energy towards this aim.

Self-healing Sadhana every Friday. White Tara Sadhana every Wednesday. Practices on Death and Impermanence every Friday. Talks on various subjects. Meeting of the Lam Rim group twice a month on Tuesdays. One week Lam Rim courses three times a year in February, June and October. One course on a specified subject and one on Tantric Self-healing for body and mind once a year each. Occasional Yoga classes. Retreats three times a year for one week in February, June and October.

Plan to offer Tai Chi classes and to organise travel worldwide with Lama Gangchen.

Founder/Guru	Venerable Lama Gangchen Tulku Rinpoche
Teachers	Founder and other lamas and doctors visit
Opening times	Daily from 10am to 2pm and 5pm to 10pm. Closed in July and August
Residents	None
Festivals	Contact centre
Facilities	Shrine room and library
Accommodation	Yes, at 500 ptas a day
Food	Use of kitchen offered with accommodation
Booking	Depends on course – usually one month in advance with 50–100% deposit
Fees	Lam Rim course: 10,000 ptas; one-week retreats: 40,000 ptas
Languages	Spanish and English
Expected behaviour	To behave ethically, quietly and respectfully to others
How to get there	Very easy – contact centre for details

Instituto Internacional Zen de Euskal-Herria (Zen – Rinzai – International Zen Institute)
Avda. de Madrid, 9 esc. dcha. 8° B
20011 San Sebastian
Tel: +34 (9)43 459885 (for Spanish) or +34 (9)41 121015 (for English and Spanish)

Town is 25km from French border. In a twelve-storey building in the Amara zone in south San Sebastian. Founded when participants met Venerable Roshi Gesshin Prabhasadharma in Holland in 1986. She offered to visit Spain and now offers advice and directs one or two sesshins annually.

Meditation sessions Mondays to Fridays 8–9.50pm. Intensive meditation practice weekend following full and new moons – see programme for dates. Please be punctual for sessions and if no-one answers the door immediately, please wait a while.

To book, Spanish people should contact the centre one week in advance for retreats and one month in advance for the Roshi's sesshin. Foreigners should contact: Maria Arrate Dharma Sukha Aguirre, Rua Mayor de Peralta 24, 01300 Laguardia-Alava, telephone +34 (9)41 121015.

Founder/Guru	Venerable Roshi Gesshin Prabhasadharma
Teachers	Visiting teachers
Opening times	See programme
Residents	No
Festivals	Contact centre
Facilities	Dojo
Accommodation	No. Can be arranged in private homes on special occasions
Food	No
Booking	See above
Fees	Contact centre
Languages	Spanish, Basque and some English
Expected behaviour	Contact centre
How to get there	Good train connections to San Sebastian

Recognize your dreams and transform illusion into luminosity.
Do not sleep like an animal.
Do the practice which mixes sleep and reality.

– Tibetan Buddhist prayer

SWEDEN

Sakya Changchub Choling (Tibetan – Sakya)
c/o Eva Tidemalm
Hagagatan 46
113 47 Stockholm
Tel: +46 (0)8 33 77 46

Usually meet in member's private homes. Founded 1979 and has been visited by H.H. Sakya Trizin in 1984 and H.E. Dagchen Rinpoche in 1980.

Emphasise both study and meditation, believing that all practices should be firmly rooted in kindness, love and compassion. Methods include Theravada, Sutra Mahayana (Paramitayana) and Vajrayana.

Founder/Guru	Venerable Geshe Sherab Gyaltsen Amipa
Teachers	Founder visits, Venerable Lama Pema Wangdak
Opening times	Call or write for information
Residents	No
Festivals	Phone or write for information
Facilities	Shrine room and library
Accommodation	Occasionally – write or phone for information
Food	As accommodation
Booking	Phone or write
Fees	Phone or write for information
Languages	Swedish and English
Expected behaviour	Respect for Buddhism, a genuine interest in Buddhism, preferably practice of the Five Precepts
How to get there	Phone or write for information

Stockholm Zen Centre (Zen – Integral Zen)
Östgötagatan 49
116 25 Stockholm
Tel: +46 (0)8 641 6382
Fax: +46 (0)8 641 6382

In a basement of an apartment building in the city centre. Integral Zen is a merging of Rinzai and Soto with koan training, founded by Sogaku Harada Roshi in Japan. Caters for lay people and offers an opportunity to practice zazen and to introduce newcomers to Zen practice. This centre founded 1982 and affiliated to Rochester Zen Center in the USA whose abbot is Sensei Bodhin Kjolhede, dharmaheir of Roshi Philip Kapleau. Leader of the Swedish Sangha is Zen priest Sante Poromaa.

Zazen times: Monday to Thursday 6.30–8.30pm; Tuesday, Wednesday, Friday 6.15–7.15am, Sunday 9–11am. Sunday session includes Dharma talk or Teisho. Introductory workshops once a month which last for a day or occasionally longer. Buddhist doctrine is taught occasionally. One day zazen sittings.

Five-or seven-day sesshins, workshops and Ango period (traditional intense three-month retreats) are held at the centre's retreat centre – Zengården, Pl 240, Finnåker, 71041 Fellingsbro, *Tel:* + 46 (0)581 63 00 61. Contact them direct for more information and programme of events.

Founder/Guru	Roshi Philip Kapleau
Teachers	Sensei Bodhin Kjolhede, Sante Poromaa
Opening times	See meditation schedule above
Residents	No
Festivals	New Year, Vesak and Jukai
Facilities	Zendo and library
Accommodation	No
Food	No
Booking	Phone for booking forms and further information one month in advance
Fees	Contact centre
Languages	Swedish and English
Expected behaviour	Five Precepts and guidelines for meditation practice in the zendo
How to get there	From Stockholm central station, take subway to Medborarplatsen, then a few blocks walk

Karma Shedrup Dargye Ling (Tibetan – Kagyu)
Hökarvägen 2
129 41 Hägersten
Tel & Fax: +46 (0)8 886950

An old wooden villa in peaceful surroundings outside the city.
Retreat centre is **Karma Dechen Ösel Ling** in Fellingsbro (see
separate entry on p321). Founded 1974. Open to everyone offering
interested people the chance to learn about the Buddhist approach
to life and the deep insight and knowledge the Buddhadharma
can offer. School classes and other interested people also visit.

Chenrezig meditation open to everyone on Sundays, Mondays
and Wednesdays (see opening times). Introduction to Buddhism
at least one Sunday evening every month except during the summer. Arranges activities which support personal development,
giving better balance and joy and stimulating communication
with others and social interaction. Classes and courses on subjects
such as Lodjong, Nyungne.

Founder/Guru	H.H. the 16th Karmapa and the Very Venerable Kalu Rinpoche
Teachers	Resident Director: Venerable Dorje Lopon Lama Ngawang; visiting teachers from all over the world including India, Nepal and France
Opening times	Sundays 3–8pm; Mondays and Wednesdays 6–8pm
Residents	Contact centre
Festivals	Contact centre
Facilities	Shrine room, library and shop for dharma books and other items connected with practice
Accommodation	No, but possible at nearby youth hostel – contact centre for details
Food	Soup as evening meal at 20 SKr
Booking	Contact centre
Fees	Contact centre
Languages	Swedish and English
Expected behaviour	No smoking in the area and no drugs and to offer at least one hour's work a day

How to get there   Underground train to Mälarhojden, pass a
shop called Kensum, along the Selmedal-
svagen and right at the next crossroads on
to Hökarvägen

Stockholm Buddhist Vihara (Theravada – Sri Lanka)
Sångvägen 9
17536 Järfälla
Tel & Fax: +46 (0)8 58031323

Near the city centre. Two-storey wooden villa with a small garden.
Meditation and recitation daily. Special Sri Lankan Bodhi-puja
every Saturday. Meditation for beginners and experienced practitioners with Dhamma discussion on Sundays. Retreats on special
days such as Vesak and when erudite monks visit. Study courses
held occasionally. Dhamma school for children on Saturdays.
Plan to organise social activities for the welfare of society.

Monks visit schools, universities and other academic institutions at least once a week. Also visit hospital and prisons to give
spiritual support.

Founder/Guru	Sri Lankan-Sweden Buddhist Association
Teachers	Resident: Venerable Kirindigalle and Dhammaratana Nayaka Thera and visiting monks from all over the world
Opening times	9am–9pm
Residents	Five monks
Festivals	New Year, Vesak and Kathina
Facilities	Shrine room, library, study room
Accommodation	Rooms available at no cost
Food	Food is offered to monks by devotees – monthly dana list
Booking	Phone the monks
Fees	Membership 100 kronor per year
Languages	Swedish, English and Sinhalese
Expected behaviour	Silence during meditation hours
How to get there	Train to Jakobsberg then 6–8 minutes walk

Föreningen Malmö Buddhistcentrum (Tibetan and Theravada)
c/o Leif Magnusson
Odengatan 8
23432 Lomma
Tel: +46 (0)40 410 419 (L. Magnusson) or +46 (0)40 81536 (Rev.
Dharmavajra)

Malmö is on the coast opposite Copenhagen. No centre, but meet
at each other's houses. Buddhist Society of Malmö founded about
twenty-five years ago. Open Buddhist group inviting teachers
from different traditions. Respect of the Five Silas. Only Buddhist
group in Sweden open to all Buddhists.

Puja and group meditation every second Wednesday. Study
programmes, private meditation instruction and counselling on
request. Daily puja and meditation possible with Rev.
Dharmavajra only on request. Regular weekend retreats and meditation days and occasional one week retreats.

Programme open for newcomers. Give information to schools.
Perform Buddhist funerals and other ceremonies on request.

Founder/Guru	Late Venerable Tao Wei Kwong Wu
Teachers	Various from different traditions
Opening times	As per programme of events
Residents	L. Magnusson – order member of Arya Maitreya Mandala and Rev. Dharmavajra – a priest
Festivals	Wesakh
Facilities	Shrine room and individual libraries
Accommodation	May be provided – contact centre
Food	Sometimes – vegetarian
Booking	Some weeks in advance by phone
Fees	Contact centre
Languages	Swedish, English and German
Expected behaviour	Five Precepts, take part in meditation sessions, no alcohol, smoking not encouraged
How to get there	Boat from Copenhagen

Karma Dechen Ösel Ling (Tibetan – Kagyu)
Solbo, Oppeby 2646
71041 Fellingsbro
Tel: +46 (0)581 633 073

An old farm rebuilt and extended with an eleven-metre stupa in the grounds. In the countryside and surrounded by forest for pleasant walks. Apart from the retreat area, the main building has a shrine room, dormitory, dining room and coffee shop open to all. Number of small houses which are ideal for individual short retreats. Founded in 1974 in Stockholm (see separate entry for **Karma Shedrup Dargye Ling** on p318) and this retreat centre purchased in 1980 to provide a place for three-year retreats – the first of its kind in Sweden. The stupa was consecrated by H.H. the Dalai Lama in 1988. Aim is to develop compassion and wisdom through practising meditation and studying the Dharma.

During courses, there is Tara meditation in the morning and Chenrezig in the evening. Occasional courses in Kum Nye. Solitary retreats for people who have participated in courses here before and under guidance either of the teachers here or one known to them.

School parties and tourists are welcome during the day.

Founder/Guru	H.H. the 16th Karmapa and the Very Venerable Kalu Rinpoche
Teachers	Resident Director: Venerable Dorje Lopon Lama Ngawang; visiting teachers from all over the world including India, Nepal and France
Opening times	Contact centre for information
Residents	Resident Director and two lay people
Festivals	Vesak and other Tibetan festivals
Facilities	See above
Accommodation	Huts from 150 SKr/day per person up to 1500 SKr for 2 weeks; 4 people pay 400 Skr/day. Small room 70 SKr/day
Food	During courses, communal cooking at 85 SKr/day
Booking	See programme; for overnight stay, contact the centre beforehand

Fees	See programme
Languages	Swedish, English and Tibetan
Expected behaviour	No smoking in the area and no drugs, to offer at least one hour's work a day
How to get there	Train to Fellingsbro, then taxi for 15km. Ask for the Buddhist centre and stupa

If things were brought into being by choice,
Then since no one wishes to suffer,
Suffering would not occur.

– Shantideva, *A Guide to the Bodhisattva's Way of Life*

SWITZERLAND

Arranged according to postcode

Dojo Zen (Zen – Soto – Association Zen Internationale)
16 av. Calas
1206 Geneve
Tel: +41 (0)22 789 32 93

Ground floor Zen Dojo created about twenty years ago. Practice only zazen at this small centre. There are around nine nuns and monks associated.
Practice times: Tuesday to Friday 6.15–8.15am, Tuesday to Thursday 6.45–8.15pm; Saturday 9–11.30am and Sunday 9.45–11.30am.
Sesshins held at other locations for around eighty people from around Europe.

Founder/Guru	Master Taisen Deshimaru
Teachers	Resident: Vince Vuillemin, visiting teachers from France, Netherlands and Spain
Opening times	See practice times above
Residents	No
Festivals	Contact centre
Facilities	Dojo
Accommodation	No
Food	No
Booking	Not necessary
Fees	8 Sfr per session or 60 Sfr per month towards rent; teaching free
Languages	French, English and some Spanish
Expected behaviour	Zen Dojo rules
How to get there	In the Champel area of Geneva

Geneva Buddhist Vihara (Theravada)
1 Quai des Vernets
1227 Les Acacias Geneva
Tel & Fax: +41 (0)22 301 0859

Fifth floor apartment. Founded in 1992 with the help of the International Buddhist Foundation and the Venerable Tawalama Dhammika, the resident monk.

Offers meditation, prayer, counselling and teaching of the Dhamma. Meditations every Saturday 3–5pm and Monday 10–11.30am. Chanting daily 7.30am, 11am and 7.30pm. Dhamma study Sundays and Fridays.

Produce *Le Journal du Dhamma* in French, English and Sinhalese.

Founder/Guru	Venerable Tawalama Dhammika
Teachers	Resident monk Venerable Tawalama Dhammika and visiting monks
Opening times	9am to 10pm daily
Residents	Venerable Tawalama Dhammika
Festivals	Contact centre
Facilities	Shrine room, monk's dwelling and small library
Accommodation	No
Food	Traditional Thai and Sri Lankan food every Monday
Booking	Contact centre
Fees	Contact centre
Languages	French, English and Sinhalese
Expected behaviour	Normal appropriate behaviour for a religious place
How to get there	5m from the main station Cornavin and not far from Geneva airport

Rabten Choeling (Tibetan – Gelug)
Centre des Hautes Études Tibétaines
1801 Le Mont-Pèlerin
Tel: +41 (0)21 921 36 00 Secretary, +41 (0)21 921 7253 Ven. Gonsar Tulku Rinpoche
Fax: +41 (0)21 921 7881

Set in three houses near a lake and with good views of the Alps. Founded in 1977 by the late Venerable Geshe Rabten Rinpoche, spiritual director is now Venerable Gonsar Tulku Rinpoche, his principal disciple. Dedicated to the transmission of Buddhism and

Tibetan culture. The first Tibetan monastic centre (**Tibet-Institut**, Wildbergstrasse, 8486 Rikon/ZH, Switzerland) was founded mainly for the approximately 2,000 Tibetans living in Switzerland, but Rabten Choeling is intended mainly for Europeans, although Tibetans are of course welcome.

Teaches aspects of Tibetan Buddhism – language, philosophy, psychology, meditation, art, medicine, astrology, etc. Two-week school in summer for Tibetan children, teaching Buddhism, Tibetan history, etc.

Every Sunday afternoon 3–4.30pm teaching for all levels. Meditations and prayers daily which visitors are free to attend.

It is always possible to make an individual retreat under the guidance of one of the lamas.

Often monthly on-going courses in Bern, Basel, Zürich, Winterthur, Geneva, Lausanne and La Chaux-de-Fonds. Associated groups include Thubten Choeling in Schaffhausen, Antenne de Rabten Choeling in Winterthur, Rabten Samphel Ling in Liebefeld, Rabten Choeling Geneve and Antenne de Rabten Choeling in Zürich.

Founder/Guru	Geshe RabtenTinpoche in the name of H.H. the Dalai Lama
Teachers	Resident: Ven. Gonsar Tulku Rinpoche, Ven. Geshe Thubten Trinley and visiting teachers
Opening times	According to programme. Closed during December/January, May and September for one month. Occasional open days
Residents	Two Spanish monks, one French monk, one French nun, around twelve lay students and the Secretary
Festivals	All Buddhist festivals, ceremonies and ritual, open to the public
Facilities	Temple, library with bookshop, shop for Tibetan handicrafts and study room
Accommodation	Limited places in dormitories (18 Sfr) or private rooms (25 Sfr)
Food	Three meals a day, international cuisine, often Tibetan
Booking	Only necessary for retreats, otherwise just

	turn up
Fees	Contact centre
Languages	Tibetan, English, French and German
Expected behaviour	Respectful and to follow the meal times
How to get there	Train to Vevey, then funiculaire to Mont-Pèlerin

San Sui Dojo (Zen – Soto – Association Zen Internationale)
Rue du Port 4
1815 Clarens
Tel & Fax: +41 (0)21 964 44 62

Building in a little street which leads down to the lake. Founded by a Zen nun in 1995.
   Zazen Monday 9am and 6.30pm and Wednesday 8pm. Two and a half day sesshin once a year in Zinel (VS).

Founder/Guru	Choulel Boiettini
Teachers	Visting: Roland Rech from Paris
Opening times	See session times above
Residents	Six nuns and monks and twenty-five lay people
Festivals	Contact centre
Facilities	Contact centre
Accommodation	No, but plenty of cheap hotels in Montreux
Food	Only when full day or full night sessions
Booking	Contact centre
Fees	Contact centre
Languages	French and English
Expected behaviour	In accordance with other participants
How to get there	Along the lake side, bus stop Rue du Port

Dhamma Gruppe (Theravada)
Postfach 5909
3001 Bern
Fax: +41 (0)31 921 68 05

Buddhist meditation retreat organisation that arranges events at various places around Switzerland and rents different places for this. Arrange up to seven retreats a year with up to eighty participants.

Retreats in Vipassana and/or Metta. Occasional meditation courses for women. Length of retreats may be from weekend to three weeks. Retreats are suitable for both beginners and experienced students. Retreats are held in Swiss German, German and English languages.

Extensive cassette tape catalogue of Dharma discourses by different teachers available in German and English.

Founder/Guru	Not applicable
Teachers	Various
Opening times	According to programme
Residents	Not applicable
Festivals	Not applicable
Facilities	According to venue – see programme
Accommodation	Full-board part of course price
Food	Vegetarian
Booking	Annual programme on request – booking details enclosed
Fees	Varies but around 400 Sfr for a week
Languages	See above
Expected behaviour	Five Precepts and maintaining silence when necessary
How to get there	See programme

Sayagyi U Ba Khin Gesellschaft (Theravada – Myanmar)
Greyerzstrasse 35
3013 Bern
Tel & Fax: +41 (0)31 992 11 62
e-mail: 100330.3304@compuserve.com

Currently looking for a suitable site for a permanent centre, but have been running ten-day Vipassana retreats for over ten years. These are in the tradition of Sayagyi U Ba Khin and held twice a year at rented sites in Switzerland. One is led by Mother Sayamagyi and Sayagyi U Chit Tin and the other by a regional teacher. Two discourses on the theory of Theravada Buddhism are given daily. Daily guidance is given by the teachers. Suitable for old and new students.

One-hour meditation meetings are held every Tuesday in Basel, Bern, Zürich and Ticino.

Founder/Guru	Mother Sayamagyi and Sayagyi U Chit Tin
Teachers	Regular teachers are from the International Meditation Centre in the UK
Opening times	As per programme
Residents	No
Festivals	No
Facilities	Depends on site rented
Accommodation	Depends on site rented
Food	First-class vegetarian
Booking	Information is sent out containing booking form; 100 Sfr required
Fees	No charge for teaching, but 500 Sfr for ten-day course towards cost of food and lodging
Languages	English, German and French
Expected behaviour	Five Precepts
How to get there	Information given when booking

> All dharmas, all beings, contain the nature of full enlightenment within themselves. Don't look for it outside yourself. If you shine the light of awareness on your own self, you will realize enlightenment immediately.
>
> – Thich Nhat Hanh, *Old Path White Clouds*

Shambhala Zentrum Bern (Tibetan – Kagyu and Nyingma – Shambhala)
Funkstrasse 116
3084 Wabern / Bern
Tel: +41 (0)31 961 24 18

In a suburb. Started in 1983 as a Dharma Study Group and has since developed until it moved to its current address in 1995. Affiliated to Shambhala International, Halifax, Canada. Interested people can contact Shambhala centres in London, Amsterdam, Hamburg, Marburg, Paris, Vienna, Munich for more information.

Shambhala offer three paths: The Shambhala Training (or Sacred Path of the Warrior) which is a non-denominational systematic training in meditation as a way to secular enlightenment; The Vajradhatu Gate which is a programme of Buddhist teaching and practice; and The Nalanda Gate which embraces all other cultural activities such as the Japanese art of archery, ikebana (Japanese flower arranging) and calligraphy.

Classes Wednesdays 7–10pm. Programme of special events, weekend programmes, etc.

Shamatha (sitting practice), Beginners' Buddhist courses, weekend intensive training seminars, one-day sitting practice, weekday evening classes. One-month group retreats and ten-day individual retreats are held on other premises.

Founder/Guru	Venerable Chogyam Trungpa Rinpoche
Teachers	Sakyong Mipham Rinpoche (spiritual director of Shambhala) and other visiting teachers
Opening times	According to programme
Residents	Seventeen lay people
Festivals	Shambhala Day (Tibetan New Year), Midsummer's Day, Vesak, Milarepa Day, Parinirvana of Chogyam Trungpa, H.H. Dilgo Khyentso Rinpoche and Karmapa Rikpe Dorje
Facilities	Shrine room
Accommodation	During events, included in price
Food	During events, included in price
Booking	Contact centre
Fees	Contact centre
Languages	Swiss German; English, French and Italian if necessary
Expected behaviour	Normal decency
How to get there	Contact centre

Dhammapala Buddhist Monastery (Theravada – Thai)
Am Waldrand
3718 Kandersteg
Tel: +41 (0)33 75 21 00
Fax: +41 (0)33 75 22 41

Ninety-year-old former hotel in a quiet corner of the tourist resort
of Kandersteg, at 1,200m altitude in the Bernese Alps. Monastery
in the Thai Forest Tradition emphasising formal meditation and
all-round mindfulness throughout daily activities. Visitors are
those interested in experiencing monastic life, learning more
about Buddhism and those participating in periodic retreats.

The daily routine is chanting and meditation at 5am, clean-up at
6.30am, communal breakfast at 7am, main meal of the day at
11am, working meditation at 1pm, tea break at 5.30pm and
evening chanting and meditation at 7.30pm. On Saturday
evenings the meditation is followed by a Dhamma talk and the
opportunity to ask questions.

Eight-day and four-day retreats. Saturday evenings,
Observance Days (new, full and quarter moon days) and the meditation weekends each month are suitable for newcomers. Run
meetings and retreats at other locations – see programme.

They can also supply a list of local meditation group contacts in
Switzerland, Germany and an Italian monastery.

They have a publication department producing books in
German and French, mostly translations from English originals
published by Amaravati Publications or Wat Pah Nanachat,
Thailand. These are available for free distribution together with
other books by Theravada teachers.

Founder/Guru	Ajahn Chah tradition associated with Ajahn Sumedho
Teachers	Ajahn Tiradhammo
Opening times	Contact centre
Residents	Four monks and one postulant
Festivals	Contact centre
Facilities	Shrine room and library
Accommodation	Shared single-sex bedrooms
Food	Two meals per day with evening drinks
Booking	Phone, fax or write beforehand

Fees	Free of charge, but the monastery is dependent on donations
Languages	English, German, Swiss-German, French, Italian, Spanish and Thai
Expected behaviour	To follow the daily schedule (see above) and the Eight Precepts
How to get there	One hour from Bern by train, 67km south of Bern by car

Dojo Mokushinzan (Zen – Soto)
Thannerstrasse 35
4053 Basel
Tel: +41 (0)61 321 42 27 or 321 92 19

Former small factory in an inner court.
  Zazen Monday, Tuesday and Friday 6.15–7am and Wednesday and Friday 7.30–9pm.

Founder/Guru	L. Tenryu Tenbreul
Teachers	L. Tenryu Tenbreul
Opening times	See session times above
Residents	No
Festivals	Contact centre
Facilities	Contact centre
Accommodation	No
Food	No
Booking	Contact centre
Fees	Contact centre
Languages	German
Expected behaviour	Contact centre
How to get there	Contact centre

Wat Srinagarindravararam (Theravada – Thai)
Buddhistisches Zentrum
Im Grund 7
5014 Gretzenbach
Tel: +41 (0)62 858 60 30
Fax: +41 (0)62 858 60 35

Set in a very small village in the valley. Building is half-Thai and half-European in style. Much of the financial support for its establishment came from the King of Thailand's late mother, Somdejphrasrinagarindra. Its main purposes are: to be a centre for Buddhist monks, to be a Theravada study centre open to everyone, to be a serene place of meditation and Dhamma study, to guide and help solve social problems using the principles of Buddhism (especially for people from Thailand, Laos and Cambodia and their partners), and to support and maintain Thai language, tradition and culture. Many visitors are Thai, especially busy at the weekends.

Organised meditation on Wednesdays 7–9pm. Beginners may come to learn meditation either Monday or Tuesday 7pm till about 9pm. Weekend retreats possible. At time of writing, it was planned to programme organised events.

Visitors who stay should follow the monks routine of waking at 5.30am, morning chanting at 6am, breakfast 8am followed by helping monks with cleaning, then evening chanting and meditation at 9pm.

Daily chanting 6am and 9am. Daily study 9am and 1.30pm.

Founder/Guru	Somdejphrapuddajinawong, Abbot of Wat Benchamabopitr in Thailand
Teachers	Resident monk: Ven. Phrasirivuddhimedhi and very occasional visiting teachers
Opening times	8am–9pm
Residents	Five monks
Festivals	Magha Puja, Songrant festival, Visakha Puja, Asalha Puja, Oakpansa Day, Kathina ceremony and Loykrathong Festival
Facilities	Shrine room, library with study room
Accommodation	Free of charge (free to make donation) up to seven days, then according to means
Food	As offered to the monks by lay people. Usually Thai cuisine
Booking	Not necessary
Fees	By donation – monastery dependent on lay community
Languages	Local people speak German, monks speak Thai and English

Expected behaviour	Respect for monks and visitors; join in routine as above
How to get there	Train to Aarau, then No. 3 bus to Gretzenbach, leaving the bus at the stop by the post office

Shambhala Study Group Ticino (Tibetan – Kagyu and Nyingma – Shambhala)
Via Rotondello 31
6517 Arbedo
Tel: +41 (0)91 829 1851

In a private apartment. Part of Shambhala International whose headquarters are in Canada.

Shambhala offer three paths: The Shambhala Training (or Sacred Path of the Warrior) which is a non-denominational systematic training in meditation as a way to secular enlightenment; The Vajradhatu Gate which is a programme of Buddhist teaching and practice; and The Nalanda Gate which embraces all other cultural activities such as the Japanese art of archery, ikebana (Japanese flower arranging) and calligraphy.

Meditations include Shamatha, Tong Len, Ngondro and Vajrayogini Sadhana. Various classes according to the Three Yana Vajradhatu curriculum. For newcomers, there are Beginners Classes and Shamatha practice.

The Shambhala Training available here and ikebana (Japanese flower arranging), Kyudo (Japanese archery), Mudra space awareness, Maitri space awareness.

Founder/Guru	Chogyam Trunpa Rinpoche, current head Sakyong Mipham Rinpoche
Teachers	Visiting senior Vajradhatu students and Sakyong Mipham Rinpoche
Opening times	Tuesday 6–10pm
Residents	No
Festivals	Shambhala Day, Milarepa Day
Facilities	Shrine room, library of audio and video-tapes
Accommodation	No

Food	No
Booking	By phone
Fees	Contact centre
Languages	Italian, French, English
Expected behaviour	Contact centre
How to get there	Train station Bellinzona or highway exit Bellinzona Nord

Zen Dojo Zurich (Zen – Soto – Association Zen Internationale)
Rindermarkt 26
8001 Zürich
Tel: +41 (0)1 261 81 59
Fax: +41 (0)1 262 75 27

Old building in a historic part of Zürich. They welcome everyone wanting to practise whatever their religion. Emphasis is on Shikantaza – the exact practice of Zazen, without any object or purpose, as transmitted by the Zen Masters Eihei Dogen, Kodo Sawaki and Taisen Deshimaru.

Practice times: Monday to Friday 6.30am, Saturday 11am, Tuesday to Thursday 7pm. Arrive fifteen minutes before session times. Sessions involve zazen, Kinhin and a short ceremony with some chanting. After morning zazen, Guen Mai (traditional Japanese rice soup) is served. On Saturdays after zazen, a vegetarian lunch is eaten together.

Two sesshins of three days each year at 160 Sfr each including food and accommodation. One-day sesshins once a month at 50 Sfr including food. All sesshins and days of zazen are suitable for both newcomers and experienced people.

Founder/Guru	Master Taisen Deshimaru
Teachers	Resident: Meiho Michel Bovay and other visiting disciples of Deshimaru
Opening times	Zazen times above, office hours Tuesday to Thursday 9am–12 noon
Residents	No
Festivals	Contact centre
Facilities	Dojo
Accommodation	During sesshins only

Food	See above – Guen Mai 2 Sfr, Lunch 10 Sfr
Booking	One week in advance for sesshins
Fees	12 SFr per session or 100 SFr per month for sessions – sesshin prices above
Languages	German
Expected behaviour	To follow zazen practice
How to get there	Within walking distance of Neumarkt tram station in the Niederdorf district of Zürich

> When the deluded in a mirror look
> They see a face, not a reflection.
> So the mind that has truth denied
> Relies on that which is not true.
>
> *– The Royal Song of Saraha*

Karma Yeshe Gyaltsen Ling (Tibetan – Karma Kagyu)
Hammerstrasse 9
8008 Zürich
Tel: +41 (0)1 382 08 75
Fax: +41 (0)1 382 08 75 or +22 (0)1 380 10 44
e-mail: 100553.3425@compuserve.com

House with several flats and a meditation room. At this address since 1990. Their lineage is about practice rather than study, but they have a Buddhist University in Delhi – Institute of Karma Kagyu. Tibetan culture is not involved as adapted to Western style.

Every Tuesday at 2pm: Three Lights meditation with explanation for newcomers. Every Thursday 8pm Chenrezig meditation or puja, every Sunday at 7.30pm, Eight Karmapa, Phowa or Clear Light meditation. Also study courses and practice of Ngondro for more experienced practitioners. One- or two-day retreats at this centre, longer retreats elsewhere. Summer courses with Lama Ole Nydahl and others.

Other associated Karma Kagyu centres in Switzerland are: **Karma Dorje Ling** in Basel, **Karma Kunsang Ling** in Bern, **Karma Tscho Pel Ling** in Bern and **Karma Wangchuk Ling** in Luzern – ask this centre for details.

Founder/Guru	H.H. the 16th Karmapa, represented by Lama Ole Nydahl
Teachers	Visiting teachers from Tibetan Buddhism and several Western lay teachers
Opening times	As per programme
Residents	Twelve lay people
Festivals	No
Facilities	Gompa, library and office with room to study
Accommodation	Only during courses when necessary
Food	Only during courses when necessary
Booking	Phone centre
Fees	Contact centre
Languages	Swiss, German and High German
Expected behaviour	Normal decent behaviour
How to get there	In the centre of Zürich

Zentrum für Buddhismus (Zen – Rinzai)
Bodhibaum Zendo
Friedheimstrasse 24
8057 Zürich
Tel: +41 (0)1 312 1062
Fax: +41 (0)1 312 1062
e-mail: 100116.3443@compuserve.com

Founded 1992.
   Zazen Tuesdays and Fridays 7.30pm–9.15pm. One-day sesshins monthly except June, July and August. Five-day sesshins twice a year in spring and autumn. Introduction to Zen Meditation and Introduction to Yoga Meditation one and a half hours a week for fifteen weeks starting in January and September. One-day Zen meditation and yoga meditation seminars.

Founder/Guru	Robert and Agetsu Wydler Haduch
Teachers	Robert and Agetsu Wydler Haduch
Opening times	See event times above
Residents	Two lay people
Festivals	Silvester
Facilities	Zendo and small library

Accommodation	No
Food	No
Booking	Phone or write for details
Fees	Zazen by donation, one-day sesshin 100 Sfr, five-day sesshin around 6505 Sfr, Courses 450 SFr
Languages	German and English
Expected behaviour	Contact centre
How to get there	Phone for details

Meditation Centre Haus Tao (Zen – Rinzai)
9427 Wolfhalden
Tel: +41 (0)71 888 41 83
Fax: +41 (0)71 888 35 39
e-mail: tao@link-ch1.limmat.net.ch

A 250-year-old mill. Member of the Foundation of Mindful Living. Vietnamese Rinzai Zen in the style of Thich Nhat Hanh. A very peaceful place.

Beginners are offered retreats and personal guidance by an authorised Zen teacher. Three-month retreat in the autumn and several shorter retreats each year. Events such as: New Year, Easter and Autumn Retreats, Women's Spirituality, Work Meditation and a Meditation Course.

Publish the magazine *Intersein*.

Marcel Geisser has worked as a therapist and teacher of humanist psychology for fifteen years and studied and practised Buddhism for twenty-six years. Ordained Dharmacharya by Thich Nhat Hanh in 1994. Has also studied with masters from most Buddhist traditions.

Founder/Guru	Dharmacarya Marcel Geisser
Teachers	Resident: Dharmacarya Marcel Geisser, visiting teachers including Thich Nhat Hanh and Ajahn Tiradhammo
Opening times	Year round
Residents	One or two lay people
Festivals	Vesakha
Facilities	Shrine room, library and study room

Accommodation	Single and double rooms at 45–50 Sfr per night (including food)
Food	Three vegetarian meals a day
Booking	Contact centre
Fees	See programme
Languages	German and English
Expected behaviour	Five Precepts and to be part of the community and help with the work
How to get there	Train or car to Rheineck, then via Thal to Wolfhalden

Finding other Buddhist centres, groups and organisations

> If you have the basic understanding that the primal Buddha-nature is that of all sentient beings, it follows that anyone who thinks that any *action* can lead to his 'enlightenment' is turning his back on the truth: he is thinking that there is a 'he' there to be 'enlightened', whereas 'enlightenment' is a name for the state wherein there is no separate individual at all, and which is that of all sentient beings, a name for what they are, but which cannot be recognized by anyone who believes himself to be an autonomous individual.
>
> – Wei Wu Wei, *Open Secret*

This Directory is not a comprehensive listing of every Buddhist organisation, centre or group. There are also meditation groups who meet in private homes on a regular basis, publishing companies and bookshops, Tibetan cultural centres and schools.

UK AND EUROPE – ALL TRADITIONS

All over UK and Europe

European Buddhist Union's European Buddhist Directory
Contact the EBU about groups and centres in your area (or elsewhere in Europe). Standard information from the EBU Directory will be given, e.g. standard information for five centres, on paper or floppy disk.

Contact:
EBU c/o BUN
PO Box 17286
1001 JG Amsterdam
The Netherlands

The European Buddhist Union Directory will be available to all. To get copies on paper or floppy disk, send in an order form. The cost will be moderate and in some instances there will be no charge.
Contact:
EBU c/o SJBN
PO Box 1519
3500 BM Utrecht
The Netherlands

They also plan during 1996 to install an internet site on which all or most of the information in the European Buddhist Union Directory will be made available.
    See **European Buddhist Union** entry in France for more details on the EBU.

Austria

Bodhi Baum Jahrbuch für Buddhismus
2722 Netting 34
For listing of centres in Germany, Austria and Switzerland (published every March):

Österreichische Buddhistische Religionsgesellschaft
Fleischmarkt 16
1010 Vienna
Tel & Fax: +43 (0)222 512 37 19
Umbrella organisation for all Buddhist activities in Austria.

Denmark

Buddhistisk Forum
Sekretariat
c/o Lisbeth Lundbye
Tjærnegade 5, st. th.
2200 Kbn. N.
Denmark
For information on all main Buddhist traditions in Denmark.

Germany

Bodhi Baum Jahrbuch für Buddhismus
2722 Netting 34
For listing of centres in Germany, Austria and Switzerland

Deutsche Buddhistische Union
Amalienstrasse71
80799 München
Tel: +49 (0)89 28 01 04
Fax: +49 (0)89 28 10 53
Umbrella organisation of thirty-seven Buddhist associations of all
main traditions. Produce quarterly magazine *Lotusblätter*.

Hungary

Buddhista Misszió
H-1221 Budapest
Alkotmány u. 83
Tel: +36 (0)1 226 10.10
Has list of Buddhist centres in Hungary

Ireland

See *UK*

The Netherlands

Boeddhistische Unie Nederland (BUN)
PO Box 17286
1001 JG Amsterdam
The Netherlands

Boeddhisme in Nederland
Book by Victor J. van Gemert, Zenuitgeverij Theresiahoeve, 1990

Switzerland

Bodhi Baum Jahrbuch für Buddhismus
2722 Netting 34
For listing of centres in Germany, Austria and Switzerland:

Schweizerische Buddhistische Union / Union Suisse des Bouddhistes
Wiedingstrasse 18
8055 Zürich
Produces list of Buddhist monasteries, centres and groups of all schools in Switzerland.

UK

Buddhist Directory (1994) The Buddhist Society London: The Buddhist Society

For a comprehensive listing of Buddhist groups, centres and related organisations in the UK and Ireland. Available from The Buddhist Society (see entry in London listings) or Wisdom Books (see Buddhist Book Service in *Further Reading*).

UNIVERSITIES

There are often Buddhist groups in Universities – contact the Secretary of the Students Union for details.

THE INTERNET

The Internet has pages dedicated to Buddhism, including a directory of centres worldwide. Some sites are dedicated to a particular organisation or school of Buddhism.

SPECIFIC SCHOOLS

Friends of the Western Buddhist Order

Friends of the Western Buddhist Order (FWBO) has centres in forty cities in fifteen countries. Contact The London Buddhist Centre (see entry in London, UK) for details.

NICHIREN

Soka Gakkai International (See entry in Berkshire, UK) run local meetings all over the UK. Contact them about the nearest meeting to you or phone their Richmond centre on 0181 948 0381/2 after 4pm and at weekends.

PURE LAND

Jodo Shinshu

In Austria, contact Buddhistische Gemeinschaft Jodo-Shinshu Österreich (see entry in Austria).

In Germany, contact Jodo Shinshu Deutschland (see entry in Bad Reichenhall, Germany).

Other

In the UK, contact the Pure Land Buddhist Fellowship (see entry in Oxfordshire, UK) for information on Pure Land groups of any denomination.

Buddha's Light International Association (BLIA) Contact the London Fo Kuang Temple (see entry in London, UK) for other centres. There is also a BLIA centre in Manchester, telephone 0161 236 0494.

SHINGON

In the UK contact the British Shingon Buddhist Association, at the Kongoryuji Temple (see entry in Norfolk, UK).

THERAVADA

Thai

Samatha Trust (see entry in Wales, UK) holds classes and groups around the country for beginners and experienced meditators. Contact this centre for groups in Altrincham, Bolton, Bristol/Bath, Cambridge, Chester, Durham/Sunderland, Ipswich, Liverpool, Llangunllo, London, Manchester, Oldham, Oxford, Pembrokeshire, Peterborough, Rossendale and Stockport. Local beginners classes held throughout the country. For beginners weekends contact: Graham Murphy, 31 Highville Road, Liverpool L16 9JE, telephone 0151 722 0893.

Dhammapala Buddhist Monastery (see entry in Switzerland) can also supply a list of local meditation group contacts in Switzerland, Germany and an Italian monastery.

Myanmar

International Meditation Centre (see entry in Wiltshire, UK) has centres in Austria, The Netherlands, Switzerland, Germany.

Sayagyi U Ba Khin Gesellschaft (see entry in Switzerland) holds one-hour meditation meetings every Tuesday in Basel, Bern, Zürich and Ticino.

Other

The House of Inner Tranquility (see entry in Wiltshire, UK) has satellite groups in London, Oxford and Toronto, Canada.

Buddha-Haus (see entry in Oy-Mittelberg, Germany) has meditation groups throughout Germany and in Austria, Switzerland, The Netherlands and England – contact centre for details.

TIBETAN

A Handbook of Tibetan Culture (1993) ed. Graham Coleman. London: Rider

The Handbook of Tibetan Culture – among other information, a list of places worldwide having anything to do with Tibetan culture whether religious, cultural or scholarly. Available from The Buddhist Society (see entry in London listings) or Wisdom Books (see Buddhist Book Service in *Further Reading*).

Guide du Tibet en France for everything connected with Tibet available in France, from Éditions Clare Lumière, Mas Vinsargues, 13116 Vernègues, France or 12 av. Henri Barbusse, 13760 Saint Cannat, France.

Gelug

Chodzong Buddhistisches Zentrum (see entry in Langenfeld, Germany) Headquarters for associated centres and groups in Germany – contact them for details.

Foundation For The Preservation Of The Mahayana Tradition (see *Index of Centres by School*) has more than sixty centres worldwide. See their twice yearly journal *Mandala* for a list of addresses, available at any of the centres listed in this Directory.

New Kadampa Tradition (see *Index of Centres by School*). Contact your nearest centre for other local groups and centres.

Rabten Choeling (see entry in Switzerland) runs courses in Bern,

Basel, Zürich, Winterthur, Geneva, Lausanne and La Chaux-de-Fonds. Also associated groups including Thubten Choeling in Schaffhausen, Antenne de Rabten Choeling in Winterthur, Rabten Samphel Ling in Liebefeld, Rabten Choeling Geneve and Antenne de Rabten Choeling in Zürich. Contact them for details.

Nyingma

Rigpa is an international association of Buddhist meditation centres in Europe, the United States and Australia under the direction of Sogyal Rinpoche. For details of other centres and groups contact Rigpa Fellowship (see entry in London, UK) or Dzogchen Beara Retreat and Conference Centre (see entry in Ireland) for centres in Dublin, Limerick and Cork.

Nyingma – the Urgyen Samye Chöling centre in France has affiliated centres in Spain, England, Switzerland and the USA. Contact them for details.

Kagyu

Austrian Karma Kagyu Centres are all part of Karma Kagyu Österreich. Contact Mag. Alexander Draszczyk, Auhofstr 39, 1130 Vienna, *Tel:* +43 (0)222 8765434.

Karma Kagyu centres worldwide An international address list is published at Karma Triyana Dharmachakra, seat of H.H. the Gyalwa Karmapa in North America. This is available from most Karma Kagyu centres. Dhagpo Kagyu Ling (see entry in Aquitaine, France) or Institut Karma Ling (see entry in Rhone Alps, France) have this list and also one specifically for France available.

Sayka

Sakya Tsechen Ling (see entry in Alsace, France) is the headquarters of the Sakya school in Europe for centres in Spain, Germany,

Sweden, The Netherlands, the UK, Switzerland and Italy.

Others

Arya Maitreya Mandala Vajrayana Order (see entry in Germany) for contact addresses in Germany, England, Sweden and Singapore.

Dzogchen International Community is a worldwide organisation – contact their headquarters at Merigar (see entry in Italy).

Longchen Foundation (see entry in Oxfordshire, UK) has local groups which meet weekly in Oxford, Worcester, Bristol, London and Leigh-on-Sea.

Shambhala International – headquarters in Halifax, Canada. International organisation with centres in London, Amsterdam, Hamburg, Marburg, Paris, Vienna, Munich and others. Contact Shambhala Europe, Wilhelmstrasse 20, Marburg, Germany for details.

Tarab Ladrang Institutes are in Denmark, France, Belgium, Germany and Austria. Contact centre in Denmark for details on others.

VIPASSANA

Although Vipassana is a meditation technique devised by the Buddha and unique to Buddhism, Vipassana centres often prefer not to classify themselves as Buddhist centres.

However, the three main centres in Europe are:

Vipassana Centre
Dhamma Mahi
Le Bois Planté
Louesme
89350 Champignelles
FRANCE

Vipassana Centre
Dhamma Dipa
Harewood End
Hereford
HR2 8NG
ENGLAND

Vipassana Meditationshaus
Kirchenweg 2
76332 Bad Herrenalb
GERMANY

ZEN

Soto

Throssel Hole Priory (see entry in Northumberland, UK) has over twenty affiliated meditation groups in the UK, The Netherlands and Germany, contact the Guestmaster for details.

International Zen Association has centres in France, Belgium, Germany, USA, North Africa and South America.
Headquarters: Association Zen Internationale, 17 rue des Cinq Diamants, 75013 Paris, France.
Contact Association Zen de Belgique (see entry in Belgium) for other centres in Belgium.
Contact International Zen Association UK (IZAUK) for some twelve more around the country, including one in Scotland and three in London and for other IZA centres worldwide.

Rinzai

International Zen Institute of America has formal branches in Florida, Germany, The Netherlands and Spain and many meditation groups in USA and Europe. Contact Zen Institut Deutschland (see entry in Sonnenbühl, Germany).

Zen Zentrum Mumon-Kai (see entry in Germany) runs nine

branches in Germany, Austria and Poland.

Ch'an

Western Zen and Ch'an Retreats (see entry in Avon, UK) for affiliated groups in Swindon, Cardiff, Manchester and Edinburgh. Also contacts in Warsaw, St Petersburg and New York.

Soto/Rinzai Synthesis

Kanzeon Sangha (see entry in Düsseldorf, Germany) for Zen sitting groups in Germany and other countries.

NETWORK OF ENGAGED BUDDHISTS

In the UK:

Ken Jones
Network of Engaged Buddhists
Plas Plwca
Cwmrheidol
Aberystwyth
Dyfed SY23 3NB
Tel & Fax: 01970 84603

A network of people trying to combine inner peace seeking and outward social concern in a mutually supportive and enriching way. It provides opportunities for sharing problems, feelings and experience in this great lifelong undertaking, embracing the concerns of ecological well-being, world peace and social justice. In trying to understand the problems of personal and social violence, it is both an affinity group and pressure group, attempting both personal and social transformation. It has a broad, non-sectarian interfaith character and the wide range of members' interests are reflected in its newsletter, *Indra's Net*.

Internationally:

International Network of Engaged Buddhists
303–7 Soi Santipap
Nares Road
Bangkok 10500
Thailand
Tel: +66 (0)233 2382 and +66 (0)233 2792

Main centres in the USA

Happy is he who has overcome his ego; happy is he who has attained peace; happy is he who has found the Truth.

– Anguttara- Nikaya

Tibetan – Gelug

The Deer Park (Geshe Sopa)
4548 Schneider Drive
Oregon
Wisconsin 93575

Rashi Gempil Ling (Founded by Geshe Wangyal)
First Kalmyk Buddhist Temple
R.R.3
Box Howell
New Jersey 07731

Tibetan – Sakya

Sankya Puntsok Ling
8715 First Ave
1510 D. Silver Springs
Maryland 20910

Tibetan – Nyingma

Nyingma Institute (Tarthang Tulku)
1815 Highland Place
Berkeley
California 94709

Tibetan – Rime

Rigpa USA
PO Box 607
Santa Cruz
California 95061-0607
Tel: (408) 454 9103
Fax: (408 454 0917

Tibetan – Karma Kagyu

Shambhala USA
1345 Spruce Street
Boulder
CO 80302
Tel: 303 444 0190 or 303 444 7881
Fax: 303 443 2975

Karma Do Nga Choeling
12021 Willshire Boulevard
Suite 667
West Los Angeles
California 90025

Karma Triyana Dharmachakra (Seat of H.H. the Gyalwa
Karmapa)
352 Meads Mountain Road
Woodstock
NY 12498
Tel: 914 679 5906

Dzogchen

Dzog-chen Community
Tsegyalgar
P O Box 277
Conway
Massachusets 6259820
Tel: +1 (0)413 625 9820
Fax: +1 (0)413 665 1142

Vipassana

Insight Meditation Society
Pleasant Street
Barre
MA 01005
Tel: 617 355 4378

Insight Meditation West
Spirit Rock Center
5000 Sir Francis Drake Boulevard
PO Box 909
Woodacre
CA 94973
Tel: 415 488 0164

Zen – Soto

Zen Center of San Francisco (founded by Shunryu Suzuki Roshi,
present Abbot Reb Anderson)
300 Page Street
San Francisco
CA 94102
Tel: (415) 863 3136

Zen – Rinzai

First Zen Institute of America
113 East 30th Street
New York
NY 10016
Tel: (212) 686 2520

Zen – Rinzai-Soto Synthesis

Zen Center of Los Angeles (Taizan Maezumi Roshi)
905 South Normandie Ave
Los Angeles
California 90006

Diamond Sangha (Robert Aitken Roshi)
2119 Kaloa Way
Honolulu
Hawaii 96822
Tel: (808) 946 0666

Ch'an

City of Ten Thousand Buddhas (Master Hsuan Hua)
Talmage
California 95481
Tel: (707) 0939 0217

Zen – Korean

Providence Zen Center/Diamond Hill Zen Monastery (Seung Sahn Sunim)
528 Pound Road
Cumberland
Rhode Island 02864
Tel: (401) 769 6464

Pure Land

Buddhist Churches of America
National Headquarters
1710 Octavia Street
San Francisco
California 94109
Tel: (415) 776 5600

Nichiren

Nichiren Shoshu USA (NSU)
Headquarters
525 Willshire Boulevard
Santa Monica
CA 90401
Tel: (213) 451 8811

Vietnamese

Vietnamese Buddhist Association
3119 Alta Arden Expressway
Sacramento
California 95825

Non-sectarian

Springwater Center
7179 Mill Street
Springwater
NY 14560

Main schools in the Far East

> Learned Audience, when you hear me talk about the Void, do not at once fall into the idea of vacuity, (because this involves the heresy of the doctrine of annihilation.) It is of the utmost importance that we should not fall into this idea, because when a man sits quietly and keeps his mind blank he will abide in a state of 'Voidness of Indifference'.
>
> – *The Sutra of Wei Lang (or Hui Neng)*, translated from the Chinese by Wong Mou-Lam

INDIA

Tibetan – Sakya

Sakya Centre
187 Rajpur Road
248 009 Rajpur
Dehra Dun
UP

Tibetan – Gelug

Drepung Monastic University
Lama Camp No. 2
Tibetan Colony 581411
Mundgod

Distt. N. Kanara
Karnataka State

Office of H.H. the Dalai Lama of Tibet
Thekchen Choeling
McLeod Ganj
Dharamsala
Distt. Kangra
Himachal Pradesh

Library of Tibetan Works and Archives
Ganchen Kyishong
Dharamsala 176215
Disst. Kangra
Himachal Pradesh

Tibetan – Rime

Rigpa House
RA46
Inderpuri
PO Pusa
New Delhi 12

JAPAN

Nichiren

Nichiren Shu Headquarters
1-32-15, Ikegami, Ota-ku, Tokyo
Tel: +81 (0)3 3751 7181

Zen – Soto

Soto Zen Headquarters
2-5-2 Shiba
Minato-ku

Tokyo 105
Tel: (03) 454 5411

Eiheiji Tokyo Betsuin (Rinzai)
2-21-14 Nishi Abazu
Minato-ku
Tokyo 106
Tel: (03) 400 5232

Zen – Rinzai

Daitokuji
53 Daitokujicho
Marasakino
Kita-ku
Kyoto 603
Tel: (075) 491 0543

Ryutakuji
Mishima-shi
Shizuoka-ken 411
Tel: (0559) 86 2206

Pure Land

Hongwanji International Center
Higashi-nakasuji
Rokujo Sagaru
Shimogyo-ku
Kyoto 600

KOREA

Zen – Korean

Songgwang-Sa
Songgwangmyon

Seungjukun
Cholla Namdo Province
South Korea

MALAYSIA

Vipassana

Malaysian Buddhist Meditation Centre
355 Jalan Mesjid Negeri
11600 Penang

MYANMAR

Vipassana

Stories of oppression continue to come from Myanmar. Be aware that visits take in tourist money which may support an oppressive regime.

Mahasi Centre (Mahasi Sayadaw)
16 Thathana Yeiktha Road
Yangon (Rangoon) 11201

Chanmyay Yeiktha (Ven. Sayadaw U Janakabhivamsa)
55-A Kaba Aye Pagod Road
Kaba Aye p.o.
Yangon (Rangoon)
Tel: (95) 01 61479

Vipassana Meditation Centre Panditarama (Ven. Sayadaw U Panditabhavamsa)
80-A Thanlwin Road, Golden Hill Avenue
Bahan
Yangon (Rangoon)

SRI LANKA

Theravada

Island Hermitage
Dodanduwa

Vipassana

Vipassana meditation centre Kandubodha
Delgoda

THAILAND

Theravada

Wat Pa Nanachat
Bahn Bung Wai
Amper Warin
Ubon 34310

Vipassana

Ven. Bodhipalo
c/o Section 1, Wat Mahadhatu
3 Maharaj Road
Bangkok 10200

Vipassana Meditation Centre Sorn Vivek Asom
Soi Prachanakul 7
Tanon Bahnbung
Amper Muang
Chonburi 20000
Tel: 038 283766

Vipassana Meditation Centre Sorn Thawee
Sametnua

Bangkla
Cha Choengsao Province

TIBET

The Chinese government's oppressive measures continue in Tibet. At the time of writing, pictures of the Dalai Lama had been banned, even in private homes, and were being removed from temples and burnt. Several monasteries had also been closed down in the last few months. The Office of Tibet in London advised that Westerners visiting Tibet would financially benefit the Chinese government and that the only benefit to Tibet is that outsiders would witness for themselves what was happening. To find out which monasteries and temples are still open, contact the Chinese embassy in your country.

Book List for Buddhist visitors to the Far East

See also the section on *Finding Other Buddhist Centres, Groups and Organisations*.

Tibet

Tibet Handbook – V. Chan (Best for Buddhists visiting Tibet)
Tibet Travel Survival Kit

Odyssey Illustrated Guide to Tibet – E. B. Booze

India

Meeting the Buddha: On Pilgrimage in Buddhist India – Ed: Molly Emma Aitken (Specially recommended for pilgrimage)

Living Tibet – B. Warren and N. Rose (On Dharamsala)

Travel through Sacred India – R. Housden

Holy Places of the Buddha – E. Cook, Crystal Mirror Series, Volume 9

Power Places of Kathmandu – K. Dowman

Nepal Travel Survival Kit – R. Everist and T. Wheeler

Buddhist Monks and Monasteries of India – S. Dutt

Buddhist Monasteries in Himachal Pradesh – O.C. Handa

Eight Places of Buddhist Pilgrimage – J. Russell

Myanmar

Guide to Burma – N. Greenwood

Japan

Pilgrim's Guide to Forty-six Temples – S. Usui

China

Pilgrims and Sacred Sites in China – S. Naquin

Appendix: Precepts

Some centres ask you to conform to the Five or Eight Precepts.

The **Five Precepts** are
to refrain from killing living beings;
to refrain from taking what is not given;
to abstain from sexual misconduct;
to refrain from telling lies and using abusive or cruel speech;
to refrain from self-intoxication with alcohol or drugs.

These are all based on behaviour which will not harm others in any way and translate positively into loving kindness, generosity, contentment, truthfulness and awareness.
    These are considered to be the minimal ethical requirements of Buddhism and practising Buddhists are expected to make efforts to work towards them. Interpretation of them may vary, especially refraining from sexual misconduct which may range from celibacy in some places to the avoidance of adultery in others.

Theravadan centres sometimes ask visitors to comply with the **Eight Precepts**. These comprise the Five Precepts and also ask you to refrain from:
taking food at unseasonable times, i.e. not after midday;
dancing, music, singing and unseemly shows;

the use of garlands and perfumes, unguents and from things that beautify and adorn the person;
from using high and luxurious seats and beds.

These are also expected of lay Theravadan devotees on auspicious occasions including full and new moon days.

Glossary

> O let us live in joy, in love amongst those who hate! Among men who hate, let us live in love.
>
> – *The Dhammapada*

5 Precepts (see Precepts)

8 Precepts (see Precepts)

Abhidharma (Sanskrit; *Abhidhamma,* Pali) (Lit: Higher teaching.) Third division of the Theravadan scriptures, which is largely a commentary and analysis of the Sermons. The Myanmar sangha specialises in its study.

Abhisamaya Alankara A discourse on the collection of sutras known as the Prajnaparamita.

Ajahn (Thai) Thai form of the Sanskrit Acharya (teacher). Meditation master.

Amida Buddha (Japanese) Buddha of Infinite Light and Life which includes Infinite Wisdom and Compassion. In Pure Land Buddhism, the intermediary between Supreme Reality and mankind.

Amitabha (Sanskrit) One of the deities of the Tantric pantheon. The Buddha of Infinite Light, the perfected state of our faculty of perception/discrimination.

Anagarika (Lit: Homeless One.) Someone who has adopted a homeless life without formally ordaining as a monk.

Anapana Sati (Pali) Meditation on mindful breathing.

Anatta (Pali; *Anatman*, Sanskrit) One of the Three Marks of Existence which are part of the basic teachings of Buddhism. Doctrine of non-separateness of all forms of life; applied to people, there is no immortal ego or self, the unchanging and immortal being the possession of no one human being.

Anila (Tibetan) Respectful form of address for a nun.

Atisha (982–1054) Indian scholar; in Tibet from 1038 till his death; Entirely reformed the prevailing Buddhism. Founded the Kadampa school of Tibetan Buddhism.

Avalokitesvara (Sanskrit) Bodhisattva of Compassion.

Ayurvedic (non-Buddhist) Traditional Indian medical system.

Bardos (Tibetan) The state between two other states of being, especially the intermediate state between one life and the next.

Bhavana (Sanskrit, Pali) Self-development by any means, especially meditation, mind development and concentration; meditative practices.

Bhikshu (Sanskrit; *Bhikkhu*, Pali) Those living from alms or offerings given by lay Buddhists. Often translated as monk.

Bhikshuni (Sanskrit; *Bhikkhuni*, Pali) The feminine of the above. Often translated as nun.

Bodhicaryavatara (Sanskrit) A text of Shantideva (Indian 7th century bodhisattva).

Bodhichitta (Sanskrit; *Boddhicitta*, Pali) Compassionate wish to gain Enlightenment for the benefit of all sentient beings.

Bodhidharma Indian Buddhist who went to Chinese court in 520 CE; founder of Zen Buddhism.

Bodhisattva (Sanskrit) A being pledged to become a Buddha so as to be able to help all other beings to escape suffering by becoming Enlightened.

Bon (Tibetan) Pre-Buddhist Tibetan religion.

Brahmaviharas (Sanskrit, Pali) The four sublime states or virtues which elevate man. These are loving kindness, compassion, sympathetic joy and equanimity.

Buddha (Sanskrit and Pali) 'Awakened One'. One who has attained enlightenment. Particularly applies to Siddhartha Gautama, also known as Shakyamuni, the founder of Buddhism. The Buddha principle which manifests in various forms. For Theradavans, only one Buddha is accepted in each age; for Mahayanans, there are countless transcendent Buddhas which represent embodiments of various aspects of the Buddha principle.

Buddhadharma (Pali) The Buddha's teachings.

Buddharupa Statue or image of the Buddha.

Chado (Japanese) Tea ceremony used as a meditative practice in some Zen traditions

Chenrezig (Tibetan) Tibetan equivalent of Avalokiteshvara, embodiment of the compassion of all the Buddhas and supreme protector and patron deity of Tibet.

Chogyal (Tibetan) Title. (Lit: Dharma Raja or Religious King or Protector of the Buddhist Religion.)

Dana (Sanskrit, Pali) One of the basic Buddhist virtues, it is the opposite of greed and translates as generosity or giving.

Dathun Month-long meditation retreat.

Dharma (Sanskrit; *Dhamma,* Pali*)* Has numerous meanings. Among other things it can mean truth or reality. Also stands for those teachings and methods which are conducive to gaining Enlightenment and thereby seeing things as they truly are, refers particularly to the teachings of the Buddha.

Dharmasala Rest house for pilgrims.

Dharmata (Sanskrit) Ground of being, the essence of everything; unifying spiritual reality; the absolute from which all proceeds.

Dogen (1200–1253) Japanese founder of Soto Zen; studied in China for four years before taking it to Japan; founded Eiheiji monastery.

Dojo (Japanese) Zen training hall.

Dokusan (Japanese) In Rinzai Zen, a question and answer session with the Master or Roshi during which progress is tested.

Empowerment Ritual performed by eminent Tibetan Lamas; an essential prerequisite for the practice of Tantra.

Enlightenment An individual's awakening to the mind's true nature. A state of perfect wisdom and limitless compassion. The achivement of a Buddha.

Feldenkrais (non-Buddhist term) Learning system using movement as a model and means of liberation from bad body habits that contribute to health problems.

Gampopa (1079–1153) Tibetan scholar, disciple of Milarepa and Marpa, whom he succeeded; one of the founders of the Kagyu school of Tibetan Buddhism.

Gen-Mai (Japanese) Traditional rice soup eaten sometimes offered after practice sessions at some Japanese Zen centres.

Geshe (Tibetan) Gelugpa title equivalent to Doctor of Divinity.

Gestalt Therapy (non-Buddhist) A psychological school founded on the principle that the mind tends to perceive events and situations as a pattern, or whole, rather than as a collection of separate and independent elements.

Go (Japanese) Japanese board game.

Gompa (Tibetan) Teaching and practice hall; isolated place or monastic site.

Green Tara (See *Tara*)

Guru (Sanskrit) Teacher, particularly a spiritual master.

Hannya Shingyo (Japanese) Diamond Sutra – main Buddhist sutra chanted by Zen practitioners.

Hatha Yoga (Sanskrit) Form of yoga involving physical exercises and breath control.

Hevajra (Sanskrit) One of the Tantric texts of Tibetan Buddhism.

Hitsuzendo (Japanese) Calligraphy used as a meditative practice in some Zen traditions.

Ikebana (Japanese) Flower arranging used as a meditative practice in some Zen traditions.

Iyengar yoga Modern energetic adaption of Hatha Yoga.

Jewels, Three The Buddha, the Dharma and the Sangha – the three highest values of Buddhism.

Kanna-Zen (Japanese) Form of Rinzai Zen founded in the 12th century.

Karma (Sanskrit). (Lit: Action.) Cause and effect; our willed actions (including mental and vocal) will have consequences for us in the future.

Karmapa (Tibetan) Title of the head of the Karma Kagyu school;

alternative name for the school itself.

Kesa (Japanese) Zen monk garment.

Khenpo (Tibetan) Title usually of an Abbot; indicates high scholarship in Nyingma, Sakya and Kagyu schools.

Khyentse (Tibetan). (Lit: One in whom Wisdom and compassion are perfectly combined). Name of a number of exceptional Nyingma Lamas during last 200 years.

Kinhin (Japanese) Formal marching during periods of rest from Zazen to loosen stiff joints and exercise the body.

Koan (Japanese) Formalised riddle, used in Rinzai Zen as a device to throw the student against the ultimate question of his own nature.

Kum Nye (Tibetan) Gentle Tibetan Yoga system.

Kusen (Japanese) Oral teachings.

Kyudo (Japanese) Art of archery used as a meditative practice in some zen traditions.

Lama (Tibetan) Spiritual teacher who may or may not be a celibate monk venerated as an authentic embodiment of the Buddhist teachings. For the Tibetan, he is particularly important because he not only teaches rituals but conducts them. May be head of one or more monasteries and possess political influence. Today, often used as a polite form of address for any Tibetan monk regardless of his spiritual development.

Lam Rim (Tibetan). (Lit: Graduated path.) System of teaching founded by Atisha (11th century Indian Master) in which all the stages of the path to enlightenment are laid out in a very clear and systematic manner. All four main schools of Tibetan Buddhism have produced Lam Rim texts.

Lodjong (Tibetan). (Lit: Mind training.) Based on Lam Rim teachings – explains how to train the mind in daily life for the development of Bodhicitta.

Longchen (1308–1363) Greatest scholar of the Nyingma tradition of Tibetan Buddhism.

Mahamudra (Sanskrit) Has several meanings; as a practice it is popular in Kagyu and Gelug schools of Tibetan Buddhism; as a path it is a sequence of systematic advanced meditations on emptiness and pure appearance.

Mahathera Title for Bhikkhu of twenty years' standing, usually called Theras.

Mahayana see *Schools*

Maitreya (Sanskrit) Embodiment of loving kindness of all the Buddhas; historical figure – a Bodhisattva disciple of Buddha Shakyamuni; the coming Buddha, fifth in the line of the thousand Buddhas who will descend to this world. Currently said to reside in Tushita – a Buddhist heaven.

Mandala (Sanskrit) In the context of Tantra, a symmetrical design used as an object of meditation.

Mantra (Sanskrit) String of sound symbols recited to concentrate and protect the mind.

Mara (Sanskrit). (Lit: Death.) Evil influences that impede one's spiritual transformation. Personified as a Tempter whose baits are the sensory pleasures.

Marpa (1012–1097) Tibetan founder of the Kagyu school of Tibetan Buddhism; most famous pupil was Milarepa.

Metta Bhavana (Pali) Meditation on loving kindness.

Milarepa (1038–1122) Tibetan poet saint; one of the founders and greatest figure in the Kagyu school of Tibetan Buddhism.

Moxibustion (Japanese) Medical use of burning herbs.

Mudra (Sanskrit). (Lit: Seal, sign.) Bodily posture or symbolic gesture imbued with symbolic significance which may be used in ritual. In Tantra, may refer to a female consort.

Naropa (11th century) Indian master and accomplished scholar; teacher of Marpa and Milarepa; particularly famous for his Six Yogas of Naropa.

Nembutsu (Japanese) Recitation of The Name of Amida Buddha which in Japanese form that most Shin Buddhists use is *Namu Amida Butsu or* Namuamidabu which literally means 'I take refuge in Amida Buddha'. Principle practice of Pure Land Buddhism.

Ngondro (Tibetan) Preliminary practices normally undertaken by a meditator prior to engaging in Tantric practice.

Nirvana (Sanskrit) Ultimate goal of Buddhist endeavour – permanent cessation of all suffering.

Nyinthun (Tibetan) Meditation practice for a whole day.

Nyung-Neh (Tibetan) Fasting ritual normally led by a monk or nun.

Osho (Japanese) Zen priest.

Padmasambhava (8th century) Indian Buddhist who visited Tibet at the invitation of the king and taught various Buddhist principles; credited with founding the Nyingma school of Tibetan Buddhism.

Panna (Pali) Wisdom.

Paramitas (Sanskrit) The Ten Perfections cultivated by a Bodhisattva. They are generosity, morality, renunciation, wisdom, energy, patience, truthfulness, determination, loving kindness and equanimity.

Phowa (Tibetan) Ejection of consciousness at the moment of death.

Transmission of consciousness.

Precepts Five, eight or ten guides to behaviour. Centres sometimes ask that visitors behave according to the Five or Eight Precepts. For a full description see *Appendix: Precepts.*

Puja (Sanskrit) Sacramental offering which may be associated with body, speech and mind.

Qi Gong (non-Buddhist term) Chinese martial art or physical meditation practice.

Rain retreat months (see *Festivals*)

Rakusu (Japanese) Zen monk garment.

Reiki (non-Buddhist term) Energy healing system based on ancient Tibetan knowledge rediscovered by a Japanese theologian.

Retreat Intensive periods of meditation which may be long or short term.

Right livelihood Fifth stage of the Noble Eightfold path. Earning a living in accordance with Buddhist ethics.

Rinpoche (Tibetan) (Lit: Precious One). Honorific of a high lama, denotes reincarnation of a realised master.

Roshi (Japanese) (Lit: Old venerable master.) Title of a Zen master who can be either monk or lay, man or woman.

Sadhana (Sanskrit) In Tantra, a type of text and the meditation practices presented in it which relate to deities to be experienced as spiritual realities.

Sakyamuni Sage of the Sakyas – a title applied to the Buddha.

Samadhi (Sanskrit) (Lit: Union.) Profound meditative state; focus on a single object through calming of mental activity; one-pointedness of mind.

Samsara (Sanskrit, Pali) World of rebirth and death; the succession of rebirths until liberation is attained; cyclic existence.

Samu (Japanese) Manual work used as part of meditative practice in Zen schools.

Sangha The Buddhist community as a whole, sometimes referring to the community of Buddhist monks, nuns and novices.

Sangye Menla (Tibetan) Prayer ritual for sick people.

Satipatthana (Pali) System of mind development by the analysis of consciousness.

Sayadaw (Myanmar) Equivalent of Mahathera or Bhikku of twenty years' standing; title given to highly respected Bhikkhus.

Sensei (Japanese) Teacher.

Sera (Tibetan) Large monastic college in Lhasa, Tibet. One of the three main monasteries in Tibet with Ganden and Drepung.

Sesshin (Japanese) (Lit: to search the heart.) Intensive zen retreat.

Shamatha (Sanskrit; *Samatha,* Pali) Basic meditation practice common to most schools of Buddhism, whose aim is to tame and sharpen the mind as a springboard for insight (*vipashyana; vipassana).*

Shantideva (7th century) Indian compiler and writer of important Buddhist works.

Shiatsu (non-Buddhist term) Japanese healing massage technique using acupressure points.

Shikantaza (Japanese) A form of Zazen consisting of just sitting with no supportive techniques such as counting the breath.

Shine Meditation for developing calmness.

Silas (pali). (Lit: obligations, precepts.) Morality or virtue.

Six Yogas of Naropa System of advanced tantric meditation originating from the Indian Master Naropa and used by the Kagyu and Gelug schools of Tibetan Buddhism.

Stupa (Sanskrit) Originally a structure built to commemorate a Buddha or other highly developed person, often containing relics; became a symbol for the mind of a Buddha.

Sutra (Sanskrit, *Sutta,* Pali) The sermons of Gautama Buddha; any collection of teachings.

Sweat lodge (non-Buddhist term)

Tai Chi or *Tai Chi Chuan* (non-Buddhist term) Chinese exercise system and gentle martial art.

Tantra (Sanskrit) Form of Buddhism using yogic practices of visualisation, mantra, mudra and mandalas, as well as symbolic ritual and meditations which work with subtle psychophysical energies; the texts or teachings in which these are described.

Tara (Sanskrit) An emanation from the Bodhisattva Avolokiteshvara. Embodies the feminine aspect of compassion, seen in both peaceful and wrathful depictions and in various colours, the Green Tara and the White Tara being the forms most frequently seen.

Thangka (Tibetan) Tibetan religious painting.

Thera (Pali). (Lit: Elder.) Bhikkhu of ten years' standing.

Three Jewels (see *Jewels, Three*)

Transmission Passing on of oral teachings and scriptures with related commentary in an uninterrupted lineage or succession form person to person from ancient times.

Tsog (Tibetan) Feast offerings.

Tsongkhapa (1355–1417) Tibetan reformer of Buddhism. Founded Ganden monastery and the Gelug school of Tibetan Buddhism.

Tulku (Tibetan) Voluntary reincarnation of a religious figure of some distinction.

Upasaka (Sanskrit, Pali) Buddhist lay member who takes refuge in the Buddha, the Dharma and the Sangha and who vows to observe the Five Precepts.

Upasika (Sanskrit, Pali) Female *upasaka.*

Vajrasattava (Sanskrit) One of the meditational deities of Tantric Buddhism.

Vajrayana (Sanskrit). (Lit: The Diamond Vehicle.) Buddhist Tantra of India and the Himalayan region. Sometimes used as an alternative term for Tibetan Buddhism. Arose in first millennium in northern India from Mahayana and spread to Tibet, China and Japan. Characterised by a psychological method based on highly developed ritual practices.

Vajrayogini (Sanskrit) One of the female meditational deities of Tantric Buddhism.

Vihara Buddhist temple or monastery.

Vinaya (Sanskrit, Pali). (Lit: discipline.) Third part of the Tripitaka containing the rules and regulations for running and living in a monastery or nunnery, especially the ethical codes involved.

Vipashyana (Sanskrit; V*ipassana,* Pali*)* Insight, clear seeing. With *Shamatha* (*Samatha),* one of the factors essential for the attainment of enlightenment.

Wat (Thai) Temple or monastery.

Yana (Sanskrit, Pali) Vehicle or means of progress to salvation from the wheel of Samsara as in Mahayana.

Yidam (Tibetan) In Tantra, a personal meditational deity embodying an aspect of Enlightenment whose nature corresponds to the psychological make up of the practitioner.

Yoga (Lit: Union.) A method of meditation or physical exercise designed to bring about spritual development.

Zafu (Japanese) Zen meditation cushion.

Zagu (Japanese) Zen monk's garment.

Zazen (Japanese) Sitting meditation used in Zen schools.

Zen (Japanese) (See *Schools*)

Zendo (Japanese) Zen training hall.

Index of centres by school

> The foolish reject what they see, not what they think; the wise reject what they think, not what they see... Observe things as they are and don't pay attention to other people.
>
> – *The Sutra of Huang Po*

EARLY BUDDHISM

FRIENDS OF THE WESTERN BUDDHIST ORDER

NICHIREN

PURE LAND

Jodo Shinshu

SHINGON

THERAVADA

Myanmar

Myanmar – International Meditation Centre

Sri Lanka

Thai

TIBETAN

Dzogchen

Gelug

Gelug – Foundation For The Preservation Of The Mahayana Tradition

Gelug – New Kadampa Tradition

Kagyu

Changpa Kagyu

Drikung Kagyu

Drukpa Kagyu

Karma Kagyu

Kagyu and Nyingma – Shambhala International

Nyingma

Nyingma – Rigpa

Nyingma and Rime

Rime

Sakya

ZEN

Ch'an

Korean

Rinzai

Rinzai – International Zen Institute

Soto

Soto – Serene Reflection Meditation Tradition

Soto – Association Zen Internationale

Soto/Rinzai synthesis – Kanzeon Sangha

Soto/Rinzai synthesis – Integral Zen

Vietnamese

Zen and Western Therapy

NON-SECTARIAN / ALL TRADITIONS

All traditions including Theravada and Soto Zen **Buddhisticher Bund Hannover,** Hannover, Germany   226
All, but mainly Theravada and Zen **Buddhistische Gesellschaft München** München, Germany   254
Main Buddhist traditions – **The Buddhist Society** London SW1, England   53
No particular school **Buddhayāna** Ilmmünster, Germany   261
Non-sectarian – **British Buddhist Association** London W9, England   60
Non-sectarian – **Centro D'Informazione Buddhista** (Buddhist Information Centre) Giaveno (Torino), Italy   275
Non-sectarian – **Centro Studi Maitri Buddha** Torino, Italy   274
Non-sectarian – **Gaia House** Newton Abbot, Devon, England   78
Non-sectarian – **Tan Kapuja – The Gate of Dharma Buddhist College** Budapest, Hungary   268
Non-sectarian – **The Barn** Totnes, Devon, England   79
Non-sectarian with strong influence of the cult of the Medicine Buddha – **Sangye Menlai Gedün, Community of the Medicine Buddha** Budapest, Hungary   270
Open for all traditions **Seminarhaus Engl** Unterdietfurt, Germany   260
Various **Waldhaus am Laacher See** Nickenich, Germany   239

MIXED TRADITIONS

Pure Land and Zen – **London Fo Kuang Temple** London W1, England   57
Theravada – but embraces all schools – **Harlow Buddhist Society** Harlow, Essex, England   88
Theravada, Zen and Tibetan Traditions – **Buddhistische Gesellschaft Hamburg** Hamburg, Germany   218
Theravada, Zen and Tibetan – **Yogacara** Neckarbischofsheim, Germany   245
Tibetan and Theravada – **Föreningen Malmö Buddhistcentrum** Lomma, Sweden   320
Tibetan and Zen – **Centre d'Etudes Bouddhiques** Grenoble, Rhone Alpes, France   204
Zen and Tibetan – **Metafor** München, Germany   256
Zen mainly – **Puregg – Ökumenisches Haus der Stille** Dienten, Austria   156

Further Reading

> There is no evil like hatred,
> And no fortitude like patience.
> – Shantideva, *A Guide to the Bodhisattva's Way of Life*

GENERAL

The Buddhist Handbook (1987) John Snelling. London: Rider

The Elements of Buddhism (1990) John Snelling. London: Element Books

What the Buddha Taught (1972) W. Rahula. Bedford: Gordon Frazer

A Short History of Buddhism (1980) Edward Conze. Allen and Unwin

Buddhist Scriptures (1959) Edward Conze. Harmondsworth: Penguin

The World of Buddhism (1984) H. Bechert and R. Gombrich. London: Thames and Hudson

An Introduction to Buddhism: Teachings, History and Practices (1990) P. Harvey. Cambridge: Cambridge University Press

Introducing Buddhism (1990) C. Pauling. Glasgow: Windhorse

The Dhammapada (1973) Juan Mascaró, trans. Harmondsworth: Penguin Classics

LIFE OF THE BUDDHA

Life of the Buddha (1971) Bhikkhu Nanamoli. Kandy: Buddhist Publication Society

The Buddha (1973) Trevor Ling. Harmondsworth: Penguin

Old Path White Clouds (1991) Thich Nhat Hanh. London: Rider Books

MEDITATION

The Heart of Buddhist Meditation (1983) Nyanaponika Maha Thera. London: Rider Books

Meditation in Action (1991) Chogyam Trungpa. Boston and London: Shambhala

Meditation (1992) Kamalashila. Glasgow: Windhorse

Being Peace (1987) Thich Nhat Hahn. London: Rider

Path to Bliss: A Practical Guide to Stages of Meditation (1991) Dalai Lama. New York: Snow Lion Publications

THERAVADA

Theravada Buddhism (1988) R. Gombrich. London: Routledge & Kegan Paul

MAHAYANA

Mahayana Buddhism (1989) Paul Williams. London: Kegan Paul

TIBETAN

The Jewel in the Lotus (1987) ed. S. Batchelor. London: Wisdom Publications

Foundations of Tibetan Mysticism (1987) Lama Anagarika Govinda. London: Century

Introduction to Tantra (1987) Lama Thubten Yeshe. London: Wisdom

A Guide to Dakiniland (1991) Geshe Kelsang Gyatso. London: Tharpa

Tibetan Book of Living and Dying (1994) Sogyal Rinpoche. London: Rider

Magic and Mystery in Tibet (1965) Alexandra David-Neel. London: Unwin

NICHIREN

Nichiren Shoshu Buddhism (1988) R. Causton. London: Century

The Flower of Chinese Buddhism (1986) Daisaku Ikeda. New York: Weatherhill

PURE LAND

Shinran's Gospel of Pure Grace (1981) Alfred Bloom. Tucson, Arizona: University of Arizona

ZEN

The Zen Teaching of Huang Po (1975) John Blofield, trans. New York: Grove Press

The Three Pillars of Zen (1989) Philip Kapleau. New York: Anchor

Zen Flesh, Zen Bones (1971) Paul Reps. Harmondsworth: Pelican

Zen Mind, Beginner's Mind (1971) Shunryu Suzuki. New York: Weatherhill

WESTERN BUDDHISM

New Currents in Western Buddhism (1990) Sangharakshita. Glasgow: Windhorse Publications

Buddhism for Today and Tomorrow (1996) Sangharakshita. Glasgow: Windhorse Publications

Buddhism in Britain (1979) P. Oliver. London: Rider Books

A Path with Heart (1993) Jack Kornfield. New York: Bantam

OTHER BUDDHIST DIRECTORIES

See *Finding Other Centres, Groups And Organisations*

BUDDHIST BOOK SERVICE

Wisdom Books: 402 Hoe Street, London E17 9AA, Tel 0181 520 5588 Distribute mainly to the UK and Europe, but will also send worldwide.